EXTREME MUSCLE ENHANCEMENT

2nd Edition

Bodybuilding's Most Powerful Techniques

By Carlon M. Colker M.D., F.A.C.N.

Extreme Muscle Enhancement — 2nd Edition

Copyright © 2007 ProSource Publications, LLC
All Rights Reserved

Cover design and layout: Passarelli Design
Photography: Per Bernal, Rick Schaff

Printed in the United States of America

ISBN 978-0-9764593-1-6

ProSource Publications, LLC
2231 Landmark Place
Manasquan NJ 08736

FOREWORD

If you're a guy with any appreciable amount of testosterone coursing through your veins, you know the feeling. It's the same emotion Charles Atlas tapped into with his classic black-and-white advertisements of the 1930s and 40s — the skinny guy getting sand kicked in his face, only to return to the scene after a few months of working out to deliver a knockout punch to the jerk who bullied him. That campaign was brilliant in delving to the core psyche of men, as evidenced by the overwhelming response Atlas received from those ads. Although the marketing ploy was crude by today's standards, the underlying message still resonates to this day.

The fact is, real men don't want to be small and unassuming. We want to be the intimidator, not the intimidated. Real men want that muscular suit of armor, and the commanding, authoritative presence that innately comes with it. We want the ability to strike a chord of fear in others and earn immediate respect as soon as they catch sight of our thick arms, rock hard chests, and powerful lats and legs. It's an unwavering aspiration that passes from generation to generation, and never dissipates. Until the day men walk the earth no more, the desire to be big and muscular will live on.

Unfortunately, countless men have only dreamed of changing their physique and accruing the mass they so desperately desire, but never actually achieve that ambition. Sometimes it's a lack of willpower, but often it's simply a lack of the right information.

To be blunt, training and dieting to build your body ain't easy. In fact, a minefield of misinformation awaits anyone who wants to join the ranks of the massive masses. From magazines and infomercials to the personal trainer down at your local gym, everyone seems to have a theory, workout, exercise or other formula meant to lead you on the path to growth, some well intentioned, some not. Who can you trust to deliver the straight-up facts?

That's where *Extreme Muscle Enhancement* comes in. A book designed to slice through the fog, to cut straight to the heart of the matter, its intentions are spelled out in no uncertain terms right from the start. This is not for the woman trying to get her body back after pregnancy. It's not for the middle-aged couple who seeks to maintain their health and vitality with a moderate whole-body routine. It's not even for the man who only wants to add a few solid pounds and get a little leaner by hitting the gym once a week.

This text is written for one very specific audience — guys who want to add slabs of fat-free muscle, period. If you want soft, "mainstream" advice, go somewhere else; but if you're serious about hitting the heavy iron and revamping your eating habits to live the life of a big man, you've come to the right place.

Hardcore training. Hardcore dieting. Hardcore attitude. Author Carlon Colker delivers it all, giving you the insider's view of what it takes to achieve the ultimate bodybuilding physique. A former competitive bodybuilder himself, he's currently a practicing M.D., the Chief Executive Officer and Medical Director of Peak Wellness, Inc. in Greenwich, Connecticut, and a writer for *Muscular Development* magazine, a publication that preaches a no-BS approach to training science.

In the first section, Extreme Nutrition, he covers all the basics of the optimal bodybuilding diet, exposing common myths and laying down the law on how you can immediately set the stage for explosive muscular growth via diet, supplementation and his 10 Anti-Catabolic Principles. Dr. Colker's advanced approach to overcoming your genetic limitations is a must-read for all men.

Section 2, Extreme Training, is a body-part-by-body-part breakdown of how to attack the weights and squeeze every last benefit out of your training sessions. Designed to blend seamlessly with the nutritional principles outlined in the first section, your blueprint for gains becomes tantalizingly clear and attainable. No more guessing your way around the gym, piecing together hodgepodge workouts without rhyme or reason — you'll know what exercises to choose and how to combine them into full-fledged, efficient and effective regimens that keep you directly on track toward your destination.

The other comprehensive sections delve into the available shortcuts to growth, post-workout nutrition, the inevitable discussion of steroids and other growth enhancers, what you need to know about these unpredictable, often volatile agents, and the bodybuilding lifestyle, including everything you need to know to compete and win. Armed with this knowledge, you can then make a fully-informed decision.

In this comprehensive guide, you'll find the answers to the questions men have constantly sought, year after year, decade upon decade. The "secrets," if you will, to physical power. The next step — implementation of these practices into your own life — is in your hands. If you're ready to commit yourself, make the required sacrifices and do what it takes to grow bigger and stronger, turn the page and prepare to fulfill your destiny.

— *The ProSource Editors*

To Zack

EXTREME MUSCLE ENHANCEMENT — 2ND EDITION

TABLE OF CONTENTS

EXTREME MUSCLE ENHANCEMENT

2nd Edition

SECTION I

EXTREME NUTRITION

1 EATING FOR SIZE

It's an all-too-common story: Regular Joe wants to build his body by gaining big, hard muscles, but just doesn't know how to go about it. Guys that want to build their bodies and gain muscle have had no single comprehensive place to turn that clearly spells out the roadmap, no authoritative text to lead the way.

As a result, countless individuals have resorted to following popular diets designed for the masses, while being lost in the gym and not really knowing how to diet and train for huge, ripped muscle. These poor souls, of which I was once one, take to the gym and go it alone, piecing together advice from friends and emulating what they see others doing around them in an effort to learn to grow as they go. Unfortunately, many who start out with big expectations end up disappointed with their lack of progress, throw in the towel and give up the quest.

Well, guess what? You're a lucky man — in your hands, you have the how-to guide to avoid the common mistakes and pitfalls others succumb to and make meaningful, appreciable gains in muscle mass. By using my book, you will super-charge your efforts as I lead you down the road. You won't be that guy, toiling away in the gym with little or nothing to show for it. The guidance I provide here will allow you to switch into high gear and take the bodybuilding fast track. Buckle up — you're going to enjoy this ride.

Courting Disaster

While many popular diet methods are designed by qualified experts, they aren't necessarily meant for everyone. The fact is, they are geared largely for overweight women. For a man who wants to drop fat but gain lean mass, the results of following such a diet as prescribed are disappointing. While some basic principles of a few of these diets have some application to bodybuilding, the rest of what they teach has little or no relevance to a male bodybuilder when it comes to extreme muscle enhancement.

Getting a lot of quality protein — a concept that many dietitians still shudder at — is vital in the quest for muscle mass. So is controlling carbohydrate intake. But these practices alone will not build an extreme physique. This book pulls no punches when it comes to telling you what you need to do to grow. It contains advice suited for the beginner as well as the more advanced bodybuilder, and reaches beyond the modern yet simplistic principles popularized in cookie-cutter dietary approaches. These pages have something for every man looking to build an extreme physique.

I will reveal to you how, through proper diet and training, you can control your ability to enter into, and remain in, a highly "anabolic" (muscle-building) state, by battling "catabolism" (tissue breakdown) head-on. While stoking your anabolic furnace, you will learn how to actually elevate your body into a sustained "anti-catabolic" environment, thus building hardcore mass while burning off body fat. In short, this book will be your guide to creating something nearly every man I know strives to achieve — an outstanding, jaw-dropping, head-turning muscular physique.

Food Fallacies

Looking back, we as humans have had many accomplishments and made innumerable advances worthy of pride. Achievements in arenas of science and technology, computers, engineering, communication and medicine are particularly inspiring. We have traveled into space and even cured diseases. We have developed an interactive, worldwide web interconnecting people and disseminating information at the blink of an eye.

Our advances have made the world seem smaller, more manageable and more accessible than ever in our history. Yet despite humanity's countless leaps forward, when it comes to healthy eating for leanness, disease prevention and longevity, we have seemingly stepped backwards. The raging obesity problem in the United States stands as a stark example of this lamentable circumstance.

Another unfortunate side effect of the reigning confusion? Dieting for large lean muscle mass has been virtually ignored. Contradictory information has left male bodybuilders perplexed and lost. However, against this stark backdrop, there is hope. Because underneath the radar of traditional media and outside the realm of the antiquated government guidelines, bodybuilders and experts in the field of muscle-building science have been hard at work in their lab, the gym. Based on those years of trial and error of countless bodybuilders and training experts, and using both my background as a real physician and my hardcore in-the-trenches experience, I spell out within this text exactly what works.

It may surprise you to realize that bodybuilders are on the leading edge of exercise and nutritional science. Bodybuilders truly fathered and nurtured the best concepts of what to eat long before any diet gurus took hold of it and claimed epiphany.

Take for instance, the now undisputable fact that a hardcore bodybuilder needs more protein than the average couch potato. While sources like the idiotic Food Pyramid and old-school nutritional textbooks claim that protein should be limited to as little as 0.4 grams per pound of bodyweight per day, bodybuilders discovered early on that you simply cannot add muscle without at least 1 gram of protein per pound of bodyweight per day. Despite mounting evidence to the contrary — try every bodybuilder who ever picked up a dumbbell and successfully put on size as your pool of examples — official government reports and a multitude of nutritional text still just can't seem to let go of their misguided guidelines. Humans are not perfect creatures by any stretch of the imagination. In fact, we are terribly flawed in many ways. But nothing is worse then stubbornness and refusal to explore new frontiers, to let go of old notions when evidence leads you down a new path.

For the bodybuilder, the frontier is always new. As a population, we're always seeking out new methods, new ideas, and new ways of taking the human body to higher levels of development. And that never-ending quest has led to the doorstep of a central concept in this book.

We used to think bodybuilding was all about anabolism by way of turning on testosterone and growth hormone secretion. But this tells less then half the story, for even when we attain that utopia, there is still something that holds our development back. The much greater need is figuring out how to become, and stay, anti-catabolic, because this variable is really the No. 1 limiting factor in muscle growth.

When you tend to that anti-catabolic "root," anabolism is the result — by addressing the problems of muscle breakdown and halted growth at their origins, the anabolic engine is exponentially magnified. Understand, however, this exciting concept of anti-catabolism is in its infancy. We are on the cutting edge of science, medicine and technology, moving forth with a revolutionary idea. While this text may be the first to usher in the concept of anti-catabolic nutrition and training for extreme muscle enhancement, our understanding as to how to unlock its full potential is an ongoing quest.

Enter The Revolution

In the old days, it was really all about training — nobody thought much about diet and supplements beyond eating more protein. Though the old-timers were not wrong about the value of protein, the idea that diet modification and manipulation offered little else in the way of bodybuilding advancement was not only primitive and simplistic, but woefully incorrect. If your goal is extreme muscle enhancement, the hour or so that you spend breaking down muscle in the gym pales in comparison to the day-in-and-day-out hours you must spend properly dieting and resting to build muscle.

With very few exceptions, I say that for every hour you spend in the gym busting a gut, you need at least 100 hours outside the gym eating properly and resting to heal, recover and grow before hitting the same body part again. Apart from getting enough sleep, which hopefully needs little support for you to believe and accept, you should be able to completely comprehend the critical nature of feeding your body properly to fuel your recovery processes.

Stoking your body's anabolic needs is beneficial, but will only result in a relatively low level of physique enhancement. To really break through and experience extreme muscle enhancement, you have to understand the concept of "catabolism" and how to counter it through your nutritional program.

Catabolism, in simple terms, is a breaking down of tissue by the body. The old timers didn't pay much attention to this natural mechanism. Yet understanding and dealing with catabolism is potentially a far more powerful approach than focusing all efforts on chasing anabolism. When you build your body to an extreme, it essentially is an unnatural state of physical being — otherwise your body wouldn't fight so hard against it. That genetically encoded fight to remain the same, smaller size is called homeostasis (or condition of being the same). The body always wants to fight to remain the same. That's why one workout and a protein drink won't instantly build a championship physique. It takes so much more, and the reason why the homeostatic mechanism in all of us is so strong is that our body's catabolic ability is so powerful.

The anabolic and catabolic forces within you are always seesawing; at any point in time, you are either in an anabolic or catabolic state, or in an occasional state of balance. When we're children, catabolism is at its lowest and anabolism wins the day so our bodies can grow at a frenzied pace. When we start to age beyond our prime, catabolism begins its unwelcome rule. Unchecked, it governs the rest of our lives until we fully succumb to it and fall ill or die. When you learn this concept, it will become infinitely clear why my techniques of extreme muscle enhancement focus primarily on keeping catabolism in check, and less on the relatively fruitless task of just magnifying anabolism.

The Genetic Culprit

One of the most powerful catabolic forces in our bodies is coded directly into our genes. Research has elucidated a genetic key to muscle growth. In the late

1990s, the presence of myostatin (then called "growth and differentiation factor 8" or GDF-8) was identified as responsible for actually inhibiting the growth of muscle tissue in animals. In other words, it's the root catabolic factor in our bodies.

To be precise, it was found that mice lacking the gene needed to produce myostatin actually gained slabs of muscle without any resistance exercise! Basically, these rodents just lounged around in their cages and got huge without even getting off their fuzzy little butts for a jog on their wheels.

Myostatin is a protein composed of a sequence of amino acids. It's produced by a specific gene sequence in the DNA of nearly every vertebrate-containing animal, from the brook trout to the animal you wake up to every morning in the bathroom mirror. Myostatin works in the embryonic phase and during development to inhibit the growth of muscle. The reason such a substance exists probably has something to do with an innate need to control and regulate the production of excess muscle. Perhaps from an evolutionary standpoint, having too much muscular bulk was actually a disadvantage to survival. This may explain why our bodies are so quick to counter our anabolic progress from working out and ingesting protein.

Having too much mass was an ancient evolutionary problem because it hindered speed needed to effectively kill prey and quickly retreat from danger. (Or, for the more religious set, perhaps the good Lord just doesn't care for big muscle dudes, and that's why we're hindered with myostatin.) For whatever reason we can theorize, the fact is that evolution has definitely selected out the myostatin-null population (i.e., those missing the gene sequence) and minimized their occurrence.

If you're looking for a bigger example then the lowly mouse, turn your attention to the cattle population. It turns out that we see the proof of the muscle growth inhibiting power of myostatin in the rare but heritable condition among a specific sub-population of cattle. The Belgian Blue bull and the Piedmontese breeds are born with mutations in the sequence of their DNA that "codes" (i.e., produces) myostatin. The result of their lack of myostatin is, to put it bluntly, a lot of bull! These animals are so big it borders on the ridiculous. In fact, one slow lumbering clip-clop to the food trough and their muscles ripple with a pump. Sometimes their rumps get so big from the lack of myostatin that folds of muscle start overlapping one another. That's correct — those folds are muscle, not fat! These super-bulls are truly a sight to behold, so much so that words can't fairly describe how your jaw will drop if you ever get a chance to view one for yourself at a county fair one day.

Proof of the myostatin effect is clear enough in the skeletal muscle of the bullish freaks I mention above. The effect of myostatin in the adult human operates the same way. We know that myostatin is secreted as a negative regulator of muscle growth when certain diseases occur in the adult population. For example, serum concentrations of myostatin are elevated in certain HIV patients. As a result, when full-blown AIDS develops, the muscles deteriorate and waste away as a result of too much myostatin.

We know there is a myostatin influence when injury occurs. Myostatin affects growth-inhibiting factors in the skin that prevent scars from healing too fast or to too great a degree. Without such regulation by myostatin, excess skin healing can result in a massively over-developed scar called a "keloid." I have seen countless numbers over my years in medical practice. Some of them can be quite minor and appear like just a puffy scar, while others can be large, shiny and unsightly. Cutting them out never helps because they tend to just reform. Radiation therapy seems to be the only solid method of treatment for the really bad cases.

Just like a cut in the skin forms a scab and eventually heals, injured muscle needs to repair itself. The role of myostatin is to control the healing process, keeping it in check by controlled expression of the rebuilding genes. More specifically, when skeletal muscles are injured (such as after a hard workout), healing cells called "satellite cells" are activated and incorporated into the muscle along with various amino acids to promote repair and growth. If this process occurs in an uncontrolled way, improper and excessive healing results. Myostatin is locally released to prevent overzealous healing of the muscle and control the rate of repair. In this way, confluent new muscle is produced in a minimal and highly restrained fashion.

A review article from a group in New Zealand made an interesting summary conclusion as it pertains to myostatin and its effect on humans. The researchers concluded that the detection of myostatin in human muscle, combined with myostatin studies of humans with wasting diseases, plus the role of myostatin in the regulation of muscle regeneration "…provide strong evidence for the role of myostatin in regulating muscle growth after birth."

Perhaps the most compelling evidence we have that myostatin in the human works the same way as we see in the animal models comes from a startling case report in a recent medical journal. Right now doctors have identified and are closely following a five-year-old boy born in Germany. He was born to two large and unusually muscular parents. Both are otherwise normal healthy adults, yet each is missing one of the two genes that are needed to produce myostatin, so their myostatin levels are very low. As a result, their son happened to be born with neither gene for myostatin, so his body produces no myostatin at all. Though he seems perfectly healthy in medical journal pictures, this kid looks unreal. He has a huge amount of lean muscle even for a youth twice his age, and has an equally unusual low fat-to-muscle ratio. Plus, the reports are that this myostatin-less wunderkind is already freakishly strong. I look forward to seeing him win the Mr. Olympia in 2025.

So the take-home message is that myostatin controls our potential to gain lean muscle mass, and understanding the dietary forces that influence its expression is quintessential for the guy looking for extreme muscle enhancement.

The Enemy Within

In the final analysis of what we know to date about myostatin, all roads seem to lead to the same profound endpoint for all muscle-heads: A nutritional approach that counters the effects of myostatin will lead to extreme muscle mass gains in the adult human. Short of training, minimizing myostatin expression through the diet is the single most powerful approach you can take to building massive muscles. In some instances, it even rivals the importance of training itself because, when your diet is dialed in correctly, you can make minor training mistakes and still pack on slabs of size.

In addition to myostatin, also worth mentioning are cortisol and the adrenergic hormones, which are other catabolic factors that work against us in our bodybuilding crusade. While they dim in comparison to the importance of myostatin expression in terms of what holds you back from an extreme physique, they're still relevant factors you must consider. These hormones, produced by the adrenal glands, can be easily triggered by certain dietary indiscretions. Estrogen, the female sex hormone, is also one of muscle's worst enemies.

All these factors taken together represent a formidable foe. You can see that our natural ability to be anabolic is slight overall in comparison. The hard truth is that we're exquisitely sensitive to the nature and presence of catabolic triggers within our own bodies. However, there's hope in the battle against these forces that would keep us small and weak. In Chapter 3, I outline 10 principles you can use to win the fight. But first, it is critical to provide a better understanding of basic nutritional knowledge and how it applies to muscle building, which you'll find in Chapter 2.

NUTRITION 101

Carbohydrates. Protein. Fat. Water. The vast world of nutrition can be boiled down to these categories. All food is derived from some or all of these four ingredients, and your body needs a specific selection of them to survive and thrive. Here's a straightforward 411 on each.

The Role of Carbohydrates

As a bodybuilder, you'll do better with a little bit of carbohydrates from the right source. But too much too frequently and your basal levels of insulin will rise too high, turning on body fat production and fat storage in a process called "lipogenesis." As a result, you'll pile on too much fat in addition to muscle.

Simply stated, carbohydrates are sugars. They have traditionally been viewed as the fuel for most body functions. Yet the fact is that your body can make all the blood sugar it needs in the form of glucose from the fat and protein you take in. It is another scientific and medical fact that your body literally requires no orally-ingested carbohydrates for this function. But countless professionals and non-professionals continually ignore this key point.

Glucose (the simplest single molecular form of sugar) marks the beginning of the energy-burning reaction known as "glycolysis." This reaction requires no oxygen and is thus considered anaerobic. It yields a molecule called adenosine triphosphate, or ATP.

ATP is the currency of energy in the human body. Every cell in your body runs on a steady supply of it in order to function. Without ATP, nothing happens, and this includes muscular contraction. When you're training, ATP is consumed in such a way that in the end, what was originally a molecule of glucose is split into pyruvate and lactic acid. The lactic acid is largely responsible for muscular fatigue and for drawing blood into the muscle belly, causing the pump associated with a good workout. Your body then works to clear lactic acid from the muscle by carrying it via the bloodstream to the liver. This process is called the "Cory Cycle."

When you start sucking wind, signaling that your body wants to pull in more oxygen, that's an indication that your body is shifting over to an "aerobic" energy system. In this case, instead of a lactic acid build-up in muscle tissue, the pyruvate mentioned earlier is put into play in what's called the "Krebs Cycle."

Both the glycolytic and Krebs cycles have been exhaustively studied; simple organisms rely heavily on glycolysis, while Krebs is an evolutionary advancement, as it allows for a more efficient production of energy in order to support larger and more complex life forms. Since these cycles begin with a molecule of glucose, it should come as no surprise that carbohydrates have literally become the star of the show in terms of the traditional nutrition textbook definitions of our dietary source of energy.

Although carbohydrates have always been thought to be the major fuel source of human energy, this couldn't be further from the ideal as to how our body should be working when we're running it properly. The truth is, fat is a far more efficient feeder of this pathway of energy production, but not if your body is too accustomed to an unnatural steady stream of carbohydrate ingestion. The only reason carbohydrates have become so important is because we've stoked our furnaces with an excessive amount of them, in essence altering our internal chemistries. We're allowing our bodies to get away with ignoring the preferable, efficient metabolic route of burning fat as a main source of energy. Unfortunately, this is the case with most of us, bodybuilders included.

In an effort to dispel this carbohydrate myth, a re-education must take place. Let's take a step back and look at carbohydrates from a more conventional standpoint. Different types of carbohydrates are valued differently. There are simple carbohydrates (sugars) and complex carbohydrates (starches). As mentioned, glucose is the simplest of all carbohydrates and exists as a single molecule. However, the public generally doesn't consume pure unprocessed glucose. Instead, the classic example of a simple carbohydrate that pervades the American diet is "sucrose" in the form of table sugar and high fructose corn syrup, found in nearly every commercially manufactured beverage in the world today. Any type of candy including cookies, cakes, pies, ice cream and the like are loaded with sugar. Interestingly, although natural, fruit juices and most fruits (especially dried) also contain a significant amount of simple carbohydrate, albeit natural fructose and not table sugar.

Most simple carbohydrates fall into a category of what we call "high-glycemic-index" foods, which are absorbed quickly into the bloodstream and cause a rapid increase or spike in insulin levels. Repetitive insulin spiking or high basal levels as a result of persistently elevated blood sugar cause insulin resistance, a condition directly related to the high incidence of diabetes in our society. As I described earlier, insulin causes lipogenesis, easily explaining the pervasive obesity in the U.S.; it should be easy to see how sugar in the form of high-carbohydrate foods is basically killing us.

Perhaps the biggest current bamboozle taking place is on our grocery store shelves. Because dietary fat is equated with body fat, coupled with the fact that one gram of carbohydrates is equivalent to four calories, while one gram of fat is equal to nine calories, carbohydrates have come to be perceived as "good" while fat has been labeled "bad." Pastry companies have wasted no time in exploiting this distorted propaganda. In so doing, "fat free" cakes and "cholesterol free" cookies have popped up everywhere. Playing on the guilt of the public, these products fly off the shelves and into the mouths of plump consumers with the notion in their minds that somehow they are doing some good for themselves.

The trouble is that simple carbohydrates in particular, although lower in gram-for-gram calories than fat, are far more calorie dense. Add to that, given what we know about the insulin spike caused by simple sugars, although not a fan of fatty foods per se, given the choice I actually would prefer a moderate amount of fat over a blast of simple carbohydrates.

Glucose also may be strung together in strands to form polysaccharides, otherwise known as complex carbohydrates. Examples include bread, pasta, potatoes and rice. Because they're complex, they tend to be digested at a slower rate, with the exception of high-glycemic processed foods like white rice and white bread. A lower glycemic-index rating translates to a lower insulin surge. Subsequently, complex carbohydrates are more filling and give you a more even source of energy over longer periods of time.

Clearly complex carbohydrates are a little less problematic. However, the best route is to take it one step further and stick mainly to fibrous complex carbohydrates (vegetables) — a topic I'll address in-depth later in this chapter.

Modern Mistakes

As discussed, processed foods, most of which are rich in carbohydrates, are some of the worst things you can put in your body. The resulting insulin stimulation leaves you with exactly what you don't want — muscle burning coupled with body fat storage.

When it comes to feeling good and looking good, processed carbohydrates shouldn't be part of your diet. Protein, on the other hand, is absolutely essential. Without eating certain amino acids found in protein, you'll become ill or die because your body can't produce them itself. The same holds true for certain fats. While some fats are harmful, others also are essential and must come from your diet. It's only carbohydrates that have no essential character.

Yet leave it to modern man to screw things up and get away from what's natural. It was modern man that introduced carbohydrates into the diet in great excess. Cave dwellers and early man foraged for food by killing animals and eating their meat as well as gathering leaves, shrubbery and occasionally berries. They didn't boil potatoes, build rice paddies, harvest cornfields or grind wheat. All of these were developed much later by man to create filler in the diet and feed the masses. Some modern lard-ass said, "It's time to make the donuts," and we all followed.

The key to bodybuilding success lies in nurturing the primordial metabolic pathways back to life. These pathways, when stirred and challenged, are actually extremely efficient energy producers. By retraining your metabolism to use what it's supposed to for energy, that being largely fat, you will be able to pile on mass while keeping your body-fat in check. Assuming your body mass and height are not way out of whack with the general populations, what should apply well to most natural bodybuilders is to limit yourself to 50–200 grams of fresh vegetable (fiber-based) carbohydrates per day, in addition to your supplements with the higher end of that range reserved for hard-training days. If you're used to taking in a lot of carbohydrates, get the high-sugar food forms and processed carbohydrate crap out of your diet by gradually descending your intake in conjunction with an increase in complete protein and healthy fats. The idea is to keep myostatin expression in check by not giving your body an excuse to become more anti-catabolic.

Don't Believe The Hype

A number of young bodybuilders still get confused, because they hear how many grams of carbohydrates some professional bodybuilders ingest and they try to follow along. Unfortunately, what they don't know is that these same pros abuse not only anabolic steroids, growth hormone and IGF-1, but insulin for its anabolic properties. Of course, the downside to insulin is that, when introduced artificially into the body, large amounts of sugar also must be taken in or life-threatening hypoglycemia can result. That's the reason for the pros' higher-than-recommended carbohydrate count.

There are proponents of a high-carbohydrate diet for natural bodybuilders. They claim the advantage is that carbohydrates promote an insulin increase — the same thing those pro bodybuilders are doing directly by taking insulin. While this is technically true, because of the high sugar levels that accompany that approach, chasing higher levels of insulin in this way requires more total calories and thus makes you fatter.

Instead, arginine, alanine, the branched chain amino acids (isoleucine, leucine and valine), and glutamine pump up insulin without the excess sugar calories. So as long as you're eating plenty of animal protein, you don't have to worry about losing out on the desired effects of insulin. Your body will still produce an ample supply, just not an excessive one brought on by a sugar rush.

As an aside, I have come to believe that an insulin response to certain amino acids is a healthy primordial reaction to animal flesh consumption, whereas a dramatic rise in response to excess carbohydrates is unhealthy when done repeatedly. Since such a response is usually brought on by excess processed sugar ingestion, I view this vigorous insulin response as an unnatural reflexive action by which your body purges itself of what it interprets as somewhat of a poison (i.e., too much blood sugar). Go too many times to this well and the body shuts down, leaving you resistant to any effect insulin might have to lower blood sugar or stimulate growth.

Fiber Facts

Fiber is crucial for good health and a strong body. Found in plants, it's the building material that gives plants their strong stems and leaves. These fibers are composed of multiple sugar units, also known as polysaccharides. Two types of fibers exist: soluble and insoluble.

Soluble fibers dissolve in water and become gummy or viscous. It helps lower blood cholesterol levels and help regulate the body's use of sugars. Soluble fibers are broken down into two classes: pectins, and gums and mucilages.

Pectins are found in apples, carrots, beets, bananas, cabbage, dried peas and okra. Pectin helps decelerate the absorption of food, allowing sugar to be absorbed more slowly by the bloodstream. This aids in controlling blood sugar levels. Pectin also removes metals and toxins, lowers cholesterol and reduces the risk of heart disease and gallstones.

Gums and mucilages are found in oatmeal, oat bran, sesame seeds and dried beans. These soluble fibers also help regulate blood glucose levels, aid in lowering cholesterol, and help in the removal of toxins. Interestingly, the soluble type of fiber is not of much consequence to the bodybuilder and of greater significance to those that have high carbohydrates in their diet because it has a softening influence on blood sugar spikes.

Insoluble fiber is beneficial for the bodybuilder looking to gain lean mass while keeping body fat low. In addition to being loaded with naturally occurring minerals, trace minerals, and ultra-trace minerals, insoluble fiber foods are also powerful anti-carcinogen and digestive aids. This type of fiber gives structure to plant cell walls and includes cellulose, hemicellulose and lignin.

Cellulose is a nondigestible carbohydrate found in the outer layer of certain fruits and vegetables. It assists in the removal of cancer-causing substances from the colon wall, and helps prevent constipation, colitis, hemorrhoids and varicose veins. Hemicellulose is a nondigestible fiber that absorbs water, aiding in weight loss, constipation prevention, and control of carcinogens in the intestinal tract. Lignin is a form of fiber that helps lower cholesterol, prevents gallstone formation by binding with bile acids, and is beneficial for those with diabetes or colon cancer. (The cause of colon cancer isn't known, but about 25 years ago scientists noted that these cancers were more common in Western countries where people ate less fiber.) Fiber-rich foods such as leafy greens and broccoli are usually bundled with nutrients, vitamins, minerals and phytochemicals, all of which help in preventing heart disease and diabetes.

A diet rich in fiber will promote optimal transit time in the gastrointestinal tract, pushing all contents through with speed. Needless to say, letting anything you ate sit around and fester in your intestines isn't a pleasant or smart idea. Healthy, regular bowel movements create normal pressure within the intestines and the abdominal cavity, helping prevent diseases like diverticulosis, diverticulitis and hiatal hernia.

A fiber-rich diet has numerous other benefits:

- It nurtures a healthy environment in the body so that the more favorable bacteria (lactobacilli) are formed and unfavorable toxin-producing bacteria and yeast won't flourish.

- It stimulates the secretion of pancreatic enzymes and bicarbonate; such substances prevent incompletely-digested proteins from reaching the colon.

- It prevents gallstones by increasing bile solubility. The binding and diluting of other carcinogenic bile acids also help prevent colorectal cancer.

Perhaps one of the most important benefits for many is fiber's ability to bind and excrete cholesterol. In addition, fiber can even bind heavy metals and toxins, thus protecting the body from harm.

Lack of fiber in many of the popular high protein/no carbohydrate diets is a health hazard, pure and simple. Yet, for our purposes, perhaps one of the nicest things about fibrous carbohydrates is their lack of calories. In other words, you can and should have large helpings, as they won't negatively impact your diet or provide excess calories that can be stored as fat.

Don't worry about the sugar in vegetables either. Any carbohydrates in fibrous veggies are what I call "incidental." For example, veggies like broccoli, cauliflower, cabbage, collard greens, lettuce, celery, peppers, spinach, squash, onions, cucumber, asparagus, tomatoes, green beans, peas, brussels sprouts, alfalfa sprouts and beets are just some examples of healthy fiber-based choices and should be a significant part of your diet.

Protein Power

Non-weight-trained younger men have more muscle then non-weight-trained older men. Why? As we age, our protein levels drop significantly. The total amount of protein in healthy older men is only about 70 percent of that found in younger men, highlighting the need for dietary protein to support a young, strong and muscular body even if you don't train. If extreme muscle enhancement is the goal, optimal protein levels are a must.

Protein deficiency is much more common than most physicians would like to believe. A protein deficiency not only lowers a person's immunity but leads to a myriad of other problems, including fat gain and an acceleration of the aging process. Plus, it's the quickest route to losing a ton of muscle.

Next to water, protein is the most common substance in the body and, because of its versatile properties and malleable nature, has an infinite number of applications. A constant supply of protein is required to repair body cells as they wear out and are replaced by new ones. This is especially true for the bodybuilder. During times of growth, the body needs extra protein to replace body tissue broken down by exercise. In addition, proteins regulate body processes and, in the form of antibodies, help protect against infection and disease. Proteins are the source of the amino acids essential for growth and tissue repair, and make up the framework of an infinite number of compounds and structures in the body.

Commercially available proteins are obtained from animal (meat, eggs and dairy) or plant sources. As far as the latter, leaves, stems and roots have been explored as possible sources of protein, with the seed being the most useful part of a plant. Though incredibly poor in quality, wheat and corn have also been used as protein sources in bakery and breakfast foods. Other familiar industrial proteins include non-fat dry milk powder, gelatin and raw whey.

Proteins are made up of a combination of approximately 20 different amino acids. Like fats and carbohydrates, the amino acids that make up any protein are composed of carbon, oxygen and hydrogen atoms. However, proteins also contain nitrogen, which makes their structure and role in health unique. Out of all the amino acids, only nine are deemed "essential," because the body can't manufacture them on its own by using other substances; hence we must obtain them from the foods we eat. The essential amino acids include histidine, isoleucine, leucine, lysine, methionine, phenylalanine, threonine, tryptophan and valine.

Certain proteins are known as "complete" because they contain all the essential amino acids. Every type of animal meat is a complete protein, and thus contains all the essentials at differing but adequate levels. Conversely, "incomplete proteins" lack one or more of the essential amino acids. Vegetable-source proteins are examples, as leaves, stems and roots have all been found to be incomplete. Wheat and corn are also incomplete non-animal source proteins.

The take-away message is that complete protein is absolutely necessary in maintaining health, promoting proper bodily function, supporting immunity, keeping youth intact, and preserving wellness. Just as important, animal source protein should be an integral part of your daily diet.

Amino Alert

Unlike fat, which has been directly targeted as something to completely avoid in many diets, protein wasn't shunned specifically as much as it was a casualty of fat-avoidance behavior. Traditionally people have eschewed what they consider to be fatty foods and in the process eliminated red meat, eggs and milk from their diet. It's my steadfast belief that protein deficiency, which is rampant in society, is a result of a systematic and proactive elimination of some of the healthiest foods known to mankind, and certainly ones that build a muscular physique. The bottom line in terms of complete animal source protein is that, as a bodybuilder, you must consume plenty of it.

Bodybuilders are susceptible to protein depletion because they're trying to gain muscle while battling fat. The optimum daily level of protein for a bodybuilder is roughly one gram per pound of bodyweight per day. If you get too far above that, it may not contribute to protein synthesis anymore, but it does become a fuel source. (As an interesting aside, bodybuilders at high altitudes may need more then one gram per pound per day in order to maintain nitrogen and protein balance.)

Try to aim for a serving size of about 20–30 grams per meal, every 2–3 waking hours. Based on that logic, a bodybuilder shouldn't be taking in much less than about 150 grams of protein each day. That fits with what my old friend and 1984 Junior USA lightweight bodybuilding champ Peter Neff used to say. I can just hear him yelling at me now: "You try taking in less then 100 grams of protein and tell me if you grow!" On the upper extreme, taking in 300 or more grams of protein a day really requires some justification. That being, you are either a monster of a man at a fairly lean 270 pounds or you live and train high atop Mount Cucamonga.

Metabolic Advantages

Our food selection and the way we eat affects our metabolism; some foods and methods raise your metabolism, while others slow it to a crawl. Beyond supplying the body with essential amino acids that you need for big beef building, protein has a natural fat-burning metabolic advantage over other macronutrients. Frequent protein based-meals will actually help you burn fat by lifting your basal metabolic rate, irrespective of total caloric ingestion. This is yet another reason beyond just bulk building as to why, in a quest for extreme muscle enhancement, a dietary foundation of high quality protein is critical.

The process of the body burning food for energy is known as the "thermic effect of food," or TEF. The TEF for protein, carbohydrates and fats are quite different from one another. Since most people eat mixed meals, the total TEF is usually an average of these components. When combined in roughly equal proportions, the TEF of protein, carbohydrates and fats together elevates basal metabolism by roughly 10–15 percent. This metabolic lift is further attenuated as you increase the proportion of carbohydrates or fat. Breaking these out and taking each macronutrient separately, the TEF value of both carbohydrates and fats elevates the metabolism by only about five percent, while protein ingestion elevates basal metabolism by as much as 25 percent.

Clinical research confirms the metabolic protein advantage. Supporting this idea that protein actually boosts metabolism beyond that of other macronutrients are studies demonstrating that meals containing mostly protein compared to mostly carbohydrates or fats resulted in a significantly higher burn rate. When you think about it, this is really a fascinating phenomenon that the general public simply has not yet caught on to. The idea that protein builds muscle is widely accepted. But the notion that, in the process, it also lifts the metabolism and helps incinerate body fat is something you almost never see written about.

Fact vs. Fiction

One of the most common fallacies continually perpetuated by the ignorant is that a high amount of dietary protein causes kidney failure. Next to the myth that carbohydrates equal energy, or that soy is good for a man, the claim that excess dietary protein somehow causes renal failure in healthy adults is perhaps the next most annoying and outlandish piece of diet misinformation that's repeated throughout the media and popular press. It's actually been perpetuated so much that bodybuilders have repeatedly asked me about it over the years. Clearly the popular distortion of truth has affected our athletes and infected their minds as well.

This belief is not just a simple media distortion, but rather another colossal fabrication that some pinhead found a way to even slip into nutrition textbooks. As a result, many of my highly respected and well-liked physician colleagues continue to espouse this nonsense and I have to keep correcting them.

This mess began with early observations of protein intake in patients with kidney failure. It was noted that an excessive amount of protein in the form of meat, fish, milk and eggs seemed to gradually worsen the functioning of their kidneys. Since the kidneys are quintessential in the excretory process of the building blocks of protein (amino acids), dietary protein was found guilty by association and the idea that excessive protein worsens kidney function obtained widespread acceptance.

Yet the critical aspect that got lost in translation was that these observations were in individuals with a disease or illness that had abnormally affected their kidneys to begin with. These were not healthy people. They were not normal young guys trying to gain muscle mass. They were people like frail diabetics with kidneys failing as a result of a rapid progression of their disease. They were not only expelling protein via their urine, but a host of other vital nutrients as well, which I might add have never been blamed for this worsening state. These were the kind of people that were so sick, that many ended up hooked up to dialysis machines for what was left of their lives.

Incidentally, in my opinion, most all of these types of patients have been murdered not by protein, but by years of carbohydrate addiction. You must understand that physicians, like the general public, have also largely viewed carbohydrates as essential, when truly they're not. As a result, instead of eliminating dietary carbohydrates altogether, doctors have made room for carbohydrates in the diabetic diet and introduced insulin injections. Of course, once this is done, carbohydrates are artificially made essential. In other words, once the doctor gives the patient insulin, the patient must take in carbohydrates or end up in a hypoglycemic coma. But I digress.

The bottom line is that dietary protein has no negative effect whatsoever on the kidney function of a normal healthy adult. (I would even go so far as to state that I'm not completely convinced that unhealthy adults with kidney problems should be limiting dietary protein.) As an example to illustrate the silliness of this flawed logic, take individuals with "bad" hearts (i.e., congestive heart failure with decreased ventricular function) and have them rigorously run around a track. Although mild exercise is recommended for most of these folks, exercising at this level of intensity could result in cardiac arrest and death for many. Does that mean running around a track will cause a heart attack and death for a normal, healthy adult? Nonsense! Get my point? In fact, for a normal, healthy adult, it's quite the contrary. Running around a track is not only indicated but extremely healthy.

Sadly, this misconception has pervaded popular thinking about protein. Nothing could be further from the truth. The position of the National Kidney Foundation, which seems to be continually ignored by naïve physicians and dietitians, is clear. The Foundation does not have, nor have they ever had, a position on dietary protein as a cause of kidney disease, or for that matter any relationship of dietary protein to kidney disease in the healthy adult.

Beyond our own American foundation, consider the European Report of the IDECG, published in the *European Journal of Clinical Nutrition*. They clearly state there's no obvious upper limit of protein intake healthy adults cannot accommodate. In fact, they go on to discuss strength training athletes taking in 1.8 grams per pound of bodyweight per day of protein and experimental studies where subjects were given as much as 3.6 grams per pound per day without any harm to the kidneys.

Recall my example of early man and what constituted his diet. This primordial link is what we have deviated far from as a society. In fact, it is estimated that Paleolithic diets were more than half protein. Men in the famous Lewis and Clark expedition across America ate as much as nine pounds of buffalo meat each day with no ill effects. That's well over 600 grams of protein as a daily minimum! In today's world, although too low in fiber for our purposes, the Eskimos and gauchos of the pampas still consume almost exclusively protein in the form of large amounts of fish and meat, respectively. I can assure you that they don't have kidney failure as a result of the protein they eat.

Post-Workout Push

As discussed, 20–30 grams of protein every 2–3 hours is about right for extreme muscle enhancement while training hard . . . with one major exception. If you've just put in a very intense workout, you have a window of opportunity just after the training session when your body can absorb a significantly higher level of protein. If you miss this opportunity, your body may actually do the opposite of what you want it to do by becoming catabolic and metabolizing muscle mass.

The notorious and late *Underground Steroid Handbook* author Dan Duchaine used to talk about this a lot. It seems that your body may actually crave a higher protein intake just after truly intense physical output (not to be mistaken for a half-assed routine). Increasing protein intake to 40–50 grams at this critical time is not at all problematic and in fact should spur considerable growth if you're training correctly and your protein source is a good one.

Another caveat is at the other extreme. Though meal timing is critical, there will be rare occasions when the thought of eating another protein meal actually turns your stomach. In this case, don't push it. Instead listen to your body and back off the meal. By that I don't necessarily mean an all-out structured fast as I discuss in Chapter 3, but rather just skipping the one protein meal.

Don't be afraid you'll lose ground. It's a lot worse to force your body to eat when it's fighting against you. Let your body reset itself. Sometimes it needs to do that to grow. By choking down protein when your body doesn't want it, you'll be stimulating a catabolic response, resulting in physiologic retribution in the form of catabolic hormones cannibalizing muscle mass. Your muscles will flatten out like pancakes. If you've ever tried it, just watch the mirror the next day. Do it a few more times and your skin becomes gummy as you retain water and get fatter. Definitely don't let this blossom into an all-out vacation from your meal plan; just be sensitive to the times when your body is not cooperating and wants a momentary break.

Drink Up

Protein-based diets require an additional element that must be present in your strategy: hydration. We'll dive more into hydration later, but suffice it to say that your body will be far better at using protein for muscle building when you also ingest adequate amounts of fluids. In addition, from a health standpoint, high amounts of dietary protein combined with a low amount of fluid intake acidifies the body and creates an internal milieu ripe for some diseases to gain a foothold.

A particular subgroup of individuals is worth mentioning at this point — those who've suffered from kidney stones in the past. For these people, combining a high protein diet with inadequate hydration can result in a recurrence of the ailment. High protein diets have the natural ability to leach calcium from the bone, bring it into the blood, and out of the body through the urine. In the otherwise healthy male bodybuilder, calcium-rich dairy-based foods and dietary supplements can easily offset this normal response, but those with a history of stones can run into problems. Ironically, a high carbohydrate intake will also increase insulin levels and thus change urinary calcium concentration, which also can be stone forming.

If you're healthy, you have nothing to worry about as long as you always take in adequate amounts of fluid, or dehydration only occurs in the short term (i.e., contest preparation). On the other hand, if you have a history of stones, consult your doctor before you run into trouble.

Speed Up, Slow Down

I doubt I need to elaborate further on the importance of taking in liberal amounts of protein when you're training hard and trying to gain muscle. That's just common bodybuilding sense and an obvious fact that even the most inexperienced gym rat will figure out in no time. The more cerebral ideas like how much protein is too much, what sources are best, and the optimal time of consumption are just some of the more advanced concepts that experts debate. Among such arguments, the latest and perhaps the most contentious and least understood from a consumer standpoint is the issue of fast-digesting proteins versus slow proteins, and which is the best for bodybuilding.

The first question I'm always asked on the subject is, does such a difference really exist? Is there any advantage of having one over the other in terms of building muscle? The short answer is yes. Now for the long answer.

Quite a number of proteins are available on the market. Most are egg- or milk-based while others are soy, beef, and even gelatin. Due to ready availability and low price point, milk-source protein supplements have made up the majority of protein supplements over the years. Although containing a number of different proteins, milk contains two major ones used in the dietary supplement industry, casein and whey.

Casein is the principal protein of milk and, up until fairly recently, the most commonly used milk protein derivative in the dietary supplement industry. Though it's a well known "slow protein" and for that reason certainly has some limited supplementary utility, casein has a biological value of only 77, which means that your body will absorb about 77 percent of this protein.

Whey protein is also derived from milk. Amazingly, it was a by-product of the cheese industry and had been regularly discarded. In contrast to casein and its biological value of 77, the biological value of whey approaches 100. Hence, when comparing casein to whey, whey easily wins. Whey is found in increasing numbers of protein supplements and meal replacement powders. It's rich in tissue-regenerating substances like branched-chain amino acids, cysteine, lactose, minerals and lactalbumin.

The difference between fast and slow proteins may not matter to the average mope, but the very real difference that exists between them matters to the bodybuilder. The issue then becomes one of whether or not this difference can be clinically relevant.

Going back to carbohydrates for a moment, complex or low-glycemic carbohydrates tend to be preferred over the simple or high-glycemic types because slower absorption and digestion does less damage in terms of insulin spiking and body fat addition. In the case of protein needs for the bodybuilder, the model tends to be reversed, with the fast types more preferential than slow.

The classic comparison of fast and slow protein involves comparing supplemental whey protein to supplemental casein, respectively. Whey protein is considered a fast protein because it's rapidly digested, absorbed and assimilated by the body. Whey protein has been proven in research to increase the serum concentration of the essential amino acid leucine much more than casein. A significant whey protein supplement will usually advance through your system within a couple of hours. On the other hand, casein is a slow protein that tends to curdle in the stomach. As a result, it creates a conglomerate mass in the gut that slowly transits through the gastrointestinal tract and thus takes significantly longer to break down and absorb. This means lower but steadier levels of amino acids enter the bloodstream.

Since a growing bodybuilder needs higher levels of amino acids with stunning frequency when compared to an average male, they must eat regularly throughout the day (no less then every three waking hours). Thus it should make intuitive sense that a fast protein is the supplemental preference based purely on rate of uptake. For this reason alone, you wouldn't want to make a slow protein like casein the backbone of any good lean mass-building diet.

In addition, the quality of amino acids and ratios, as well as the presence of certain biologically active milk sub-fractions like IGF-I, alpha-lactalbumin, beta-lactoglobulin, immunoglobulins and lactoferrin, provide further reasons why a properly microfiltered whey protein is better for the health and growth of the bodybuilder. While many of these biologically active milk sub-fractions are destroyed in the stomach acid and by enzymes in the small intestine, when the ingested levels are lofty enough and in a form that's quickly absorbable, clinically relevant amounts can actually be taken up. Perhaps this is nature's logic behind breast milk being so high in these nutrients.

However you look at it, the issue for bodybuilders of choosing between fast and slow proteins centers on ease of digestion and speed of absorption. The system needs rest. The more energy your body has to spend on digestion means less energy in the coffers for muscle recuperation and building. This digestibility factor may be the reason that whey protein has been shown in research to stimulate more protein synthesis then casein.

My opinion shouldn't be taken to mean that I think there's nothing at all good about casein. Objectively speaking, some research points to a better anti-catabolic inhibition of protein breakdown attributed to slow proteins like casein. Some experts believe this is due to the fact that, although insulin activity doesn't seem to differ between the two types (recall that certain amino acids are non-sugar stimulators of insulin), sustained levels of consistent amino acid concentration may be the cause. Yet one needs to keep this in perspective; if your fast protein meals are frequent enough, not only should you be able to sustain consistent amino acid levels, these levels should be considerably higher then those achieved with less frequent slow protein ingestion. This is because, unlike slow proteins, fast proteins don't face digestibility as a limiting factor.

The next logical question would seem to be, what would happen if you simply took in slow protein with a high frequency? The answer is probably that you would, at the very least, decrease your appetite for solid food and become flatulent. At worst, you would probably get some stomach upset and nausea from the periods of ingestion and curdling in which incomplete digestive periods overlap as your gut works overtime.

I vividly recall the times of training and gaining long before the advent and widespread availability of whey protein supplements. Many of the available formulas were basically just casein and milk-solid powders. I remember the sluggish, bloated feeling as my body tried to manage these difficult drinks over many hours — a little too much slow protein after a post-morning workout and you could forget about any appetite for lunch. When it came to the old meal-replacement shakes, swallowing and re-swallowing partially digested, refluxed liquid just so we could wrestle in another meal behind it was about the grossest thing I remember. We made our bodies work so hard trying to process large volumes of this stuff that we really would have been much better off just eating regular solid food.

Overall, slow proteins like casein are okay in small amounts once in a while. But if you're trying to put on mass, crafting your diet around a slow protein like casein is a mistake. I've found in my practice that slow protein ingestion is better suited for a few select high-level competitive athletes that must endure lengthy training sessions and go longer stretches without meals. Only in such athletes do I occasionally favor casein-based slow protein supplement feedings.

An interesting exception among bodybuilders would be those who have a sub-optimal dietary routine and can't seem to manage to get in more then two or three meals a day. Obviously, gains will be seen minimally if at all in this scenario, so the name of this game is maintenance. Even the best and most committed bodybuilders go through periods where they can't go to the gym as often or can't get in proper meals and supplementation. In these situations, taking in fast/slow combinations of protein is actually most helpful in maintaining what you have. Getting a quick protein jolt from whey will help feed the need for whatever immediate anabolic repair your body might require, while a bit of slow protein from casein helps to counter tissue breakdown by sustaining blood levels of at least some essential amino acids for longer periods of time as your body goes significant stretches without nourishment. It's not optimal, but a little shift toward slow proteins when times like these arise can actually be beneficial in order to hang on to your past gains from better days.

Just remember that this is the exception. If you're training optimally for bodybuilding, then you should be supplementing optimally. Let the only slow proteins come from the foods you take in and not from your supplements. When the stars are aligned and everything is clicking with your training and dieting, your supplemental protein of choice should be frequent, fast whey protein.

Fat Is Your Friend

If your aim is to remain healthy and grow, you need fat in your diet — at least the right kind of fat.

Most of the bad fats are the saturated fats. While a little saturated fat isn't harmful and is probably helpful in incidental amounts, excessive saturated fats have been linked closely to some of the most serious diseases known to man. Though I believe it's usually on the backdrop of a diet too high in carbohydrates, excess saturated fats probably contribute to heart disease, stroke and cancer.

Invariably, you've heard recommendations to decrease your intake of processed saturated fat. Many of us are making efforts to cut down on consumption of fast foods, cold cuts, sausage, bacon, hot dogs, etc. Unfortunately, society's taken this to mean cutting out all fats, which is a big mistake. As discussed, a total ban on all fat is an error not only for the casual health seeker, but for those reaching for an extreme physique.

Saturated animal fat isn't the only unhealthy fat. Some bad fat comes from vegetable sources. Unlike animal fats, polyunsaturated fats are derived from vegetables and remain liquid at room temperature. For several decades, polyunsaturated fats were considered the more healthy option. Reminded that polyunsaturated fats are cholesterol free and very low in saturated fat: we were urged by the food industry, the media, and even our doctors to use margarine and vegetable shortening (corn, safflower, soy and sunflower oils) instead of butter and lard. However, in recent years we've learned that even these vegetable fats and oils are linked to obesity, cancer and heart disease, and that we therefore need to discriminate even further.

Unfortunately, much of the nutritional information available today fails to mention the essential fatty acids from fish oils and olive oil. Again, as with amino acids, the word "essential" refers to the inability of the body to manufacture the nutrient and the necessity to obtain it through the diet. The two essential fatty acids, and the ones that should be focused on for our purposes, are both polyunsaturated fatty acids (PUFAs): alpha-linolenic acid (an omega-3 fatty acid, or "n-3"), and linoleic acid (an omega-6 fatty acid, or "n-6"). These two types of PUFAs are metabolically and functionally distinct from one another.

Alpha-linolenic acid (n-3): When obtained through the diet, n-3 isn't particularly metabolically active until it undergoes a labor intensive and often energetically unfavorable conversion to two metabolically active forms. These forms are the eicosapentaenoic acid (EPA) and docosahexaenoic acid (DHA), which are found in great amounts in fish oils (i.e., mostly cold-water fish, but also found in rabbits and wild game). For this reason, I recommend bodybuilders eat a great deal of sashimi (raw fish) in order to get the greatest amount of healthy fat from their diet and thus limit the need for excess fat supplementation.

Only taking in alpha-linolenic acid requires a conversion to EPA and DHA through the aforementioned multi-step biochemical reaction. This inefficient conversion means a diet adequate in alpha-linolenic acid but low in supplemental EPA and DHA is actually insufficient to meet one's health needs. Although plant sources of alpha-linolenic acid are useful (i.e., flaxseed oil contains more than 50 percent alpha-linolenic acid by weight), often flaxseed oils are rancid, especially when kept at room temperature. For male physique enhancement purposes, I lean more toward fish oils because of the flavone content in flaxseed oil may represent a slight estrogenic problem for the male bodybuilder. Fish oil from the diet, or supplemental EPA and DHA from a liquid EFA, are great ideas. If you can't get enough from food, liquid fat doses of anywhere from 4–10 tablespoons per day (depending on your size) work well. It can be added to salad, on meats, or into protein shakes.

Linoleic acid (n-6): Most people seem to get not only enough n-6 in their diet, but actually far too much. In the distant past, humans relied heavily on a diet with a balance of n-3 to n-6 fatty acids. As such, this balance has been incorporated into our genetics. We now have a pre-programmed need to have an equal, 1:1 ratio of n-3 to n-6 fatty acids in our diet. However, over time, modern diets have come to rely on processed food, excessive carbohydrates, cooking oils and lard, to name a few culprits. The result has been a grossly disproportionate shortfall of n-3 as compared to n-6. Some data quote the ratio as being as lopsided as 1:25 in some cases.

If your thinking cap is on, you might be asking this question: If both n-3 and n-6 are essential and must be obtained through the diet, what's the problem with too much n-6 as long as your getting a high enough level of n-3? Well, the answer is this: An n-3 deficiency is accentuated when n-6 is elevated beyond that 1:1 ratio, because this excessive concentration inhibits the synthesis of DHA from alpha-linolenic acid. Thus, diets rich in corn, safflower and peanut oils (all are low in n-3 and high in n-6), can promote an n-3 deficiency. Meanwhile, the converse is not true; you don't have to worry about an excess of n-3, especially in the form of EPA and DHA.

Weighing The Benefits

With all of that explanation under our belts, just what in general are the benefits of these healthy fats? First are the health considerations:

- They're cardio-protective and ease the passage of blood and blood constituents through the coronary arteries.
- They have antiarrhythmic effects and can protect the heart from potentially fatal rhythms.

- They can reduce blood clotting and thrombosis nearly everywhere in the body.

- They're converted to hormones that can lower blood pressure, serve as a diuretic and rid the body of excess water, exert a positive effect on the immune and nervous system, and enhance efficient digestion and absorption by stimulating gastric secretions and natural smooth-muscle contraction.

As such, I have found in my practice that essential fatty acid supplementation has been successful in treating innumerable cases of constipation, as well as aiding in alleviation of elevated cholesterol and triglycerides, skin disorders, arthritis, allergies and unexplained hair loss (alopecia).

In my assessment, missing any nutrient deemed essential spells big trouble. How can any of your body systems function optimally, whether directly related to the deficiency or not, when your system is focused on adjusting to survive because something essential is missing?

Further, I believe the gravest indirect influence a deficiency of essential fatty acids causes is a disturbance in the balance of both sex and growth hormones, both critical to the male bodybuilder. These hormones have such widespread effects that EPA/DHA supplementation thus becomes, in my assessment, one of the most powerful things you can do for yourself to stave off the aging process and maintain a strong immune system.

While complete protein may be your best anabolic and fat-burning macronutrient, essential fats may be your best anti-catabolic macronutrient. General fat rules for bodybuilders include getting plenty of healthy fat from your diet, and not worrying about counting grams as long as you're avoiding processed carbohydrate foods. Eat red meat and don't worry about the incidental saturated fat, because the benefits far outweigh any downside as long as you keep to the other aspects of the diet. Eat plenty of cold-water fish like sashimi (that's just the fish, unlike sushi, which includes rice). If you start feeling like a seal after a while, don't worry, you'll be a big seal. Use olive oil when you fry instead of animal fat or vegetable oil. Finally, take supplemental fat if you need to.

Big Fat Myths

For what seems like forever, we've been fed false propaganda that says "fat is bad." We've been told to avoid fat in our diets at all costs. This is not only a theme in mass media, but also emanates from scientific literature as well. Even professional bodybuilders as recently as 10 or 20 years ago were eliminating all fats from their diet and, in the process, limiting their growth. Yet we know that, like protein and unlike carbohydrates, fat is essential. In other words, without the proper fat in your diet, you'll likely die prematurely.

All of this "fat is bad" nonsense probably stemmed from early calorie counting. One gram of either protein or carbohydrate is equal to four calories, while one gram of fat equals nine calories, so, on a per-gram basis, fats are more than double the calories of protein or carbohydrate foods. It seems that this single comparison has woefully distorted the facts. This archaic perspective takes none of the many good qualities of proper fat into account — our knowledge has evolved considerably since the early days and we're just now realizing how absolutely vital proper fats are in the diet.

Ketosis is yet another big fat myth. It's a state characterized by an accumulation of substances in the blood called "ketones" (specifically, acetoacetate, beta-hydroxybutyrate, and acetone). Such a presence is caused by burning fat for energy and not carbohydrates. Sound like a good thing? Well, it is. I'll explain.

A "spilling over" of ketones into the urine marks ketosis. It actually signifies a condition whereby the body relies on stored body fat to provide energy to the brain, organs and tissues. Not a bad thing at all if you think about it. So why has ketosis received such widespread negative press? Well, it's another case of guilt by association.

In the medical and scientific literature, ketosis has always been considered to be of concern because the condition was traditionally associated with starvation. Other pathologic conditions associated with ketosis have included uncontrolled diabetes mellitus (there's that sugar problem again) and inadequate nourishment during pregnancy. With these frightening associations, it comes as no surprise that ketosis has received such a bum rap anytime it appears. But I posit that the bad publicity surrounding ketosis is less fact-based and more distortion.

Commonly, high-protein, low-carbohydrate diets are considered ketogenic because they can cause ketosis. During a prolonged fast, the body's carb stores deplete quickly, resulting in lower levels of blood glucose. Although it's classically considered critical to maintain a certain blood sugar level to provide the brain with energy, if the transition to lowering carbohydrates is gradual enough, the body then uses fat and protein for energy. In order to preserve protein, the body uses less glucose and relies more strongly on fat metabolism. Sound logical?

However, fat is unable to cross the blood-brain barrier and provide energy to the brain. As a result, the liver converts these fats to ketones, which the brain readily uses for energy. Many of my colleagues tend to forget that little point and think our brains starve. If that were the case, every time someone dropped their carbohydrates they'd be driving off the roads and into trees.

The body has a very efficient and sensible metabolic pathway involving ketones. Just because the formation of ketones results from some abnormal disease conditions, this hardly means they have anything to do with causing such conditions (again a case of twisted logic). Though they can be a sign of problems under certain conditions, ketones by themselves are not some kind of nasty byproduct of toxic destruction. They actually are of considerable use. When our bodies are tuned and centered, we awaken metabolic pathways that have long since been forsaken. When we stop the narcotic diet of over-feeding ourselves carbohydrates, we rediscover old energy routes of great efficiency that don't require ingesting sugar foods for energy.

As long as you experience only a mild, transient ketosis and you eat adequate amounts of essential vitamins, minerals and fiber-based carbohydrates in the form of fresh vegetables, you're on the right track. You won't likely be in a state of ketosis much, and if you are now and then, know you're burning more body fat.

Severe ketosis can result in nausea, hypotension, dehydration and fatigue. But these are usually only seen in cases associated with starvation. In the absence of severe dehydration and metabolic stress, starvation ketosis does not normally progress to ketoacidosis, a condition where the plasma ketone concentration becomes high enough to cause a dangerous drop in pH (i.e., the blood becomes more acidic). In fact, you'll find little evidence in the literature to suggest that ketogenic diets actually induce ketoacidosis. This is largely due to the fact that dietary protein, if high enough, can be converted to carbohydrates. In fact, a study from the Department of Nutritional Sciences at the University of California-Berkeley showed a hundred grams of dietary protein provides about 55 grams of carbohydrates, which is more than enough to prevent ketosis.

Because of the lean away from processed carbohydrates and the lean toward fiber-based carbohydrates, the proper bodybuilding diet might be classified by some as mildly ketogenic on occasion, at least in the beginning adaptation phase. However, such a label is incorrect. Your diet should be high in protein and fiber-based carbohydrates, essential fats, fiber, water and other essential nutrients, thus making ketosis unlikely and infrequent. I believe that the occasional transient ketone production actually works for you by rapidly and safely stripping the body of flab during times of more intensified training while sparing muscle mass. Yes, healthy dietary fat is an awesome anti-catabolic bodybuilding tool.

Hydrate!

For more reasons then I can even begin to capture in writing, proper hydration is an absolute necessity for muscle growth. Water is the most common substance on the planet and, I believe, the most neglected of all essential nutrients.

When we look at our body composition as a model for what to consume, we find that the body is made up of an enormous amount of water, followed by muscle, fat, and trace carbohydrates and elements. So it seems incredibly logical that our diet should reflect this composition.

On average, an adult's bodyweight is nearly 70 percent water. This corresponds to about 12 gallons. Of course, this specific percentage varies depending on body composition, age and gender, among other factors, but the point remains the same — water is fundamental.

Lean muscle contains much more water than body fat does. Thus, the more muscle you have and the leaner you are, the higher proportion of water your body contains. Water accounts for about 75 percent of a newborn's weight, decreasing in the elderly to about 55 percent. As we age or become ill, our bodies dry out. Sadly, although we're in desperate need of hydration as we age and lose muscle, we tend to drink less, thus compounding our dilemma. The first piece of your anti-catabolic front in preventing premature muscle loss should be making sure you're always adequately hydrated.

Water contains no calories, yet every cell, tissue, and organ, and almost every life-sustaining body process needs it to function. It transports nutrients and oxygen to your cells, carries waste products out of your cells, lubricates body tissues, moistens your mouth, eyes and nose, and constitutes the tissues that cushion your joints and protect your body organs. Water is also the main constituent of all body fluids, including blood, gastric (stomach) juice, saliva, amniotic fluid (for a developing fetus), and urine.

The value of proper hydration cannot be underestimated. In fact, whenever someone becomes sick and is brought to the hospital, be it fever, infection, trauma, blood loss or other affliction, the first thing that's almost always done is to set up an intravenous line and pump fluid into the body. When faced with severe illness, the hydration of the patient is a first consideration for the physician when a life is at stake. Thus, it should come as no surprise that this should be a first consideration for you as well. Dehydration can result from a disease process or result in a disease process. Either way, poor hydration equals poor muscle retention and growth.

Water For Workouts

To keep muscles functioning during a workout, you need a near-continuous water supply. If you train with true muscle-building intensity and you're one of those guys that sweat a great deal, it's truly amazing to see how much fluid you require. Losing one or two pounds of your body's water weight can create a feeling of thirst. With more fluid loss, strength will fade. With even more loss, you'll suffer exhaustion. Too little water for too long and your muscle tone will flatten and the inexorable skid begins.

The more intense your workout, judged by how much sweat you're throwing off, is a perfect barometer to measure how much fluid you need to put back in. Try to listen to your body and drink instinctively during your routine, but make an attempt to drink smaller sips more frequently as opposed to chugging a lot down in big gulps. This is especially true when performing heavy lifting or doing movements that involve bending at the hips (i.e., squats, deadlifts, bent-over rows, etc.), as those compress the midsection and may result in nausea, reflux or vomiting.

For moderate- to high-intensity routines that last no more then 45 minutes, fluid requirements can and should be easily satisfied by drinking pure water. But if you perspire profusely, it may not be enough, and you may need to consider a sports drink. Dehydration occurs with amazing rapidity under these conditions and can actually inhibit physical performance, flatten muscles, and rob you of a pump in a surprisingly short amount of time. This may be due to the fact that, in addition to water loss during periods of intense training, a high level of critical minerals called "electrolytes" are also expelled in sweat, including sodium, potassium, magnesium, phosphorus, chloride and calcium.

Any worthwhile hydration formula must contain a variety of electrolytes; otherwise, it's just sugar water. Picking a rehydration formula for these times of great physical exertion can be a little daunting because many of the popular products on the market, to be honest, suck.

The Ideal Sports Drink

The premier consideration for sport-drink formulation is something called "tonicity." The tonicity of a solution is also referred to as the "osmolality" of a solution. These terms refer to the concentration in liquid of sodium, sugar, and to a lesser extent, other electrolytes. Your body has a normal concentration of these substances that can be calculated and given a numeric value (equal to about 280).

A fluid that contains a higher concentration of sugar and electrolytes relative to this number is said to be hypertonic. A fluid that contains the same tonicity or osmolality as that of the body is said to be isotonic. A fluid that contains a lower concentration of these substances relative to the human is hypotonic.

Fluid flows through tissues in the direction of the highest concentration. So a hypertonic solution (like so many of the more popular retail sports drinks on the market) will actually draw fluid out of the body and actually temporarily worsen dehydration. Though the body eventually secretes enough water into the intestines to dilute the hypertonic solutions, the temporary water shift into the gut can expose the bodybuilder to sluggishness, and even cramping. Many bodybuilders note excess mucus formation and an ironic, persistent need to drink plain water after drinking these types of sports drinks. As a result, you'll never see a professional bodybuilder quench their thirst with these popular mainstream beverages.

As far as an isotonic solution, once in the stomach it won't go anywhere fast because it has the same osmolality as the body. It'll just sit in your gut until your system can remove it. As a result, you're left bloated with abdominal distention.

Finally, a hypotonic solution is rapidly absorbed. Because of its lower osmolality compared to the body, it empties quickly from the gut for absorption into tissues, nourishing working cells.

Pure water is a most extreme hypotonic solution, with an osmolality of less then 20. Yet while water is well absorbed, it can't replenish electrolytes and critical micronutrients, because it doesn't contain an appreciable amount of these electrolytes needed to assist in the cultivation and maintenance of a good pump. Even traditional electrolyte formulas that contain sodium and potassium may not be enough for intense training, because they lack magnesium and phosphorus, which are critical to cell fluid resuscitation and functional recovery after intense exertion.

The rehydration formula you choose should have these electrolytes and the osmolality should be significantly lower then 280 (otherwise it won't get absorbed quickly enough), and preferably more then 200 (otherwise it's probably too low in electrolytes). In other words, you want to be reasonably sure that absorption happens quickly due to the hypotonic aspect while being certain that you are getting an appropriate concentration of electrolytes. By the way, if a company doesn't publish their osmolality, don't buy their hydration formula.

Perhaps the most annoying thing about many popular sports drinks is that they're loaded with sugar. After all I've said about focusing on healthy fiber-based carbohydrates in the form of fresh vegetables, the last thing you need to do is blow it all by drinking high amounts of sugar during your workout. Also, if the total carbohydrate content of a sports drink exceeds 10 or more grams per eight fluid ounces, it's too much. If that's the case, you can reasonably conclude the solution is either hypertonic and won't be quickly absorbed, and/or contains too much sugar and not enough electrolytes.

THE ANTI-CATABOLIC PRINCIPLES

As mentioned in Chapter 1, we as humans are up against a host of factors, all conspiring against our abilities to build appreciable mass. However, those forces can only succeed in defeating your bodybuilding efforts if you let them. Instead, learn how to control and minimize them by tapping into the 10 anti-catabolic nutritional principles outlined below.

Principle No. 1: Avoid Starvation Alert

One of the hallmarks of dieting to gain mass is to not let your body starve all day and then dump in a truckload of food at once. The temporal relationship of your meals is critical. Although there is a time and place for caloric deprivation, the body must be fed on a regular basis or you simply won't gain size. You'll gain fat. In other words, when you eat is as important as what you eat. Even a small amount of calories eaten at the wrong time, after hours of caloric deprivation, can cause you to rapidly gain blubber. It's a phenomenon I call "starvation alert."

Starvation alert is an age-old mechanism whereby your body attempts to resist change. Every warm-blooded animal has an internally programmed physiologic drive to preserve energy and not change when times are good. When an African tiger, cheetah or other predatory creature has had unsuccessful hunts and has gone hungry for days, times are bad. The animal's body knows that, and internal adjustments automatically occur. Metabolism slows, hormone levels change and sleep patterns alter. They enter a state of starvation alert. The period of starvation throws the body into a shocked state in which it makes necessary survival adjustments, including activation of fat-storage pathways so any calories ingested that aren't needed up front are tucked away for later use. This is the nature of the starvation alert mode — preparing for another harsh time of deprivation by causing the body to hoard fat.

My favorite example illustrating the principle of starvation alert in men is the Japanese sumo wrestler. I have spent quite a bit of time in Japan and have made many friends of Japanese heritage. In my time abroad, over the years I feel I have come to know the culture fairly well. I can tell you firsthand that the Japanese aren't an obese culture by any stretch of the imagination. This is so much the case that it leads one to believe that genetics and not just dietary habits are at work here. They tend not to be great bodybuilders, but they are not traditionally fat either. However, like a blip on a radar screen or a spike on a seismograph, emerging from these people of modest streamlined physiologic stature, there is sumo.

Thousands of years old, the sport of sumo seems more like a religious tradition at times than a sport. These massive blobs grow to staggering proportions, with some weighing well over 500 pounds. Doesn't it make you wonder how a man from such an innately trim culture can produce so much fat? The answer is this: The Japanese sumo tradition must be credited with discovering the earliest application of starvation alert and basically using it to create the otherwise inconceivable girth on these men.

Contrary to what you might think, most sumo wrestlers traditionally eat only one meal a day in the evening. It's called chanko and is made up of a pot of broth with pieces of meat, poultry and fish mixed in with vegetables. The dish is served with a pot of rice and tea. It doesn't sound that excessive to most people, and it's puzzling to attempt to determine what exactly is so bad about this meal. But to me, the problem is clear. Even though the total calories consumed are not that huge in number, the issue is one of timing. The meal is served in the evening and, worse yet, before sleep. The result is a cultivation of the worst aspects of starvation alert, sending a catabolic, fat-accumulation message through all points of the body.

Steeped in the tradition, sumo wrestlers purposely starve themselves all day. This puts them into a state of starvation alert so that when the evening feeding comes, the body is fully prepared to stockpile nearly every calorie as fat, all in preparation for what the body perceives as necessary for "surviving" the next period of deprivation. On top of that, they fall asleep immediately afterward, which seals the deal.

Interestingly, as with animals, this extreme fatigue to the point of falling asleep is an integral hallmark of the body being immersed in a deep state of starvation alert. The way to decrease fat and put the brakes on this catabolic impulse is taking the reverse approach — having smaller meals frequently throughout the day, higher in calories in the morning, decreasing to nothing by bedtime.

Perhaps the best real-world example of my theory of starvation alert in action is Thanksgiving Day. It seems like everyone at one time or another has approached this gluttonous day with a similar flawed logic, and thus experienced the same outcome — starvation alert and subsequent fat gain. It starts a day or so before Thanksgiving, as we begin tapering our intake in preparation for the large meal to come. Thanksgiving Day hits and we only have a cup of coffee for breakfast and skip lunch altogether, somehow thinking that if we eat less during the day we'll be able to get away with stuffing ourselves at night. Sound familiar? Just like the sumo wrestler, we have put ourselves in a state of starvation alert. That will easily lead to the storage of plenty of fat while curbing quality muscle growth.

Hitting the dinner table in our deprived condition, we gorge ourselves with turkey, gravy, stuffing, sweet potatoes, giblets and cranberry sauce, among other specialties of the feast. What's the result? Like the predatory cat in the wild and not much different from the sumo wrestler, we're barely able to keep our eyes open. As we deliriously rise from the table with our belt buckle discreetly unsnapped, the blur of our gastronomically-stretched consciousness comes into focus. Like fat, lazy dogs we eye a quiet warm spot on the carpet near the television and collapse into a deep sleep. That is, of course, until we come back to life about a half-hour later, just as the pumpkin pies are carried in.

So as it applies to bodybuilding, the take-home message is to understand starvation alert and avoid it completely: Eat more early than later, eat frequent smaller meals, and don't go to bed on a full stomach. This leads into the next concept of meal cadence.

Principle No. 2: Maintain a Proper Meal Cadence

One of the biggest dietary mistakes you can make as a bodybuilder is to go for long stretches with little or no food intake. Nearly everyone in their life has gone too long at some time or another in a wait for food. Think back to a time when you were starving. Remember how you felt? Your stomach was probably growling and you were literally salivating at the thought of a sloppy cheeseburger, some salty fries and an icy cold soda.

Think of a time when you were in this ravenous state but couldn't get access to food. Recall the next thing that happened — you became agitated. Then your core temperature went up and you began to sweat. At the peak, perhaps you were out of your mind with aggravation and you could feel your pulse shoot up. Shortly after that, it all subsided and you were mysteriously fine, at least for a little while.

What happened to your body from a physiologic standpoint was that you slipped into starvation alert. After those first telltale signs, it's usually too late to reverse even with a quick feeding. The relief you feel in that state is due to a triggering of catabolic hormones such as cortisol and epinephrine, every bodybuilder's worst enemy when they're secreted in excess, as they cause your system to break down muscle and store energy as fat.

The best way to avoid this hyper-catabolic state is to ensure you never reach that point in the first place. Ingesting smaller, more frequent meals spaced throughout the day is the best way; I have generally found that a male bodybuilder wanting to gain mass should space their meals no more then three hours apart. That's what I call good meal cadence, because it virtually eliminates the possibility of long stretches of caloric depletion and the destructive hormonal sequence that follows.

Just remember that what constitutes a meal in this case isn't necessarily the traditional, grab-the-knife-and-fork-for-a-four-course-meal affair. For optimal results, a bodybuilder should have small, workman-type meals — a chicken breast with a side of rice, a bowl of oatmeal, even just a protein shake.

I'll touch more on the content of perfect muscle-building meals later. The focal issue right now is that you understand meal cadence — never allow yourself to reach the point of having a high hunger level. You should eat because it's feeding time, and never because you're starving.

Principle No. 3: Utilize Structured Fasting

As I described in great detail, regular feeding is critical to countering catabolism. You should never feel starved, nor should you gorge until you're stuffed. Yet, even if you follow this moderate feeding program, you'll still have rare times when the thought of more food literally sickens you. This is a critical time when you must temporarily go against Principle No. 2 and avoid food for a short period. Here's where you use fasting to your metabolic advantage.

Avoiding starvation alert and paying attention to proper meal cadence should generally rule nearly every day of a bodybuilder's life. However, on occasion, very short-term, structured caloric deprivation has its place because it not only resets your metabolic ability to burn fat but also spurs anabolic growth factors that build muscle.

Now, I realize this goes against years upon years of conventional bodybuilding wisdom. The thought that you must constantly force-feed calories when you're trying to put on solid weight, never missing a meal no matter what, is a mantra passed from generation to iron-pumping generation. Honestly, such consistency is often necessary, but it's a delicate balance that all too often is taken too far, leading to disappointing outcomes for the hardgainer dutifully following this approach.

I remember Ray, a former training partner, who used to compete in the Mr. America. Like everyone at the time, he was convinced that you had to gorge yourself between shows to get results. You had to eat, even if you weren't hungry. He'd push the feedings on me. I respected Ray so much because he was a bit older than me and had a whole lot more bodybuilding and competitive experience. There he was, constantly shoving a fork and a plate of food at me, egging me on with his war cry, "Ya gotta eat to grow!"

I listened. I ate. And in less then 10 weeks I gained about 15 pounds of the most disgusting, fat-riddled mass I'd ever put on. My muscles were flat and I was softer than ever. It took me the next few months to realize the error of my ways and finally correct it.

Sure, the guys back then grew, but it was more in their waistlines than in their chests. Unfortunately, little has changed, as an unwitting new generation of lifters is all too open to listening to the sloppy sages of yesteryear who just love to perpetuate their flawed logic to any audience willing to listen.

True bodybuilding sapience now tells us that continuously pigging out on all that food without a break will only serve to develop that massive belly you always wanted. If you're just now realizing that you're one of those victims, don't feel bad. You're not alone and there's plenty of hope. Just remember my story about Ray. I was also snookered by what were, at the time, his good intentions to try and help me. Of course, the only thing Ray helped me gain was a lot of gas and bloating, which I was more than happy to finally lose, along with all the bonus fat I gained on his grotesque regimen.

By the way, if you think you're fine but still have a waist bigger then 35 inches, you might be in denial and will need to ask yourself a simple additional question. Do you have to periodically unsnap your pants and let your flab-alanche expand to stuff more food into your cake hole? If so, you might have won a prize and until now, you didn't even know it. You might actually be a blue-ribbon bodybuilding pig. Head to the county fair and see if you make it to the podium. Or better yet, swallow your pride, admit the error of your ways and take a new path while you still have time.

After years of education and coaching bodybuilders, I can assure you that if this game was as simple as chronic overfeeding, muscle growth would be effortless for all of us. As I've explained, the only prerequisite would be to eat non-stop and become a blob-in-training. Gyms are filled with many of these misguided souls, so don't become one. Put the utensils down, wipe your face and listen up on how to use rare times of caloric restriction in order to grow.

It might surprise you to learn that restricting calories when your body is sending signals it doesn't want food isn't just for dieting and losing weight. When done correctly, it will actually stimulate muscle growth. I think back to the year I won my class at the East Coast championships. While moderately sized, I certainly was not the thickest in my class. So my game was getting shredded, and boy was I ripped for that one. Even the muscles in my face were cross-striated through the skin.

Getting in great shape and taking a class was not the most memorable aspect of the experience. Instead, my greatest recollection was of coming off that show and making some of the biggest gains in fat-free muscle I'd ever packed on. It wasn't just the usual weight rebound that one experiences after dieting for a show. I had certainly done that enough to recognize it. No, it was different. I was actually packing on muscle and very little fat. This was all years before medical school or any of my formal training in sports medicine or sports nutrition, so I wasn't really sure what was happening to me at the time. But I watched things carefully and took great notes, hoping I might one day figure it out.

It turned out that what I was experiencing was not all that uncommon. The guy helping me at the time, Peter Neff, was a master at dieting and knew his body as well as anyone I'd ever met. People who've heard of him know he was a legend in the sport of amateur bodybuilding. As a matter of fact, it's been said that with the exception of Robby Robinson, Pete had won more bodybuilding titles as an amateur than anyone else in history. So it should suffice to say that when it came to contest preparation, this guy knew his stuff. He told me how this symptom of piling on real mass after extreme dieting (not just gaining fat or simply putting back on the pre-diet weight) was something he'd noticed himself over the years. This was precisely how he actually used to make notable short-term gains between shows. He couldn't explain why it worked, but it did.

I now speculate that the reason it works has to do with a down-regulation of myostatin and a subsequent stimulation of growth hormone during a time of extreme caloric depletion immediately followed by a vigorous re-feeding. To understand this, consider these five points:

1. *The body's in a constant struggle for homeostasis, or a fight to maintain the status quo.*
2. *Building bulky muscle mass challenges this homeostasis.*
3. *Hard training inhibits myostatin and stimulates growth hormone secretion, since the body must respond to the workload by increasing muscle repair and growth.*
4. *Brief and severe caloric restriction also temporarily slows myostatin expression and stimulates growth hormone secretion, along with up-regulating the sensitivity of growth hormone receptors as the body responds to preserve muscle.*
5. *Although avoiding starvation alert and honoring proper meal cadence is critical to keep myostatin expression in check, over many months, a constant flow of calories may actually put a damper on growth hormone secretion as your body fattens in response to an environment of over-abundance. This moment is signaled by a physiologic rejection of food (i.e., the thought of eating another meal makes you want to puke).*

So while you're experiencing periods of intense training, you can periodically use short-term caloric restriction to take advantage of the brief surge of growth hormone and the up-regulation of growth hormone receptors. I call it "structured fasting." Note that this isn't the same scenario as what occurs under starvation alert. The difference is, when you're in starvation alert, your body actually wants food as you pass through moments of starvation. Starvation alert is fostered by a lifestyle of daily food deprivation and nighttime re-feeding. This is bad for bodybuilding and in sharp contrast to moments necessitating structured fasting. In the latter, you're reading a different set of signals from your body, a negative reaction to the thought of food or a disinterest in eating.

If you've never experienced it and find that you're always hungry when mealtime rolls around, then your meal cadence is not good enough. Take note of this: When you eat enough bodybuilding meals with enough frequency, food rejection is inevitable. With structured fasting, you learn to not fight it, but go with the flow and actually make it work for you.

Remember that structured fasting is only half the approach. It will only work in combination with a vigorous calorie intake immediately after the fast. Pay attention to the following five caveats for your fast and re-feed:

1. *Don't completely deprive your body of all calories for an entire day, as one does when truly fasting. Instead, have one liquid meal. I prefer a low-calorie liquid protein shake in the morning and then fasting the rest of the day and night.*
2. *The most critical time to keep calories in check is at night because it's while sleeping that one enjoys the greatest growth hormone response to fasting.*
3. *Do not perform structured fasting more than once every few weeks, and don't ever pass over to the other extreme and force your body to fast if it does not signal for it. I've found that when done unnecessarily or with too great a frequency, it will work against you and diminish your returns.*
4. *You must immediately re-feed the morning the fast is over. Do not wait until later in the day to re-introduce food.*
5. *When re-feeding, take in plenty of protein, healthy fat and fluid. Be careful of carbohydrates because they will cause your insulin to spike and that can lead to fat gain. You want to exploit a natural myostatin downgrade along with the rise in growth hormone, all the while keeping your insulin levels from surging. After that, it's back to your normal dietary pattern.*

Structured fasting may be one of the best dietary methods you can try to keep spurring muscular growth and warding off excess body fat. A rare structured fast is not only good for muscularity, but it's good for your health as well. It breaks the cycle of continuous caloric overabundance. Although the bodyweight of animals that are continuously fed a surplus of calories climbs dramatically, they eventually top out and then start to lose lean muscle mass with a double-whammy of pure fat gain. Man is no different.

In longer studies on animals exposed to continuous caloric excess, incidence of cancer and other diseases increases. Compared to animals on diets with boundaries, the lifespan of the overfed will decrease dramatically. As a positive example from my own life, I remember the dogs I had growing up. My dad loved dogs and still does. He made sure they stayed active but hated feeding them a lot. He always said too much food made him broke and made them fat and lazy. Our dogs, fed in a very controlled way, were always thick with muscle, fit and game for a fight. My Dad's last great pooch lived over 23 years.

As a last thought, when implementing structured fasting, if you think you need a day like this but are afraid of getting smaller, losing strength, or feeling weak for the relative few hours it takes, relax and suck it up. You're suffering from an irrational fear — one day won't derail you. Indeed, it may just be the catalyst you've been sorely lacking, the very piece of the puzzle that's been holding you back from the growth spurt you've been striving for. Just dive right in and do it; you won't regret the decision.

Principle No. 4: Eat For Your Somatotype

Learning how to tailor your diet to fit your somatotype is an enormously powerful way to ignite your progress. To begin, take a look at these classic somatotype descriptions to figure out where you fit (hint: many people don't fall neatly into one category but fall more in between as a mix of two):

Ectomorph: This is the typical, skinny hardgainer. If he happens to gain body fat, he can lose it easily. He finds it very tough to gain appreciable muscle. Physically, he possesses thin bones and joints, with a naturally narrow waist. A "skin and bones" type, but sometimes possesses wide, square shoulders which taper to the waist — a good thing in bodybuilding terms.

Mesomorph: This is the naturally muscular, athletic-looking guy we'd all like to be (but so few of us are). He tends to gain muscle very easily while not carrying a lot of body fat. Big bones, thick joints, and a well-shaped muscle structure throughout his body. Although a mesomorph can often get a solid six-pack, he's usually not narrow or small in the waist.

Endomorph: The endomorph is the guy who constantly battles his weight. Wide in the waist, narrow in the shoulders and often chubby, he can add muscle with some degree of ease, but unfortunately puts on fat just as easily. It takes a huge effort for an endomorph to "get ripped" he invariably has to diet harder, longer and more consistently to build a bodybuilding physique.

Have you determined where you fit? If so, here are a few guidelines you can use, tailored to each type.

The ectomorph who wants to bodybuild is the most dependent on frequent feedings. He should be eating small, protein-heavy meals as frequently as every two hours. He needs to be aware of his carbohydrate intake — for ectomorphs, filling up on carbohydrates at the expense of complete proteins (such as steak or eggs) and healthy fats is a bad idea. Endomorphs load up on pasta and bread and seemingly instantly get fat, which warns them off of such foods — that same "warning signal" doesn't occur with ectomorphs because they're metabolism is quicker. However, if not kept in check, a high intake of carbohydrates will hurt your chances of long-term success. You won't get fat, but your muscles won't grow either.

One of the most potent problems facing an ectomorph in his teens and 20s is his penchant for a limited appetite. It's common for an ectomorph to claim he eats a lot of food but "just can't gain weight," when in reality, if he truly tracked his intake, he would find he doesn't eat nearly as much as he thinks. He simply doesn't eat the amount of food necessary to keep up with his revving metabolism.

The classic ectomorph often finds it tough to get enough quality calories without feeling bloated. As a result, in addition to healthy foods I recommend a great deal of protein shakes to round out the daily diet. Liquid calories are easier to assimilate and digest than whole food, and they don't leave you feeling as full, which makes them a valuable addition to the muscle-building nutrition program of the ectomorph.

Overall, the ectomorph's body is stubborn and resistant to change. You really need to steadfastly stick to your diet and training. New muscle comes slowly, and can disappear in the blink of an eye if you slip off the bodybuilding wagon for even a moment. But if you can adhere to your plan, you do enjoy a few edges in that you often have a nice V-shaped body frame to build upon, and you can burn excess body fat easily when the time comes to get cut.

The mesomorph has a very responsive physique when it comes to bodybuilding diet and nutrition. Like the ectomorph, limiting simple carbohydrates and saturated fat is a good thing and frequent feedings are the right strategy in the chase for big mass gains. Interestingly, unlike the ectomorph, the mesomorph is not as intensely dependent on frequent feeding simply because his body doesn't lose lean muscle as easily in response to missed meals. He can go three hours between feedings without ill effect. Again, high-quality, complete protein (preferably red meats and poultry in the meso's case) and healthy fat should dominate his diet.

Dietary supplements in general can have profound effects in the mesomorph. Unlike the ectomorph body, the mesomorph is far less resistant to change. The right dietary supplements for the mesomorph can produce an easily detectable change when coupled with hard training.

The endomorph, when left without guidance, is basically a train wreck when it comes to eating, and should almost always be on a restrictive diet. His desire to eat, coupled with a propensity toward excess body fat, makes him difficult to manage and gives him little room for error.

Although an endomorph stacks on muscle in much the same, responsive way as the mesomorph, he finds it difficult to keep his body fat levels under control. As with all three body types, the same ideal formula of taking in high-quality protein and healthy fats while limiting carbohydrates and saturated fats holds true.

Late-night carbohydrate eating is probably the most egregious diet sin for the endomorph. They are like sumo wrestlers, so following this model will lead to the same results. While at one extreme, an ectomorph might actually need an evening meal to stave off overnight catabolism, the same protocol will cause an abrupt fat gain in the endomorph.

Protein shakes are helpful for endomorphs. But unlike the ectomorph who must use them in addition to meals, the endomorph must use them in place of some meals as a way to limit the total number of calories consumed. Since he typically likes to eat, taking up to half his meals as lower-calorie protein shakes can be extremely effective. Dietary supplements can affect the endomorph as easily as the mesomorph, but until he gains lean mass in just the right places, the effects of dietary supplements are less easily noticed due to the poor body structure and high percentage of blubber. So the good news for an endomorph is he gains muscle easily — the bad news, he needs to be much more cognizant of holding his body fat in check.

Principle No. 5: Say Yes to Beef

Something about the savagery of eating meat seems to satisfy a deep-seeded carnivorous human need. We have incisors for a reason. Though brutal sounding, we were obviously meant to have the ability to rip and tear the flesh of other animals. The position of our eyes in front of our heads, and not on the sides, dictates that we are hunters rather than hunted. Front-placed eyes, like those of the meat-eating lion, wolf, hawk and snake, are the natural hallmark of the hunter because they allow for vision in three dimensions. (Just try covering one eye and see how much depth perception you lose.) This is in stark contrast to the herbivore, whose eye position is on the side of the head, as in the cow, deer, rabbit, pigeon and antelope, to provide the ability to see 360 degrees and watch out for predators.

Added to that, we humans have a dietary need for essential amino acids that are found whole only from the flesh of other animals and from their byproducts. The essential amino acids are never found in complete form in any vegetable; the few essential amino acids found in plants are seldom in appreciable quantity, and can only be made complete by combining different vegetables.

Spending your days combining vegetables in an optimal way is completely impractical. Vegetables should be nothing more than a regular healthy side dish for the bodybuilder because they contain only sparse amounts of essential amino acids and healthy fats. Science proves that meat, not vegetables, quenches the anti-catabolic thirst at the cellular level. Like it or not, nature says we are meat eaters. If you haven't yet guessed, I'm no vegetarian. So if you're the vegan sort and not already completely offended, stop reading now and forget about extreme muscle enhancement.

When I think of the raw human savagery of the macho meat eater, the image of King Henry VIII comes to mind. I recall paintings and pictures of him sitting at a massive table of food, holding a half-eaten turkey leg. Maybe it's a "guy thing," but tearing apart a turkey carcass or Cornish hen just seems to satisfy some kind of testicular need. Yes, it's weird fun for us guys, but true.

While I recommend that, unless you're a very fat endomorph, you should make beef your anti-catabolic preference, poultry is also a bodybuilding staple. I don't think it's much of a problem, but there are some caveats. Poultry is a relatively good source of essential amino acids and certainly comparable to beef in many ways. However, the estrogen content can be quite high. This is especially true for turkeys around the holiday season. I mean, did you ever stop and ask yourself how they get a 20-pound bird to have breasts as big as those on a woman? Some of these birds are artificially jacked up with estrogens, causing them to develop prematurely and hold a great deal of water (since nobody wants a dry turkey, estrogens are a sinister way to juice them up artificially). While these perils can be easily avoided by going the route of organic, kosher or hormone-free birds, the cost can add up, since these are of considerably greater expense.

Regular chicken or free-range chicken can be a happy compromise, as these tend to be less adulterated than some of the hormone-happy holiday birds you can find year-around in the freezer section. When at my family holiday shindig, I usually ask for a Cornish hen or small chicken to be made alongside mom's extra-feminine thunder-chick. In addition, when ordering deli meats, I try to ask for chicken and not turkey breast.

By the way, in case you are wondering why I suspect that turkey is worse than chicken in terms of estrogen content, the answer is fairly straightforward. The smaller the bird, the less cost-effective it would be to add estrogens to their diet. This is in sharp contrast to turkey meat, which comes from a far bigger bird that sells for significantly more. That's not to say I don't believe estrogens make it into the food of some chickens, just that I think it's less prevalent overall. In terms of flavor, I really love the taste of chicken. I've been known to go through heavy training phases during which I seriously deplete the free-range chicken population all by myself.

Now, back to beef. I must confess that for me, there are few, if any, gastronomic satisfactions equaling that which comes from eating a quality steak. Maybe it's the sight of blood that makes my testosterone boil, or maybe it's the iron from the blood that jacks me up, but I suspect it's something far greater. Many of these animals are also adulterated with hormones. The only difference is that, in the case of beef, we're talking about the male hormones of testosterone and testosterone derivatives. Having lots of lean beef on a carcass that goes to market and is weighed is critical to the cattle rancher. As such, hormones of the male type are considered ideal.

While one could, and certainly should, argue that the addition of these hormones may be as problematic from a health standpoint as the estrogens in poultry, bodybuilders have already seized upon the extra hormone boost in the meantime. I don't know of a single quality bodybuilder with an extreme physique who avoids beef. In particular, steak seems to be the favorite of countless strength athletes and bodybuilders I've known over many years. By the way, hormone-free beef is available at a bit of a premium. Kosher beef is also an option, but the taste tends to suffer because much of the blood is purged.

Though far more advantageous, beef is surprisingly not the main staple protein food for the bodybuilder. In terms of total volume consumed, poultry wins by a long shot. Just think of how many bodybuilders walk around with plastic containers filled with chicken breasts and not beef fillets. Perhaps it's a function of convenience. Maybe it's that poultry tends to taste better then beef when cold. It might also be the irrational fear related to thinking beef is always higher in fat. So, although bodybuilders generally recognize the importance of beef, for whatever reason, few eat the optimal amount for muscle growth.

As I said, I'm a big-time beef eater. Though I like the usual bodybuilder filet mignon, occasionally I go for a rib-eye. It has more fat in it, but much better flavor. The ultimate steak highlight for me was having Kobe beef in Tokyo at Aragawa (perhaps the best steakhouse in all of Japan and certainly one of the best in the world). Authentic Kobe steak is only from the island of Kobe just off the central island of Japan. Each animal is hand-selected by some kind of "meat sensei" and they can only come from a strict lineage. They actually show you a chart in the restaurant with the family tree of the cow you're eating! These animals are fed a special diet that includes sake. Unaware of their future, their pristine life includes frequent bathing and deep-tissue massage treatments to keep their flesh supple.

At any rate, the taste was indescribable, but I'll try. First of all, it was well cooked on the outside, but not black or charred in any way on the surface. It was as thick as any steak I've eaten, but I was able to press a fork through it and didn't really have to use my knife! The flesh was red, very finely marbled throughout, and fairly bloody. There were no runs of fat or edges to cut away, nothing to waste. With no saucy crap to glop over it, the natural taste was clean and impeccable. It was a mildly salty beef with a hint of sweetness at the end. It lacked that overpowering beefy aroma that, for me, made most traditional steaks taste like dog food by comparison. It was simply unlike anything I'd ever eaten before. By the way, the steak was $500! And no, I didn't have to pay. I mean, can you imagine how many chopsticks I'd have to wash if I got stuck with that bill?

Principle No. 6: Say No To Soy

Battling estrogens is a key approach in squelching catabolism. Testosterone is the male sex hormone and estrogen is the female sex hormone. While both sexes have both hormones, testosterone vastly predominates in the male body and estrogen dominates the female body.

Just like too much testosterone in the female is a bad thing, too much estrogen in the male is equally problematic, actually resulting in a feminizing effect. At its mildest, the muscles soften and reduce in size, fat storage increases, metabolism drops, and you retain more water. At an extreme, female breast tissue begins to develop, fertility can be negatively affected, and male sexual development is interfered with. All that said, in my opinion, the single most insidious food product available that damages our health as men and wreaks catabolic mayhem is soy protein. It's a powerful industry — soy even has an absurd "heart-healthy" claim to back it.

In recent years, society has increasingly developed a love affair with soy protein. But much to the chagrin of soy proponents, the sordid facts surrounding this perverse form of protein are rapidly unfolding. Although the soybean is the most complete of the vegetable proteins, soy is not an adequately complete source of high-quality protein. Unlike meat proteins, vegetable proteins lack a relatively large number of the essential amino acids. The fact is that soy protein, unless specifically fortified, is deficient in one or more of the essential amino acids.

In particular, an almost insignificant amount of methionine creates an insurmountable issue. Methionine is an unusual and valuable essential amino acid in that it contains sulfur, making it very important for tissue growth and development (anabolism). The soy cheerleaders try to bury or minimize this downside of soy protein. They avoid the issue by pointing to the fortified soy products on the market that correct for the methionine deficiency. Unfortunately, they ignore the fact that most people are driven by the steady propaganda toward soy-based foods and soy products that aren't fortified.

Some soy folks encourage you to combine your soy with other foods to make the protein complete. Unfortunately, most of the plant sources of methionine are carb-based foods and simply add unnecessary excess calories to the diet. Soy over-enthusiasts call methionine a conditionally essential amino acid to downplay it. (By the way, many experts don't buy into this logic and do list methionine as an essential amino acid).

Perhaps the greatest coup for soy fans was the whorish kiss of approval soy received from the U.S. Food and Drug Administration. Specifically, they allow soy-containing products to list themselves as able to reduce the risk of heart disease. This government embrace was not only premature, but potentially dangerous. There was, and still is, no solid research or scientific fact to back such cavalier support by our government. It makes me pause and wonder how a government that is steeped in the practice of correctly forcing products to be thoroughly researched and tested before claims can be made would do something so reckless.

Soy has no more provocative research to support such broad-based government support than that which supports whey protein (one of my personal favorites) in the area of heart health. The research supporting soy as cardio-protective is epidemiological bull.

Also along the way, soy somehow got labeled as being cancer preventive! While this may be true in some carefully select cases, I laugh at the absurdity of this flawed logic, while crying at the potential health ramifications of this misinformation. The theory behind soy helping in cancer prevention stems from the fact that the phytoestrogens in soy protein, although estrogen-like in function, are weaker receptor stimulators than the estrogens in our bodies. When this weaker estrogen is put in the body, it competes with the body's own estrogens for receptor sites. As a result, a temporary "blocking" effect is exerted because these estrogen-like compounds don't stimulate the receptor to the same degree as actual estrogens. Soy supporters point to soy protein as working in a way akin to the mechanism of chemotherapeutic estrogen blockers.

The problem with this theory is that, while an estrogen-like substance might have a weaker stimulatory property on one area of receptors in the body, it may be stimulatory to the same degree as true estrogen at other receptor sites in the body. For this exact reason, drugs with more estrogen-site specificity are currently being developed. New drugs appear to have estrogen-site selectivity so that, for the postmenopausal female, the risk of osteoporosis is reduced without stimulating uterine or breast cancer.

In an interview published in the *Journal of the American Dietetic Association,* Dr. Mark Messina, Program Director of the National Cancer Institute's Diet and Cancer Branch, made some poignant comments. "Genestein [the phytoestrogen in soy], the most estrogenic of the soy isoflavones, binds more weakly than tamoxifen [a prescription estrogen blocker] to the estrogen receptor in breast cells. Although it can reduce estrogen binding to the receptor, genestein can also elicit an estrogenic response itself. Concern has arisen, therefore, that in some cases phytoestrogens may pose a cancer risk. Genestein can stimulate proliferation of cells that have estrogen receptors…"

Paralleling this perspective, in conversations with several prominent cancer specialists and colleagues at the world-renowned Memorial Sloan-Kettering Cancer Center in New York, the subject of soy protein came up. Not surprising to me, all three of the specialists I spoke with are telling successfully-treated breast cancer survivors to avoid soy products. Of even greater interest was that they maintained this recommendation even for those individuals whose cancer was deemed "non-estrogen dependent" (i.e., estrogen receptor negative). They said that they did this "just to be on the safe side." I, of course, agreed with his logic.

As far as I'm concerned, as a physician, my recommendation would be to examine your family history very carefully. If you have a history of cancer (especially breast, even for a male), I think soy is dangerous. While the phytoestrogens in soy might function as a weaker estrogen at some sites in the body and thus help prevent cancer spurred by the body's own unopposed estrogens, it has no receptor-site specificity and thus may actually stimulate cancer in other areas of the body.

If that isn't enough reason to avoid soy protein, consider its potential adverse effect on the thyroid. An epidemiological study done at Cornell University Medical College in New York found that children with thyroid disease had a clear history of consuming soymilk formulas. A subsequent and very provocative study done in Japan seemed to confirm this negative potential of soy. In fact, well-established but equally well-hidden research shows rodents given a long-term diet of soy products repeatedly demonstrate thyroid tumor production.

Still other studies implicate soy in diet-induced goiter (a type of hypothyroidism). Genestein (the main phytoestrogen found in soy) has been shown to inhibit thyroid hormone synthesis. The exact mechanism appears to be the result of an inhibition of thyroid peroxidase (an enzyme responsible for thyroid hormone synthesis) within the gland itself.

Adding to the case against soy protein is alarming research published in the April 2000 edition of the *Journal of the American College of Nutrition*. The study showed subjects consuming a soy-based diet experienced a significant and measurable decrease in their cognitive function. Talk about soy screwing with your head! That would explain why I never seem to get through to those soy enthusiasts out there. Apparently they are literally brainwashed by this little pod.

The problems we see with soy phytoestrogens in men get worse the closer you look. Research indicates that these phytoestrogens aren't as selective and harmless as the soy lobby would lead you to believe. In fact, when genistein was given to mice in doses similar to those contained in an average soy-based diet, in only nine days testosterone concentration dropped dramatically in these animals. The reduction seemed to stem from a decrease in production of luteinizing hormone (LH), secreted by the anterior pituitary gland. In fact, there have been several other animal studies that clearly indicate the rather frightening feminizing effect of unopposed estrogen stimulation in the form of dietary phytoestrogens. Clearly it appears soy can wreak havoc on an otherwise healthy male endocrine system.

The distress deepens when you consider the potential ramifications of the FDA's position on soy as a broad-based recommendation. For example, soy is now added with increasing frequency and amounts to infant formulas. This is occurring despite a clear position by the American College of Pediatrics, whose own Dr. Susan Baker, chair of the nutrition committee and professor of pediatrics at the Medical University of South Carolina, indicates a preference of milk protein over soy. Relative to traditional milk formulas (human and cow), Dr. Baker was quoted in an article in *The New York Times* as believing that they ranked ahead of soy "because the protein quality seems higher" and because "premature or low-weight babies do not create bone mass as quickly on soy milk."

Of course this is just the beginning of the increasingly recognized problems of soy exposure early in life. The same article went on to highlight a 1997 study published in the medical journal *Lancet* that "found that phytoestrogen levels in babies fed soy formula were several thousand times higher than in babies who drank breast or cow's milk. This led to concerns among parents that puberty could be delayed in boys and accelerated in girls."

As if infant exposure to a substance like soy with its uncertain qualities isn't bad enough, soy also continues to be added in increasing amounts and with frequency to children's school lunches, leaving kids the unknowing victims of our inappropriate overconfidence in this product. We shouldn't simply discard or ignore possible early indicators of what could become a serious health issue, as the soy juggernaut rolls on seemingly unopposed.

In any case, if you're a guy looking for extreme muscle enhancement, read food and dietary supplement labels carefully, or you might find yourself unwittingly getting in touch with your feminine side.

Principle No. 7: Avoid Aspirin

Research tells us that muscle cells repair and ultimately grow after resistance training along an ordered set of occurrences called "fusion events." These fusion events are governed by prostaglandins — basically signaling molecules synthesized from arachidonic acid (a chemical found in cell walls throughout the body). When the body detects that muscle injury from a workout has occurred, enzymes begin to convert arachidonic acid to prostaglandins.

These prostaglandins activate protein utilization and the rebuilding begins. Prostaglandins have also been implicated in muscular growth and proliferation.

Aspirin and aspirin-like derivatives, a class known as non-steroidal anti-inflammatory drugs (NSAIDs), inhibit the production of prostaglandins. You should also be aware that white willow bark (a commonly used ingredient in many dietary supplement formulations) may also exert a similar effect.

Some bodybuilders rely heavily on these over-the-counter medications. In many gyms across America, bodybuilders pop NSAIDs along with their post-workout protein shakes in an effort to reduce the discomfort of post-workout soreness. By reducing this pain, many believe recovery is enhanced.

However, reducing normal post-workout muscular pain with NSAIDs doesn't mean you're increasing recovery. In fact, for the reasons I indicated, you're likely doing more harm than good. Not only will you cloud your read on your muscles to know if they're recovered prior to hitting them again with another workout, you're also killing mass gains in the process.

Unless you have a medical necessity, avoid these medications and don't make them a regular part of your dietary regimen. Again, too many bodybuilders make the mistake of casually using these substances just to get rid of simple soreness, when the truth is that regular use will cut into muscular growth.

Principle No. 8: Rely On Whey

Proteins are obviously the fundamental anabolic food component for the male bodybuilder. If you're a bodybuilder who's not taking in adequate amounts of protein, you're doomed. Proteins are made up of building blocks called amino acids. In turn, amino acids are found in every tissue and cell in our body. They are essential for growth, repair, and DNA/RNA synthesis. These amino-acid building blocks of protein provide the backbone of an infinite number of enzymes and hormones needed for muscle growth. In short, dietary protein has many absolutely essential properties for normal, healthy cellular function.

Although there was and, to some, still is a controversy as to the amount of protein one should have in his diet, it's of no confusion to me. Despite the ever-oscillating position of my physician and scientific brethren, take it from me: if you're a bodybuilder, weightlifter or serious and hard-training athlete, you need more protein then the average non-training male. We've already covered that in the previous chapter.

We also talked about fast proteins (whey) versus slow (casein). But it's so vital that I would like to reiterate it in these principles: Your protein supplement of choice should be whey-based. If you're keeping to a proper meal cadence by eating every 2–3 hours in order to maximize anabolism and avoid starvation alert, the last thing you need is a slow protein with a relatively low biological value. So while whey/casein mixes definitely can have their place for athletes where physical endurance performance is more of an issue, when taking only the pure considerations of the bodybuilder, it should be easy to understand why the fastest protein with the highest biological value wins the day. Clinical research has demonstrated that whey protein increases leucine concentrations more rapidly and to a higher degree than casein. Add to that, slow proteins like casein simply do not possess the antioxidant power of whey isolates. This power is critical at the cellular level to curb the catabolic process in each muscle cell, making whey the superior anti-catabolic protein.

Filtration processes allow for the purification of whey. Whey protein commonly comes in powder form, either in concentrate or isolate. The concentrate has up to about 80 percent purified whey in dehydrated, powder form. The purer isolate form can be concentrated in dry form to as high as about 93 percent purity. For anti-catabolic purposes, look for a whey protein isolate and not a concentrate. Whey protein isolate has unique and fascinating properties not found in the other proteins, including concentrates.

For example, isolates possess unusual immune-enhancing properties. In one study, a whey-protein diet enhanced the liver and cardiac glutathione concentration, increasing the lifespan of mice. Whey protein, which is approximately 2.5 percent cysteine, has been shown to increase cellular glutathione levels that are diminished by strenuous physical activity. Sub-optimal levels of cellular glutathione have been shown to alter the structural and functional integrity of muscle.

Isolates have been shown to increase intracellular GSH along with having a positive effect on immunity. GSH is necessary for lymphocyte proliferation in the development of a vigorous immune response. The amino acid cystine (which is reduced into cysteine upon cell entry) aids in the coordinated response of macrophages (special white blood cells) and lymphocytes in immunity. Systemic availability of GSH is negligible in humans, since it's synthesized within the cell (intracellularly) from precursors. Thus, whey protein isolate, with its high concentration of the GSH precursors cystine and glutamyl-cysteine, will form GSH in the cells. In turn this will aid in decreasing the amount of oxidative damage that is induced by heavy physical activity.

As an interesting aside, GSH depletion has been implicated in the pathogenesis of a number of degenerative conditions and disease states including Parkinson's, Alzheimer's, arteriosclerosis, cataracts, cystic fibrosis, malnutrition, aging, AIDS and cancer. Thus, going back to the idea that catabolism is one of the key reasons our bodies not only succumb to age but illness as well, it's conceivable that whey protein isolate may help stave off overtraining syndrome (OTS) in the high-performance athlete.

Further refining your choices with an eye toward anti-catabolism, the type of whey protein isolate also seems to matter. Higher quality whey protein isolate products basically utilize either the "ion exchange" or "microfiltration" method to make their isolate. Ten years ago I was a big fan of ion exchange isolates and wrote a lot about them because they seemed to produce a purer form of isolate. I still think that argument holds, and the average ion exchange whey protein isolate probably does beat the average microfiltrate in terms of purity, but now there's another consideration. Recent technology has revolutionized the filtration process, and certain high-quality microfiltrates actually preserve biologically active sub-fractions that the ion exchange methods always failed to do.

Having done clinical research on these sub-fractions, I can tell you firsthand that their presence and activity is key, especially when talking about anti-catabolism. In certain whey protein isolate microfiltrates, sub-fractions remain because of the process of using a filter and not an ionizer to purify the liquid. As a result, in the best microfiltrates, biologically active sub-fractions like immunoglobulins and growth factors are preserved in the final product. In rank order, my supplemental anti-catabolic preference is this:

1) *A high end microfiltered whey protein isolate*
2) *An average microfiltered whey protein isolate*
3) *A high-end ion exchange whey protein isolate*
4) *An average ion exchange whey protein isolate*
5) *A mixed whey protein isolate/concentrate*
6) *A simple whey protein concentrate*
7) *Casein*

Principle No. 9: Include Essential Fats

Elimination of fats from the diet is one area that bodybuilders, until recent years, were no smarter then the general public. The conventional wisdom among both was that dietary fat equals body fat, so it was avoided at all costs.

Of course, this could not be a more inaccurate statement. Dietary fat is not only essential for cellular repair and growth, but without it many of the hormones and natural glandular steroid molecules produced in the body down-regulate to sluggish levels. Nonetheless, it took a while before bodybuilders figured this out and started adding fat back into their diets.

I remember the great bodybuilder Lee Labrada, who tried so hard to beat Lee Haney and squeeze in for an Olympia title of his own, but to no avail. He always had good cuts and he had a classic physique that really lacked nothing other then any one single, jaw-dropping body part. But his real problem was that he just never made the big muscle gains needed to make a bona-fide run at Haney. Simply put, he was just too small.

I wasn't helping him back then, but years later while training together he told me how he used to eliminate virtually every gram of fat from his diet in an effort to get ripped. He did this at the cost of tremendous gains in muscle he could have made. Not only do I believe he could have been 20–30 pounds bigger onstage, but I even think he would have been harder in the process. I always thought, while very cut at times, Little Lee was never truly shredded like Big Lee was on at least two Olympia occasions.

I did end up convincing him how wrong he was and he agreed. He actually started adding fat into his diet and saw the difference. But alas, it was a bit too late to catch Haney.

Principle No. 10: Drop The Junk Food

Ronnie Coleman captured the Mr. Olympia title in 2005, winning for the eighth straight time overall. Though his 2004 condition was the high point to date in bodybuilding history, it was his 2003 performance that was the real jaw dropper.

Ronnie did not make history just by winning the 2003 Mr. Olympia. In fact, his win was a foregone conclusion in the eyes of most experts even before he took the stage. He simply had no viable competition. What was historic that hot night in Las Vegas was his condition compared to just one year before. What I witnessed sitting front and center in the press seats was mind blowing. The minute Big Ron took the stage, Flex Wheeler (who was sitting next to me at the time) looked at me in disbelief. There he was at a ripped 287 pounds and probably 10 pounds less body fat. (Remember that big Ronnie isn't even six feet tall.) He was easily the thickest bodybuilder to ever take the stage. The key here was that he had gained more than 30 pounds of rock-hard muscle compared to only twelve months prior.

While we might eventually see a guy that big and conditioned take the stage again someday, I doubt that anyone for a quite a while will match his epic one-year improvement. It was such a difference that not only had I never seen such a transformation from one year to the next, but chatting with Joe Weider (the godfather of our sport and great friend) revealed he was equally stumped. In his more then 80 years, he never saw such a transformation. Joe loves to chat, and he's always schooling me about something, but on that subject I have to say it was one of the very few times I've ever seen him speechless.

Speaking to Ronnie after the show, we tried to piece together exactly what it was he did differently. We thought he'd changed his routine in some major way. He denied it. We thought he had some special drug from another planet. He denied it. We thought he stumbled on the next wonder supplement. He denied it. All that was left was to ask him about his diet. Then a big grin spread across his face.

Interestingly, it wasn't a special diet in the sense of changing his macronutrient breakdown, or the times when he was eating, or anything basic like that. At nearly 40 years old, he knows what works for his body and, with a multitude of Mr. Olympia titles already under his belt, he was way too smart to tinker with any of that.

What did he change? He stopped eating junk food. It seemed that Ronnie was no different then the rest of us in relying a bit too much on burgers, fries and all sorts of poor food choices to fill up in the off-season. But after his 2002 victory, he ditched the junk and relied on real food of the natural, home-cooked type. Knowing this, I was no longer surprised at his turnaround, and I'll explain why.

Junk food is high in one fat you don't want to get too much of: trans-fatty acids. They do the opposite of the anti-catabolic fats that I like to call "smart fats." Junk food also contains a boatload of chemicals, preservatives, stabilizers and tenderizers that simply aren't found in natural home-cooked fresh foods. These bad substances toxify the body by a process called oxidation, increasing catabolism at the cellular level.

Oxidation causes electrons to be released as cells are damaged. These electrons are known as free radicals. Their release perpetuates more cellular damage and destruction. Simply stated, anytime a substance loses an electron, oxidation has occurred. When a cell is stripped of its electrons, the cell itself begins to show instability and impaired function.

Unfortunately, the damage doesn't end there. As the cell expires, it releases its own set of harmfully-charged particles, which in turn exert damage to neighboring cells. This chain reaction is ultimately overcome by our bodies, and we live to gorge on fast food another day, but our muscle-building process is hampered.

We cause enough free-radical production by damage to our muscles in the gym, so we certainly don't need the very food we're eating to cause yet more free-radical stress on our bodies. To build an extreme physique, our physiologic processes must be focused on countering muscle catabolism and not trying to recover from junk food toxicity.

Apart from building muscle, when your body can't get a handle on free-radical production, illness, aging and death at the cellular level skyrockets out of control. All of this can be countered by not only avoiding junk food, but by eating healthy, freshly prepared foods. Unlike junk food, which loads the body with pollutants that must be cleansed out later, healthy foods are filled with antioxidants, which lead the battle against free radicals.

Scientists universally acknowledge the fact that free-radical production via oxidation is perpetually ongoing in our bodies as cells die and new cells are produced. It's an unavoidable consequence of cellular function of any higher organism. This being the case, much of the research efforts in nearly every discipline of science and medicine, from cancer to immunology, have centered around cellular oxidation and the scavenging of free radicals at the molecular level.

Meanwhile, from a disease based perspective, we know as scientists and physicians that a deficiency of fresh foods and a surplus of junk foods will result in disease. Simply put, eating junk food will lead to you being small and sick, while eating fresh foods equates to being healthy and thick. The choice is easy, isn't it?

4 DIETARY SUPPLEMENTS

I want to start this chapter by stating there's absolutely no substitute for healthy eating. If your eating is screwed up, you can forget about extreme muscle enhancement, because you can't correct for it no matter how many supplements you take. I'm a strong believer in dietary supplements, but don't assume this to mean that they should, or even could, take the place of a smart nutritional program.

On the other hand, while you could make great strides toward extreme muscle enhancement with only a diet of whole foods, I doubt you'd come even close to realizing your true muscle-growth potential without the addition of dietary supplements.

With 1994's passage into law of the Dietary Supplement Health and Education Act (DSHEA), the supplement industry was transformed. I look back and remember quite clearly what was available before DSHEA. Basic things like Vitamin C capsules, lecithin granules, cod-liver oil, and maybe clumpy, disgusting egg protein powder was about all you could find. Back then, some physicians scoffed at the idea of taking vitamins, and those who did believe in them were scorned as sort of a modern hippie subculture among their peers.

Nowadays, things are different. Many of my colleagues actually take dietary supplements they couldn't get before DSHEA — even though some are still reluctant to recommend these same supplements to their patients! It baffles me. But the tide is turning nonetheless. Evidence continues to mount that vitamin, mineral and special micronutrient supplementation not only reduces the risk of disease, but actually counters certain illnesses and optimizes physical performance.

Common examples include Vitamin E being clearly indicated as an aid to prevent prostate and colon cancer and to reduce the risk of cardiovascular disease. Studies also prove the importance of calcium and Vitamin D in lowering the risk of osteoporosis. Supplemental folic acid has been proven to diminish the occurrence of newborn neural tube defects in pregnant women while decreasing the risk of heart disease in older adults. Vitamin C has been shown to reduce the risk of bladder cancer. Zinc lozenges treat mild upper respiratory pharyngitis unlike anything available by prescription. Saw palmetto is a great treatment for certain cases of benign prostate hypertrophy. Even selenium is rapidly gaining ground as a preventive aid in a host of various cancers. These are just some popular examples, and I could go on almost endlessly.

Examples for the bodybuilder include whey protein isolate for post-workout recovery and reducing delayed-onset muscle soreness; branched chain amino acids (BCAAs) for athletic recovery; glutamine to reduce overtraining syndrome (OTS) and increase nutrient absorption; and creatine for increased muscle power and weight gain. Arginine and ornithine naturally stimulate growth hormone. Even substances like oral glucosamine and chondroitin have been shown to help bodybuilders by soothing aching joints and tendons. Just as with the popular health examples, I could go on almost endlessly.

The bottom line is that, by using the natural substances that exist around us, we have considerable control over the way our bodies respond. It's really a philosophical belief on my part. I'm a strong believer in balance in life. Forces like the Chinese Yin and Yang perhaps best describe my belief that life is a concoction of equal but opposing forces, neither one really good or evil, just opposite. We see it in science as well. Newton put an equation to the ups and downs of gravity and Einstein told us that every action has an equal and opposite reaction. All that said, I can't believe for a second that man was put here on Earth along with all the diseases and ailments we face without a natural coexisting countermeasure. This follows the universal laws and must be consistent with what Einstein described.

That's not to say that I'm in any way minimizing the great pharmaceutical advances we've made in medicine. After all, I'm a physician and I rely on prescription medications every day in my practice. Rather, what I'm saying is that these synthetic compounds are nothing but unnatural shortcuts to that which we have not yet figured out in nature. I don't believe for a second that something like cancer plaguing mankind could naturally exist without a natural coexisting countermeasure. Natural solutions to every ailment must lay undiscovered around us in our environment.

A New Paradigm

A disturbing pattern among physicians is that we're strictly trained in a disease-based model of thinking. As is reflected in the way we're trained, we typically wait for people to be sick, debilitated and even hospitalized before we address their needs. We're not trained as much on how to keep people healthy and disease-free. Physicians, along with far too many health care professionals, tend to be most comfortable addressing diseases and illness. Since this wellness-based model I preach isn't the standard, I find few of my colleagues adept at keeping their patients lean, energetic and healthy. While I'd like my patients to thrive, comparable others just survive.

Your average physician visit can last as little as a few minutes. I've always asked myself how one can be a good listener with only a few minutes to get the job done. Sure, we can slap together a spot diagnosis and a treatment plan with such limited exposure. But is this really good listening, or for that matter, good medicine? A good listener means allowing someone to speak more than two sentences. A good listener asks questions and takes the time to probe what's being presented.

In asking questions, I've found that nearly every patient is very interested in dietary supplements but are hesitant to ask their doctors. And, although they won't admit it, many physicians believe that if you aren't sick, your body doesn't need much attention, including the type of nutritional and supplemental attention that could help keep one healthy. It's a crazy way of thinking, and probably explains why so many are closed-minded when it comes to supplements.

When treating illness, many physicians believe they must have all the answers for their patients and are too hesitant to explore new ideas on prevention. Unreasonable physicians hate admitting when they don't know something. On the other hand, progressive physicians are quick to admit when they don't have a traditional answer and are open to new ideas, including natural supplemental-based remedies.

The truth behind this reluctance is that many doctors simply lack knowledge about dietary supplements. This is why so many are skeptics. In this way, they fail to recognize the incredible options for disease treatment and wellness maintenance. We can take control of our health and optimize our bodies by simply using what's around us in nature, and by making the proper choices about what nutrients to include in our diet.

It's an odd juxtaposition. Generally, we physicians are a curious bunch because we rely heavily on medical and scientific journals regarding so many disease-oriented subjects. Yet when it comes to vitamins, minerals and other supplements, doctors ignore the published information. In any case, one thing is certain: When you study the available science, it's clear that dietary supplements work for not only our health, but for extreme muscle enhancement as well.

Supplemental Solution

Unlike the days of early man, we no longer spend our days foraging for food. Instead, we sit at our desks pushing papers, surfing the internet or writing emails. Many ages ago, food was the major driving need of survival, so nourishing oneself was always a high priority.

Today, food is more available for most of us than ever, yet our complicated lives have made nourishment a low-rated task. Deadlines, obligations and commitments have taken the place of making the act of feeding ourselves a priority. But those hard-driving ambitions for personal success don't change the fact that our bodies need food and nutrients.

In our lives exist so many concerns and distractions, you really can't expect healthy dietary compliance without some easier way. The recommendation by the American Dietetic Association to obtain nutrients from a wide variety of foods in order to maintain health and reduce the risk of disease is simply unrealistic. That is, unless you use a cost-effective and time-efficient way to bridge the gap — and that way is supplementation. New supplement technology now allows us to quickly nourish ourselves while on the go and insure that we receive a generous portion of the essentials.

The obligation to eat is even more critical for the bodybuilder. You simply cannot develop and maintain your extreme physique without the ample use of dietary supplements. Achieving a proper meal cadence and satisfying your complete protein and essential fat needs alone would be nearly hopeless unless you had absolutely nothing else in life to do, and money to burn.

If one just focuses on protein powders and meal replacement products for bodybuilding, there are at least two major practical reasons supporting their use: They help foster smart habits, and they make the pursuit much less cost prohibitive.

On that first point, bodybuilders of yesteryear had to consume a great deal of excess calories in order to build muscle, and in the process inadvertently fostered bad eating habits as a result of eating all of their calories in the form of whole food. Then they carried those habits with them until their older years, when their activity levels fell, leaving them out of shape and putting their health at risk.

Perhaps the best example I have from memory is that of former Mr. Olympia Sergio Oliva. He was known as "The Myth" because his body was of mythic proportions. Along with Frank Zane, he was the only other bodybuilder to ever beat the great Arnold Schwarzenegger on a professional stage. But Sergio was a classic example of the old-school bodybuilding chow hound. Man, he loved to eat. Maybe it came from his tough life, having escaped Cuba by defecting from the Olympic weightlifting team and working endless hours in the steel mills before he found his way into our sport.

Whatever the reason was, he loved food, and it showed. He was huge but never quite ripped in his entire career.

Sergio took in massive amounts of food after his workouts, and carried his monster eating habits into his later years when he simply wasn't training as hard. The result was that his activity level and metabolism were not able to offset the calorie intake he had long since habituated himself to consuming.

The last time Sergio and I sat down and ate together, he was still gulping heaps of food but now was sporting a big belly. Don't get me wrong, Sergio knows I love him and that he's always been one of my favorite bodybuilders, beyond being a super nice guy. But the facts are that he ate like an old-time bodybuilder and now he's paying for it by struggling with his weight. He knows how I feel — I only hope that if he keeps it up, his health still holds out for a long time to come.

With the advent of supplementation, protein shakes and meal replacements now allow you to not have to eat all of your food. That makes for a much easier transition to your older years; when it's time do dial down your calorie intake, all you need to do is drop the drinks, which is infinitely easier than acclimating yourself to eat less than you have for years upon years.

Another practical reason supporting the use of protein powders and meal replacement products beyond their functional aspects has to do with these tools being so much more cost effective than whole food. Building an extreme physique requires not only a time investment in the gym, but a serious fiscal contribution in the direction of your local grocery store. Beef, chicken, fish and fresh vegetables all cost a pretty penny. While healthy foods should make up the majority of what you take in, protein powders and meal replacement products have the added advantage of substantially defraying this cost.

Making Your Selection

Beyond just protein powders and meal replacements, there are a ton of products and ingredients on the market today to address specific facets of what the male bodybuilder is trying to achieve. Whatever your game —mass building, fat burning, recovery, pump enhancement, energy augmentation — you can find a supplement to meet your needs.

The more edgy products are touted as testosterone boosters, estrogen blockers, fat absorbers, anabolic steroid substitutes, and fat and carbohydrate blockers. I've seen them all. Some are the real deal. Others are bull. Sorting through the choices and understanding which ones are right for you can sometimes be a daunting task.

Keep in mind that DSHEA has allowed us to have these choices, and though I'm passionate about my support of DSHEA, I don't want to give you the impression that I think everything about it is rosy. The world has a fair share of hucksters who test the limits of the freedoms allowed under DSHEA, and try to sell products that don't do what they promise. Some companies use the freedoms permitted under DSHEA to exploit the consumer and not deliver a quality product.

Yet the benefits DSHEA has given us far outweigh those issues. We get the personal freedom we've all come to expect in the United States — the right to evaluate products for ourselves and make the choice to use supplements in the first place.

Like any purchase you make in life, it pays to be smart and to do your homework. In this book, I would like to help you with those buying decisions, with a rundown of the major types of ingredients available in supplements and what they can do for you. Since products can come and go quickly as science advances, I believe it's more helpful for you to understand the underlying ingredients, giving you a head start in evaluating different formulations you find out there.

The following section focuses on substances that, when combined with proper diet and training, catalyze your progress. Since I've already discussed protein powders and supplemental fat earlier in this text, I skip them here. Also, if I don't mention a particular ingredient, don't necessarily take that to mean it has no use or doesn't work; my goal in this chapter is to simply highlight those that I've found in practice to have the most benefit in most guys for the purposes of extreme muscle enhancement.

By the way, when dosage isn't indicated, follow the directions on the label (in any case, label directions should always supersede this generalized advice).

Arginine

Considered a conditionally essential amino acid, since under some conditions the body can't make enough and we must therefore obtain it through the diet, arginine is found in several types of nuts, including almonds.

While in the sedentary adult population, arginine is considered to be a non-essential amino acid, infants, growing children, the injured, and hard-training athletes and bodybuilders need more of it. In particular, children need ample supplies to build up an adequate immune system.

Benefits:
- Involved in many metabolic processes, including hormone secretion, detoxification and immunity.
- Has a powerful antioxidant ability, supporting the immune system by scavenging free radicals.
- A precursor of nitric oxide (NO), it's used in the support of male sexual function. (NO is normally produced in the body to increase vascular flow

throughout the body, notably the genitalia.)

- Works as a natural magnifier of growth hormone production by inhibiting a chemical messenger in the brain called somatostatin, which normally inhibits GH release. A higher growth hormone level can boost muscle mass by increasing protein synthesis and improving recovery.

Dosage:

Typical doses among bodybuilders range from as low as 1 gram to as high as 5 grams taken 1–3 times a day. Over the years I've tended to favor doses between 1–2 grams per day. I've used it successfully combined with certain types of L-ornithine at roughly one-third to one-half the dose of arginine. L-lysine is another amino acid that works in a complimentary way for bodybuilders when taken with arginine.

Watch for:

Too much arginine can lead to diarrhea, weakness and nausea, so start with a small dose and progressively increase as your tolerance allows.

Arginine-Alpha-Ketoglutarate (A-AKG)/ Ornithine-Alpha-Ketoglutarate (O-AKG)

Arginine-alpha-ketoglutarate (A-AKG) and/or ornithine-alpha-ketoglutarate (O-AKG) based formulas have been popularized in the last few years as "NO" ingredients touted as having a specific advantage over their respective core amino acid backbones. A-AKG and O-AKG based diets have been studied and observed in science with a certain fascination in the field of immune boosting and cancer prevention research, anti-catabolism (preventing muscle breakdown), amino acid sparing, and growth hormone stimulation. In particular, there are quite a few compelling scientific studies on the utilization of O-AKG in helping burn patients recover. These naturally occurring amino acid variations may in fact introduce some added benefit over the straight amino acids. That's not necessarily to say with absolute certainty that they are better in every case, but just different in adding another dimension to curtail muscular breakdown and support hormone production. Few head-to-head trials test the core amino acids against their respective alpha-ketoglutarate derivatives. But it seems that from a practical and clinical standpoint, there are some differences. Alpha ketoglutarate itself has been tested in research as improving amino acid metabolism (arginine in particular), as well as electrolyte profile in hemodialysis patients, both aspects of which may help bodybuilders who seriously tax their body. Alpha ketoglutarate and arginine may be considered to exert both anabolic and anti-catabolic effects in certain situations through their involvement in protein metabolism. Magnifying normal dietary concentrations by way of supplementation may further support these effects. For these reasons, the popularity of incorporating A-AKG and O-AKG into various formulations has soared.

Benefits:
- While standard arginine might be a more practical magnifier of growth hormone production in the body, the A-AKG derivative is the better vasodilator. So if you're looking to maximize delivery of a particular ingredient to the muscle via blood circulation, I think A-AKG is a better bet.
- Four grams of A-AKG — the major active ingredient in most NO products — or placebo was given to 35 male weightlifters three times a day. At the end of the eight-week study, the placebo group increased their bench press by about 5 pounds, while the A-AKG group boosted their bench by 20 pounds.
- O-AKG may simply be better all the way around when compared to pure ornithine. At least one compelling study shows O-AKG has a stronger influence over amino-acid metabolism and hormone secretion. While I think standard ornithine may have some utility, I have found that O-AKG is a better compliment to straight arginine, when combined with A-AKG, or when given alone.

Dosage:
For A-AKG I have generally found that 1.5–2 grams per day is about optimal for increased circulation and delivery as well as for protein sparing and anti-catabolism.

I generally keep O-AKG between 250–500 milligrams per day for optimum anti-catabolic recovery and, when combined with arginine, for growth-hormone support.

Watch for:
You have to be more careful with higher doses of O-AKG because, unlike A-AKG, O-AKG has a potentially vigorous high-dose influence on the pancreas and subsequently on blood-sugar levels.

Branched-Chain Amino Acids (BCAAs)

While we know that different amino acids are consumed at a variety of different places and for a variety of different purposes throughout the body, research has identified certain amino acids that our skeletal muscles seem to have a very specific hunger for. This has proven of critical significance to the bodybuilder striving for gains.

The essential amino acids L-leucine, L-isoleucine, and L-valine have a certain branched-chain substructure in common, so they're grouped together and collectively referred to as the branched-chain amino acids, or BCAAs. These BCAAs share not only a certain chemical substructure, but when it comes to muscles, they can ostensibly be viewed as synonymous with one another and thus taken together.

BCAAs are metabolized to the greatest extent in the muscle itself as opposed to the liver or other organs (they comprise nearly half the mass of lean skeletal muscle). BCAAs get depleted during times of stress or intense exercise — heavy training results in a rise in cortisol, causing the breakdown of muscle proteins and a release of amino acids. One study found a 14 percent drop in muscle BCAA levels after weightlifting. When you lose them, you want to put them back, and that's where a BCAA supplement comes in.

Benefits:
- Provides an alternative energy source for almost all tissues of the body, such as muscle.
- Promotes protein synthesis in part by activating two proteins that play critical roles in a process called phosphorylation. This protein activation at the cellular level exerts its greatest effect by sparing muscle tissue during training. In other words, BCAAs are a great anti-catabolic, and as such are among the most beneficial and effective dietary supplements for all athletes, not just bodybuilders.
- Can enhance growth hormone (GH) release. One study in triathletes who took BCAA supplements for one month showed that, when the subjects took 10 grams of BCAAs before a 60-minute bout of aerobic exercise, GH levels were 95 percent higher after exercise than when they had consumed milk protein instead.
- Appears to increase fat loss, as discovered in a study of wrestlers. Scientists found that those taking BCAAs in addition to a low-calorie diet had significantly greater loss of overall body weight and body fat, including greater loss of fat from the abdominal area.

Dosage:
I generally use a dose of about 6 grams per day, with a breakdown of between 3–4 grams of L-leucine, 1–2 grams of L-isoleucine, and 1–2 grams of L-valine. I generally take my BCAAs within 30 minutes after training. I've found this is when your body has the greatest thirst for amino acids and uptake is at its highest.

Caffeine

Caffeine occurs naturally in numerous plants, the most common and popular of which is the coffee bean. Other popular sources are tea and cocoa. Interestingly, caffeine is also added artificially into many beverages to give them a kick. In fact, some of the most popular drinks among bodybuilders and the young fitness crowd boast about extra caffeine.

Caffeine, also known in chemical circles as trimethylxanthine, in low doses is a mild stimulant as well as a mild diuretic (i.e. it helps you urinate more). It operates by more or less the same mechanisms as do amphetamines and cocaine, stimulating the brain and heart.

Benefits:

- The best use of caffeine for the bodybuilder is as a mild stimulant before a workout, or as a metabolism enhancer and fat burner in conjunction with green tea extract.
- A thermogenic, caffeine has the ability to rev up the cells of your body, causing them to produce more heat at the cellular level. The result is mobilization of fat stores and caloric energy consumption. In this way, caffeine increases levels of free fatty acids in your blood, thereby facilitating the use of body fat for energy.
- Research also confirms that caffeine boosts performance during exercise. The exact mechanism is not conclusive, but theories suggest it may be either due to the stimulant effect or its ability to enhance fat use and thereby spare muscle glycogen.
- A study out of the University of Georgia demonstrates caffeine's ability to dull muscle pain. Scientists examined the effects of ingesting two doses of caffeine on the perception of leg muscle pain during cycling exercise. College-aged males were given either 2.3 milligrams or 4.5 milligrams of caffeine per pound of bodyweight or a placebo, and one hour later completed 30 minutes of moderate-intensity cycling exercise. Caffeine significantly blunted leg muscle pain, with the higher dose offering the greatest effect.

Dosage:

A typical cup of coffee contains about 100 milligrams of caffeine. Typical brewed tea contains about 70 milligrams of caffeine per cup. Caffeinated sodas contain about 50 milligrams of caffeine per can. Energy drinks generally contain between 70–80 milligrams per can.

In sharp contrast, over-the-counter drugs like Vivarin® and Dexatrim® contain about 200 milligrams of caffeine per tablet. All that said, it should not surprise you to find out that countless Americans easily consume more then 1,000 milligrams per day of caffeine and don't even realize it, which is too much. About 600 milligrams per day is the maximum I'd recommend.

Watch for:

In higher doses caffeine can cause symptomatic heart palpitations, tremors, and even anxiety. When taken at higher doses on a regular basis, it can be addictive, signified by withdrawal symptoms such as extreme fatigue and irritability coupled with extreme cravings to resume caffeine intake.

Chromium

Chromium is an essential trace mineral that plays a role in carbohydrate metabolism and insulin regulation.

Benefits:
- May be helpful with various issues such as weight loss, preventive medicine and even anti-aging.
- Helps maintain proper blood sugar levels. Research offers evidence that chromium supplementation improves glucose tolerance for both hyper- and hypoglycemic subjects, alleviates hypoglycemic symptoms, improves insulin production and sensitivity, and increases the number of insulin receptors.
- Some studies have found that daily supplementation with chromium results in a significant increase in lean body mass and a decrease in percent body fat when compared to placebo. In one notable study, body composition measures were completed in the beginning, midway and at the end of a 24–week period where the swimmers received either 400 micrograms per day of chromium picolinate or a placebo. Compared with the placebo group, the chromium group had significantly higher levels of lean body mass (more muscle), lower levels of fat mass, and a lower percentage of body fat. Another study found similar results with a lower daily dosage of chromium, at 200 micrograms per day.
- Chromium picolinate leads to significant improvements in body composition, observed through both underwater hydrostatic weighing and DEXA (the gold standard for body-composition testing), even when differences in caloric intake and energy expenditure are corrected for.
- Chromium is an effective way to curb your carbohydrate cravings. Scientists at Duke University Medical Center found that 600 micrograms of chromium given to patients with atypical depression (these individuals tend to have intense carbohydrate cravings) was effective at reducing carbohydrate cravings and aiding fat loss.
- Low levels of chromium in the body have been linked to cardiovascular disease. People who die of heart disease often have abnormally low chromium levels in their aortas, and patients with existing heart disease have as much as 40 percent less chromium in their blood than healthy individuals.

Dosage:
A smart dosage level is no more than 200 micrograms per day.

Watch for:
Although supplemental chromium seems generally beneficial, avoid excessive intake because minerals like chromium are stored in the liver and kidneys.

Conjugated Linoleic Acid (CLA)

Conjugated linoleic acid (CLA) is a polyunsaturated, conjugated fatty acid that actually promotes body-fat burning. It was first isolated back in the 1980s from cooked ground beef, but also can be found in dairy products, although these sources have undergone a 75 percent decline in CLA content over the years due to the popularity of grain feeding (as opposed to grass diets) for cattle herds.

The average daily intake of CLA in the United States has declined dramatically in the last few decades, to only about 200 milligrams per day total. Coupled with the easy access to convenient carbohydrates and fast foods, CLA deficiency is believed by many experts to be contributing in part to the steady rise of obesity in the U.S.

Four different biologically active isomers of CLA have been tested in clinical studies, namely cis-9, trans-11, trans-10, and cis-12. Commercial sources of CLA isolate the cis-9 and trans-11 isomers, both found in meat and milk, because they have a higher biologic activity. (A higher concentration of biologically active ingredient means there can be a more appreciable effect on the body at a lower total dose.) This is important because lower levels of the less active isomers are simply not as effective.

Interestingly, in animal research, the trans-10 and cis-12 isomers induce more fat loss. Of course, the study of CLA is ongoing.

Benefits:
- Reduces body fat by reducing the activity of our fat-storing enzyme system. Note that this doesn't stop your body from absorbing and using the healthy dietary fats you need to function; instead, excess fat is just not as easily stored.
- Also seems to have cancer prevention, immune enhancing and antiviral properties.
- Has been shown in laboratory animals to enhance the amount of fat burned during sleep.

Dosage:
Diet sources of CLA are unfortunately bound up along with foods high in

saturated fat, so you won't have much of a chance of finding foods with high concentrations of CLA without a lot of bad fat to go along for the ride. (For example, ice cream is a great source of CLA — but you would need to consume about four gallons of ice cream to equal the amount of CLA that has been shown effective for fat burning.) Because of that, supplemental CLA is the best option.

Doses of up to 6 grams per day for eight weeks at a time have been used with success. Some studies go out as far as a year — a recent one found that overweight males and females who consumed 4.5 grams of CLA for a year lowered their body fat percent by almost 10 percent as compared to the placebo group — but I always like the idea of cycling a few weeks on and off to allow the body to reset and re-sensitize.

My feeling is that as long as you are eating plenty of red meat as part of your diet, taking in as little as 250 milligrams per day of additional supplemental CLA should be plenty. I've found in practice that bodybuilders respond favorably to this lower dose of CLA and adding more doesn't seem to bring benefits. This may have to do with the higher proportion of lean mass relative to fat mass that male bodybuilders have compared to regular men.

Watch for:
I've never seen any problems with people taking supplemental CLA. You might come across some references in scientific literature to excessively high levels being related to insulin resistance, but my understanding is that this effect was attributed to the trans-10 and cis-12 isomers and these isomers in supplemental form are supposed to be unavailable to the public. A recent study out of the University of Wisconsin in obese but generally healthy people taking 6 grams per day of CLA (the cis-9 and trans-11 isomers) for one year while following a planned diet showed no adverse effects, as measured by blood tests and a biweekly questionnaire evaluating side effects and adverse events.

Creatine

Creatine is a natural combination of three amino acids (arginine, glycine, and methionine) that is found in meat and fish. It works as a shuttle molecule for elemental phosphorus during muscle contraction by more efficiently regenerating ATP (recall ATP is the currency of energy in the human body). Though creatine can be created by the body through assembling these amino acids, since these very same amino acids are used to form numerous other proteins for higher priority metabolic purposes, natural creatine production is simply not a big priority. For that matter, neither is it a natural priority of the body to build big muscles. The body has to be forced to do this and as such requires exogenous creatine supplementation to more efficiently fill this need.

When oral creatine is ingested into the body and taken up by the muscle cells, it binds with a phosphorus molecule to create creatine phosphate. It is then either used during muscular contraction or stored in the muscle sarcoplasm. So the more phosphorylated creatine that is stored in your muscle cells, the more potential energy for contraction each muscle cell has available. This translates to a more powerful muscular contraction and power output, plus a higher tolerance for a heavier workload.

This difference in the workout is usually obvious for most people. Some research indicates that giving creatine along with a carbohydrate helps deliver the creatine more efficiently. While I have found this to be somewhat true, too many formulas have an overabundance of sugar. Look for formulas that minimize sugars. Most importantly, I tend to like buffered creatine; it's not always that easy to find and it is generally a bit more expensive, but it's worth it because not only do you get a theoretical increase in absorption efficiency, but it's less upsetting to the stomach. Stomach upset and nausea is the major complaint among creatine users.

Some trainers claim that creatine dehydrates the athlete and causes cramping. But this is only true if they don't take in enough fluid. The fact is that creatine actually helps the body retain more fluid by allowing the muscle cell to pull more fluid into the sarcoplasm. It is for this reason that, while it is an excellent ingredient for off-season mass building, I don't use creatine for competitive bodybuilders as they approach the day of the contest. In such cases I usually stop it about five weeks in advance of the show so they can shed water and get that dry, ripped look.

Benefits:
- Works as a shuttle molecule for elemental phosphorus during muscle contraction by more efficiently regenerating ATP.
- When oral creatine is ingested and taken up by the muscle cells, it binds with a phosphorus molecule to create creatine phosphate. The more phosphorylated creatine you have, the more energy you have for muscle contraction. This translates to more power and a higher tolerance for heavier training.

Dosage:
Doses have been classically described with a loading phase of 20 grams per day for five days and 5 grams per day after that. I personally have found that, assuming you are using a high quality buffered creatine product with a minimal to moderate carbohydrate profile, loading is simply unnecessary and may carry with it some of the minor annoying side effects of stomach upset and diarrhea. In my estimation, 5–10 grams at any one time is plenty.

As far as duration, after 4–5 weeks of creatine, take a break from it for a few weeks. This will keep your body sensitized to its effects.

Watch for:
Low-quality creatine is a concern to be aware of. While one German company I've worked with has attended nicely to the issue of proper creatine manufacturing, a few others aren't so careful. Creatine made by substandard production may contain high amounts of dicyandiamide (a cyanide derivative) and/or dihydrotriazine (a chemical byproduct of synthetic creatine production). These byproducts may or may not represent a health hazard; scientists as yet aren't precisely sure.

In addition, creatine that comes to the U.S. from certain foreign countries may sit too long in shipping containers (weeks to months). As a result, this creatine degrades to creatinine (a naturally occurring waste product of the kidneys). As long as you have normal kidney function, extra creatinine probably won't hurt you, but it just adds up to more waste, and more wasted money. Stick with the industry's most well-respected and well-known supplement manufacturers, and you should be fine.

D-Ribose

D-ribose, often referred to as simply ribose, is a naturally occurring sugar found in all living cells. While not an essential nutrient, since it can be made in the body from various other substances, it's nonetheless essential for life. D-ribose is everywhere in living matter, we all ingest it in our diets.

Benefits:
- Increases energy levels, cardiovascular fitness, performance and endurance; reduces recovery time after strenuous activity and post-workout muscle stiffness and cramping.
- Needed for the production of the adenosine triphosphate, or ATP. The more ribose available, the more ATP you can make and thus the more energy you can produce. ATP is critical for muscular contraction and optimal physical performance, and has been shown to enhance the recovery of skeletal-muscle ATP following high-intensity exercise.
- Many clinical studies contain research and information gathered from animals and humans alike concerning the effects of ribose on the heart. These studies have revealed several positive effects, including improved heart function and increased exercise tolerance. Ribose is an effective nutrient at improving and/or maintaining energy in heart and skeletal muscles.

Dosage:

Though D-ribose is generally well tolerated, one of the most limiting issues has to do with effective dosage used in research, which can be as high as 30 grams per day in at least one study. Though I have found that much lower doses work effectively, it's just something that you should be aware of.

Glucomannan

Glucomannan is a gel-forming, soluble dietary fiber from konjac flour, which is derived from Amorphophallus species. Grown throughout Asia, glucomannan in the form of konjac flour has been widely used as a food substitute and herbal remedy. In fact, it has been part of the Japanese diet for more than 1,000 years.

Benefits:
- Used as a general health aid, topically for skin care and as a starch-like, thickening agent for foods. As a thickening agent, it is up to eight times stronger than starch and expands about 50 times its original volume when combined with water. As a result, in controlled studies glucomannan has demonstrated that it can promote satiety and weight loss, lower LDL cholesterol, improve diabetic control and correct constipation. One study reported average weight loss after eight weeks of about 6 pounds in adults when just 1 gram of glucomannan was taken with a cup of water one hour before meals.
- When trying to control appetite, glucomannan can be taken before a meal, in order to give one a feeling of fullness, thereby reducing appetite. As an added benefit, it slows the rate of food absorption, thus reducing the total number of calories absorbed by the body.
- May also improve glycemic control and blood lipid profile (coronary risk). Taking up to 5 grams of glucomannan with meals can reduce insulin spikes by slowing carbohydrate absorption. Even though glucomannan slows the absorption of dietary carbohydrates, studies show that it does not cause severe malabsorption; thus glucomannan tolerance has generally been excellent.
- Like other soluble fibers, glucomannan binds to bile acids in the gut and carries them out of the body in the feces. This means the body has to convert more cholesterol into bile acids, which results in the lowering of blood cholesterol and triglycerides. Several studies have shown that supplementing with several grams of glucomannan per day significantly reduced total blood cholesterol, LDL ("bad" cholesterol), and triglycerides, and in some cases it even raised HDL ("good" cholesterol).
- Is a highly-effective remedy for constipation. Any time you feel like your dietary fiber intake has fallen off and you find yourself a little constipated from all the protein, glucomannan is a great way to jump-start your system.

Dosage:

Glucomannan can be used when you're bringing your body-fat levels down by cutting calories. It helps take up space in the gut and cut the edge off the initial strain of going from that massive-but-smooth build to that hammer-hard muscular physique. It works as a nice transition while your gut shrinks and readjusts to reduced food intake.

Watch For:

Glucomannan capsules are generally preferred. Since glucomannan has the innate ability to expand, one must be careful with the powder form, as without enough water, too much can cause throat obstruction. Don't overdo glucomannan because it may reduce the absorption of fat-soluble vitamins, according to at least one study. Finally, avoid inferior grades. I've found that sourcing from Japan is almost invariably superior.

Glucosamine/Chondroitin

Glucosamine, a naturally-occurring amino sugar, is a critical building block of the cartilage matrix. Without it our tendons, ligaments, skin, nails, bones, mucous membranes and other body tissues cannot form, and damaged tissue cannot be replaced or repaired.

Like glucosamine, chondroitin sulfate is needed for connective-tissue formation. The difference is, chondroitin is primarily found in joint cartilage, whereas glucosamine is dispersed in tissues. Used in conjunction with one another, these substances support healthy joints.

Normally, our bodies can produce sufficient amounts of glucosamine from molecules of glucose and glutamine, but generally at a rate only equal to that which it's used for general repair. In sharp contrast, when our bodies undergo the rigors of weight training or other strenuous physical activity, it's not always able to keep up. That's where the supplemental form comes to the rescue.

Benefits:
- Research has demonstrated that the combination of the two supplements was more effective than with either substance alone in inhibiting injury and inflammation.
- One study determined that a glucosamine-chondroitin combination relieved symptoms of arthritis.
- A meta-analysis (a comparison of the results of numerous studies) of 13 trials studying glucosamine and chondroitin found concrete, positive results that it helped alleviate hip and knee pain.

- Another meta-analysis of nine studies found that glucosamine taken alone was superior to or equal to ibuprofen in providing relief.

Dosage:
Typical dosage for glucosamine is 1,500–2,000 milligrams per day as 2–3 divided doses; for chondroitin, 800–1200 milligrams as 2–3 divided doses. Most brands require a three-times-per-day dosing schedule. I prefer time-released versions that allow for twice-daily dosing.

I've used these supplements with a reasonable degree of success in my practice, but I've had the best results with bodybuilders and athletes over 40.

Watch for:
Two words of advice when taking glucosamine-chondroitin supplements — be patient. They don't work in every case and it can take as many as four weeks for you to start feeling a difference. Also, stay away from chondroitin if you're allergic to sulfur, because it usually comes in the form of chondroitin sulfate.

Glutamine

Glutamine is an extremely common nonessential amino acid that's found in virtually every dietary protein and can readily be synthesized in nearly every tissue in the body. Glutamine is fascinating because, while it isn't often listed as a conditionally essential amino acid, experts in the field of sports nutrition still consider it conditionally essential in athletes who undergo extreme physical exertion. Glutamine becomes quite depleted during the course of a catabolic insult such as a heavy workout, injury or even infection. Thus, despite the relative predominance of glutamine in the diet and our body's own ability to manufacture it, when we're taxed beyond the normal state of health, we have an immediate requirement for more than that which can be readily attained in the diet or produced in our tissues.

Benefits:
- Bodybuilders have for years successfully used glutamine to curtail symptoms of delayed onset muscle soreness (DOMS) and to prevent overtraining syndrome (OTS). Glutamine has been widely, and I think correctly, viewed as a recovery agent.
- Has been shown to support and stimulate growth hormone production.
- Very helpful in supporting the health of the gastrointestinal tract and assisting in nutrient absorption.

Dosage:

Since up to eight percent of the naturally occurring proteins that an average sedentary person might consume contain glutamine, it can be estimated that such a diet contains as much as 10 grams of glutamine in a single day. In the case of the bodybuilder, once the body is taxed with regular training, muscles are challenged and broken down. Glutamine needs increase at the cellular level beyond that which can be readily satisfied by just this 10-gram dietary contribution.

I generally use about 2 grams of glutamine per day. Doses of up to 5 grams seem to me to be equally effective but not of greater effect. Some bodybuilders take in as much as 10 grams of additional glutamine per day, but I have seldom seen this higher dose as being of added benefit.

Green Tea Extract

Green tea extract, also known as *Camellia sinensis*, contains four major catechins in its leaves, the most abundant and powerful being (-)-epigallocatechin gallate (EGCG). On the surface, green tea is really nothing more then regular black tea that has not undergone fermentation. Yet this is a critical difference because during fermentation these catechins are enzymatically oxidized and destroyed in the process. Green tea has been used for centuries in China and Japan for its health-promoting effects.

Benefits:

- Some support exists in the scientific literature, albeit epidemiological, pointing to its cancer preventive and anti-atherogenic properties.
- Green tea extract also contains caffeine. As mentioned, caffeine is a mild stimulant that can provide a boost of energy prior to a workout. It also works as a thermogenic. But in the context of green tea extract, we find some interesting additive effects. Research reveals that green tea has a thermogenic property that promotes body fat oxidation beyond that which can just be explained by the caffeine alone. This appears to be due to its ability to inhibit the enzyme that degrades norepinephrine.
- Has anti-inflammatory, anti-viral, anti-microbial and antioxidant benefits.
- Some naturopaths argue that green tea helps to "alkalinize" the body. Since bodybuilders produce so much lactic acid during higher-rep workouts, and tend to take in foods that can be acid producing, alkalinizing with green tea has been said to help equilibrate the system.

Dosage:

I have found that green tea, green tea extract and green tea products have been helpful for me personally. For supplemental purposes, my typical doses are around 200 milligrams per day of catechins, but I tend to rely more on drinking actual green tea. Interestingly, I don't feel much from the caffeine, so I tend to use it after the workout and toward evening. I have found it helps curb appetite when I'm trying to get tighter and certainly helps to emulsify body fat when taken this way.

Typical doses in popular formulas using green tea appear to be about 90 milligrams EGCG, three times a day, or a total of 270 milligrams EGCG daily. Watch for doses more than 300 mg per day because it may decrease levels of IGF-1.

L-Carnitine

L-Carnitine, an amino-acid derivative found in nearly all cells of the body, was first identified and chemically characterized in the early 1900s and has been gaining attention as a therapeutic agent and nutrient since the mid-1960s. A nonessential nutrient synthesized from vitamins and the amino acids methionine and lysine, its primary function is to assist the production of cellular energy (ATP) but also has the ability to remove toxic metabolites.

Benefits:
- Highly concentrated in the tissue of the testicles (specifically the epididymis), L-carnitine plays a crucial role in sperm metabolism and maturation. Various studies state that L-carnitine, at total daily amounts of at least 3 grams per day, can significantly improve sperm concentration and total sperm count. Theoretically this action should work in conjunction with a stimulatory response on testosterone production, because the presence of significant testosterone is a necessary prerequisite for sperm development and maturation. In fact, at least one published study compared fertile and infertile men and discovered that infertile men had significantly lower seminal (testicular) carnitine levels.
- Believed to be helpful in keeping body fat storage under control.
- Stimulates lipid metabolism and speeds up recovery from exercise stress.
- Has been shown to have an effect on muscular responses to training, thus improving athletic performance in training and competition, and recovery from strenuous exercise.
- New research has shown that L-carnitine may play a role in enhancing blood flow to exercising muscle and thereby minimize muscle damage.
- A recent study suggests carnitine may be effective at enhancing testosterone's anabolic actions in skeletal muscle. This appears to work by enhancing the number of androgen receptors (what testosterone binds to to begin its anabolic effects) within the muscle.

Dosage:
Common doses range from 1-3 grams per day.

Niacin

Niacin is a member of the B-vitamin family, sometimes referred to as vitamin B3. Niacin is found naturally in meat (especially red meat), poultry, fish, legumes and yeast. It is also present in corn and wheat.

Benefits:
- Involved in a wide range of processes, including energy production; synthesis of fatty acids, cholesterol and steroids; and the regulation of gene expression.
- Effective in lowering cholesterol and triglycerides, in turn protecting against atherosclerosis. Various studies have shown that niacin can significantly lower total cholesterol, LDL-cholesterol (so-called "bad" cholesterol), triglycerides and lipoprotein levels while increasing HDL-cholesterol levels (so called "good" cholesterol). The largest study of its kind tested for niacin's effects on cardiovascular-disease risk factors. In this randomized, six-year study of 8,341 men who had suffered heart attacks, nicotinic acid, given in one gram doses three times per day, significantly decreased cholesterol and triglyceride levels; recurrent non-fatal heart attacks decreased by 27 percent. Another five-year randomized, placebo-controlled study discovered a significant decrease in total and cardiac mortality by 26 percent.
- Perhaps best known in bodybuilding circles because it causes skin flushing, niacin dilates cutaneous blood vessels, resulting in more blood flow to the extremities and skin surface. In an attempt to appear more vascular, some bodybuilders have ingested niacin an hour or so before stepping onstage to compete.
- May also work as a pre-workout pump enhancer, and is a powerful adjunct to arginine alpha-ketoglutarate.

Dosage:
Some men are very sensitive to the effects of niacin, so initial doses should not exceed 200 milligrams, though higher doses have been safely administered in research.

Phosphatidylcholine

Phosphatidylcholine is important for muscle cell repair and assists in the healing and protection of liver cells. From a chemistry standpoint, phosphatidylcholine is more or less the same thing as lecithin in that phosphatidylcholine is present in commercial lecithin in concentrations up to 90 percent. But the commercial source is critical because, depending on that source, concentrations can be as low as 20 percent. For example, egg lecithin naturally contains 70 percent phosphatidylcholine, while soy only contains about 20 percent. Yet due to cost, soy and sunflower have become the major sources of commercial lecithin.

Though available from a few companies, egg yolk lecithin is not considered a major source of lecithin among nutritional supplements. Egg yolk lecithin as a source of phosphatidylcholine has received a bad rap because of the whole cholesterol issue. However, when you take a more careful look, you realize that lecithin has the unusual property of emulsifying fat and allowing fat and water to mix. For this reason, the popular myth that "eggs increase your cholesterol" never really proved to be true. Even so, this has become yet another reason consumers unfortunately have been steered toward soy lecithin.

Benefits:
- Responsible for a "fluidizing" effect on cell membranes at the molecular level. This process protects the cells from the kind of breakdown associated with disorders that include liver and nerve diseases, cancers and toxic-cell death. It's for this reason that I've used phosphatidylcholine in my practice to counter the liver problems (transaminitis, hepatitis, etc.) associated with patients abusing anabolic steroids.
- A good anti-catabolic, phosphatidylcholine has the natural ability to protect cells and thus counterbalance surges of cortisol (an anti-inflammatory steroid released by the body during times of stress that destroys muscle tissue and makes you fatter).

Dosage:
Phosphatidylcholine dosage in the form of egg lecithin for the male bodybuilder should be anywhere from 10–20 grams per day, taken post–workout.

Watch for:
No major side effects seem to exist, but in higher doses — in excess of 25 grams per day — you might experience sweating, nausea, diarrhea and even vomiting. Pure phosphatidylcholine has been used at doses of up to 9 grams per day. In my practice, I've also successfully used krill oil, which has the added benefit of providing omega-3 essential fats, at up to 2 grams per day.

Phosphatidylserine

Like phosphatidylcholine, phosphatidylserine is an important structural component of cell membranes and is also found in high concentrations in the yolk of eggs (yet another reason not to wash those yolks down the drain).

Benefits:
- Due to its high concentration in nerve and brain tissue, phosphatidylserine has primarily demonstrated its usefulness in treating conditions of cognitive impairment.
- Emerging research on phosphatidylserine as an immune enhancer that reduces the stress of exercise has received much attention. The mechanism is believed to be modulated by an inhibition of exercise-induced spikes in cortisol. This has been achieved at doses of 400–800 milligrams per day. So, like phosphatidylcholine, phosphatidylserine is a good anti-catabolic.
- Has the natural ability to protect cells and thus balance surges of cortisol. It's conveniently found in the same food sources, but has a distinct advantage of necessitating much lower dosing relative to phosphatidylcholine for effect.

Dosage:
In my practice, I rely on phosphatidylcholine when phosphatidylserine is ineffective. Also phosphatidylcholine has broader health effects. As a result, I tend to use them together for the best effect. Dosage varies considerably.

Zinc

Zinc is a mineral essential to the body and present to some degree in almost every cell. It's a necessary stimulatory cofactor in numerous enzyme pathways in the body.

Benefits:
- Has been shown to support a healthy immune system, assist in wound healing, and function in protein synthesis. In so doing, zinc supports normal growth and development during childhood and adolescence.
- For men, zinc is a key component in normal testosterone production. (I theorize that it may be for this reason that oysters have long since been considered an aphrodisiac, because they contain more zinc per serving than any other common food.) Hard training causes testosterone levels to temporarily wane; these levels need to be built back up, and zinc assists in this regard.
- If you've noticed that the harder you train, the lower your sex drive, you

might be dealing with a testosterone fluctuation issue that can be countered by supplemental zinc.

Dosage:

Though the RDA is 11 milligrams per day for men 14–70 years old, I have found that most male bodybuilders do better on about 30 milligrams per day.

An excess of supplemental zinc can deplete the body of copper stores, so make sure that for every 15 milligrams of zinc you take, you also have about 500 micrograms of copper.

Zinc absorption is actually greater from a diet high in animal protein (including red meat) when compared to a diet rich in plant proteins like soy, according to research.

Some experts claim zinc picolinate is a better form of zinc. I've seen some literature but no comparative studies that would convince me that this form of zinc offers any real comparative advantage over other forms.

Watch for:

Over-consumption of breads and cereals can decrease zinc absorption.

POST-WORKOUT NUTRITION

Though I've been somewhat careful throughout the text in not making my scientific references too obvious or using too much medical jargon, I'll ask you to please forgive me for this chapter's heavily referenced indulgence. But I feel it is warranted because the subject of the science of post-exercise supplementation is such a hotly disputed discourse in which there is much debate among experts. So when discussing the specific area, the nuances of ones opinions must be carefully described and specifically referenced lest I be a goat among my medical and scientific colleagues!

That said, proper weight training in the way I describe leads to a significant increase in skeletal muscle mass. Added muscle mass (hypertrophy) can occur through an increase in muscle protein synthesis, a decrease in muscle protein degradation, or both. While stimulus (i.e., resistance exercise) is important for muscle hypertrophy, nutrient availability plays a critical factor in regulating the degree to which the muscles hypertrophy. Obviously, and as discussed, the muscle's hormonal milieu has a major impact on muscle protein synthesis.

It's now abundantly clear that both increased insulin and increased availability of amino acids are important to maximize muscle protein anabolism. The importance of availability of amino acids for the stimulatory effects of insulin to be evident was highlighted by Bennet and colleagues, who reported that insulin, given with sufficient amino acids can significantly stimulate protein anabolism via stimulation of protein synthesis and inhibition of protein breakdown. This is in line with the recent data by Borsheim and co-workers, who showed that protein balance over the muscle

---

remains negative after resistance exercise, when only carbs are ingested. In sharp contrast, amino acid ingestion alone significantly increases muscle protein anabolism after resistance exercise. However, consumption of both amino acids and moderate carbs result in much greater effects on muscle protein anabolism, suggesting an interactive effect between insulin, amino acid availability and resistance exercise. Also, it's well established that the stimulatory effect of amino acids after exercise is greater than the effect of amino acids on muscle protein synthesis, when given at rest. Thus, nutrient timing is also an important consideration.

There is an important lesson here for those looking to gain lean muscle mass. While we know that carbohydrate intake must not be out of control otherwise muscular sharpness is sacrificed, there are critical times (like the post-exercise period) in which carbohydrates, though non-essential in the literal sense, actually bolster gains. Though some amino acids are insulinogenic, even they cannot raise insulin to the degree carbohydrates can. On the other hand, we know as health care practitioners that stimulating too much sustained insulin is the route to health deterioration, fat gain (turning on lipogenesis), and diabetes. If this all sounds like a contradiction in terms, look a little closer. If you are careful about when, how much, and how you administer your carbohydrates, you can reap the benefit of short term hyperinsulinemia, while not suffering the ravages of sustaining this level and seeing your sharpness blur or your health suffer.

Given the fact that raising the blood insulin level is key to stimulating muscle protein synthesis and limiting protein degradation following exercise, it is not surprising that some hardcore gym rats abuse insulin to increase muscle mass and strength. According to drug guru William Llewellyn, insulin injections can produce "rapid and noticeable [muscle] growth ... almost immediately after starting insulin therapy." Most athletes choose to administer insulin immediately after a workout (the most anabolic time of the day to use this hormone). However, insulin abuse is extremely risky business—one mistake in dosage and/or in the diet can be extremely damaging, even fatal! Fortunately, recent studies have focused on safe nutritional mixtures containing protein hydrolysates, certain added amino acids (especially leucine) and high-glycemic (fast-acting) carbs.

The best available evidence suggests that dietary supplementation-induced post-exercise hyperinsulinemia (a high level of insulin in the blood) supported by protein hydrolysate and leucine ingestion-induced hyperaminoacidemia (high levels of amino acids in blood) increases net protein deposition in muscle, leading to increased skeletal muscle hypertrophy and strength in conjunction with appropriate resistance training. Let's examine some science behind this hypothesis.

Amino Acid & Insulin Secretion

Insulin is a peptide hormone produced by the beta cells of the pancreas. It was once believed that insulin secretion was controlled almost entirely by blood glucose concentration, i.e., by eating carb-containing foods. However, scientists later realized that amino acids also play a very important role in controlling insulin secretion. Certain amino acids cause insulin release in humans, even under conditions where the blood sugar changes little from its basal level. However, changes in blood sugar levels markedly influence the responsiveness of beta cells to individual amino acids. Studies have demonstrated that physiological amino acid mixtures and even pharmacological concentrations of individual amino acids require the presence of permissive levels of glucose to be effective beta cell stimulants. However, leucine is an exception.

Leucine & Muscle Protein Synthesis

The key branched-chain amino acid leucine acts as a nutrient signal to stimulate muscle protein anabolism. Leucine affects muscle protein metabolism by decreasing the rate of protein degradation, most likely via increases in circulating insulin. In addition, leucine activates key molecules involved in the regulation of protein synthesis, which has been shown to occur even in the absence of an increase in circulating insulin concentrations. After exercise, recovery of muscle protein synthesis requires dietary protein or branched-chain amino acids to increase tissue levels of leucine. The important bottom line is that insulin and leucine allow skeletal muscle to coordinate protein synthesis with physiological state and dietary intake. If you wish to read a more detailed review, see the excellent publication by Norton and Layman in *The Journal of Nutrition* (136:533S-537S, 2006).

Rapidly Absorbed Protein Hydrolysates

Protein hydrolysates (i.e., partially pre-digested proteins) are produced from purified protein sources by either heating with acid or preferably, the addition of enzymes, followed by purification procedures. The hydrolysis process mimics our own digestive actions; thus, many experts feel it's an ideal way to process dietary protein, especially when rapid absorption is important (e.g., immediately after exercise). However, extreme bitterness has been traditionally a negative attribute associated with the taste of most protein hydrolysates (particularly the high-grade sources). That's what makes so many of them tough to use for the bodybuilder.

Fortunately, specific de-bittering methods have produced relatively neutral-tasting protein hydrolysates. Extensively hydrolyzed proteins containing mostly di- and tripeptides (chains of two and three amino acids) are absorbed more rapidly than free-form amino acids, and much more rapidly than intact (non-hydrolyzed) proteins. The considerably greater absorption rate of amino acids from the di- and tripeptides (compared to the amino acid mixture) appears to be the result of uptake by a system that has a greater transport capacity than the amino acid carrier system, thus minimizing competition among its substrates.

Current evidence indicates that only di- and tripeptides are absorbed intact. Larger peptides appear to require hydrolysis before their breakdown products can be absorbed. While the starter protein and method of hydrolysis affect absorptive characteristics, the peptide-chain length is the most important variable. Protein hydrolysates produced from various sources showed increased amino acid absorption in humans when the proportion of di- and tripeptides was increased. Thus, in order to maximize the absorption rate, the ideal protein hydrolysate should contain mainly di- and tripeptides, which seems to produce the most immediate hyperaminoacidemia. In general, it's the kinetics of the absorption (rather than the net absorption of amino acids) that determines the greater nutritional value of the protein hydrolysates.

The use of a protein hydrolysate in post-exercise drinks can be a useful tool because it results in a faster increase in blood amino acid concentrations during a two-hour period than do intact proteins. In turn, the levels of essential amino acids in the blood regulate muscle protein synthesis. A practical advantage is that one can ingest a protein hydrolysate-containing supplement immediately after exercise without excessively suppressing appetite, so one can eat another meal sooner, possibly optimizing the post-exercise "anabolic window." In addition, protein hydrolysates strongly stimulate insulin secretion.

Clearly, hydrolyzed whey protein is the most powerful and popular protein hydrolysate among serious athletes. Whey protein has been singled out as the ultimate source of protein based on an excellent amino acid profile. Whey may offer other benefits, too. Casein hydrolysate is also utilized in some protein mixtures, but when it comes to hydrolysates, I prefer whey. By the way, the biological value of hydrolyzed collagen (also known as gelatin) is zero; thus, collagen supplementation as a protein source isn't recommended, so stay away from those poor-quality protein bars containing collagen. However, it's been suggested that hydrolyzed collagen may be useful in counteracting degenerative joint diseases (e.g., osteoarthritis). Finally, some commercial products are enriched with wheat gluten hydrolysate (i.e., "glutamine peptides"). Wheat gluten has a unique amino acid profile: glutamyl residues account for about 40 percent of the amino acids. Glutamine is an important fuel for some cells of the immune system, and may have specific immunostimulatory effects.

Protein Hydrolysate/Carb/Leucine Drinks, Insulin Secretion & Nitrogen Utilization

A study at the Copenhagen Muscle Research Center was implemented to determine the effects different protein-containing solutions have on insulin response and amino acid availability in healthy humans. Four different 600 mL solutions were used. The glucose solution (control) contained only glucose (25 g/L), and the three additional solutions contained the same quantity of glucose plus protein (0.25 g/kg body mass), but proteins were derived from different sources: whey hydrolysate, pea hydrolysate and a complete cow's milk solution. This study indicated that:

Ingestion of glucose and protein hydrolysate results in synergistic and fast increases in blood insulin. In fact, protein hydrolysates stimulated an increase in blood insulin that was two and four times greater than that produced by the intact milk protein solution and glucose solution, respectively.

Protein hydrolysates are absorbed at a faster rate from the gut than are intact milk proteins, as reflected by the rapid increase in the blood concentration of amino acids in peripheral blood.

Whey protein hydrolysate elicited the greatest availability of amino acids during the three-hour postprandial (occurring after meal) period. The authors attributed this difference to the rapid increase in blood amino acids evoked during the first 40 minutes of the digestive period, during which the increase was about 37 percent greater after the ingestion of whey protein hydrolysate solution than after ingestion of the intact milk protein solution.

It's likely that the high levels of blood amino acids and increased insulin explains a superiority of protein hydrolysates over intact proteins in promoting better nitrogen utilization (i.e., protein anabolism). The co-ingestion of carbs appears to affect the absorption kinetics, as Calbet and Holst showed that whey and casein proteins and their respective hydrolysates administered alone produce similar rates of intestinal absorption of amino acids. It should be noted that the degree of hydrolysis (i.e., the peptide-chain length) also affects absorption kinetics. Unfortunately, many scientists don't provide any information on protein hydrolysates used in their studies.

More recently, Kaastra and colleagues determined the extent to which the combined ingestion of high-glycemic carbs and a casein protein hydrolysate, with or without additional leucine, can increase insulin levels during post-exercise recovery. Fourteen male athletes were subjected to three randomized crossover trials in which they performed two hours of exercise. Thereafter, subjects were studied for 3.5 hours during which they ingested carbs only (0.8 g/kg/h), carbs + protein hydrolysate (0.8 and 0.4 g/kg/h, respectively), or carbs + protein hydrolysate + free leucine (0.8, 0.4 and 0.1 g/kg/h, respectively) in a double-blind fashion.

The results revealed that blood insulin responses were 108% and 190% greater in the carbs + protein hydrolysate and carbs + protein hydrolysate + leucine trial, respectively, compared with the carbs-only trial. This study also indicated that the addition of free phenylalanine, as applied in earlier studies, isn't necessary to obtain such high post-exercise insulin responses. Similarly, Manders and co-workers examined blood insulin responses after co-ingestion of casein protein hydrolysate, with and without additional free leucine, with a single bolus of high-glycemic carbs. Again, the subjects participated in three trials in which blood insulin responses were determined after the ingestion of beverages of different composition: carbs only (0.7 g/kg), carbs + protein hydrolysate (0.7 and 0.3 g/kg, respectively) or carbs + protein hydrolysate + leucine (0.7, 0.3 and 0.1 g/kg, respectively). The results indicated that blood insulin responses were 66% and 221% greater in the healthy subjects in the carbs + protein hydrolysate and carbs + protein hydrolysate + leucine trials, respectively, compared with those in the carbs only trial. In other words, this study also demonstrated that co-ingestion of a protein hydrolysate with additional leucine strongly augments insulin secretion after the consumption of a single bolus of carbs.

The notion that the protein hydrolysates have strong insulin-boosting properties is also supported by the studies examining the effects of intact protein-containing post-exercise drinks. Ivy and co-workers compared effects of carb + intact protein drink (80 g of carbs, 28 g of protein, 6 g of fat), low-carb drink (80 g of carbs, 6 g of fat), or high-carb drink (108 g of carbs, 6 g of fat) and concluded that blood insulin levels didn't differ at any time among treatments. However, Zawadzki and colleagues observed that blood insulin levels for the carbs + intact protein treatment (112 and 40.7 g, respectively) was somewhat higher than those for the carbs-only treatment (112 g of carbs). A post-exercise drink containing a mixture of free amino acids also has a potent effect on insulin secretion. However, a large dose of amino acids can cause gastrointestinal discomfort.

Protein Hydrolysate/Carb/Leucine Drinks And Post-Exercise Muscle Anabolism

A sophisticated study by Koopman and colleagues investigated post-exercise muscle protein anabolism and whole body protein balance following the combined ingestion of high-glycemic carbs, with or without whey protein hydrolysate and/or leucine. Their nutritional protocol was rather rigorous; the subjects received a beverage volume of 3 ml/kg every 30 minutes to ensure a given dose of 0.3 g high-glycemic carbs/kg and 0.2 g/kg of a protein hydrolysate every hour, with or without the addition of 0.1 g/kg/h leucine. Repeated boluses were taken every 30 minutes until t = 330 minutes after exercise. The results revealed that the carbs + protein hydrolysate + leucine trial had a greater mixed muscle fractional synthetic rate and less whole body protein oxidation

Similarly, muscle anabolism in the vastus lateralis muscle was significantly greater in the carbs + protein hydrolysate + leucine trial compared with the carbs-only trial, with intermediate values observed in the carbs + protein hydrolysate trial. Thus, the authors concluded that, "The additional ingestion of free leucine in combination with protein and carbohydrate likely represents an effective strategy to increase muscle anabolism following resistance exercise." This study used rather large doses of added leucine; however, other recent studies have shown that relatively small doses can improve exercise performance and enhance the acquisition of strength.

Although the Koopman study indicates that dietary supplementation-induced, post-exercise hyperinsulinemia plus hyperaminoacidemia can have favorable effects on the acute phase response to resistance training, the effects of repeated supplementation on long-term adaptations to resistance training are currently unclear. To shed some light on this issue, Bird and co-workers examined the effects of chronic, high-glycemic carb and/or essential amino acid supplementation on hormonal and muscular adaptations in untrained young men. All subjects followed the same supervised, resistance-training protocol two times per week for 12 weeks. Following resistance exercise, the subjects consumed either a high-glycemic carb, an essential amino acid (6 g), a combined high-glycemic carb + essential amino acid supplement, or a placebo containing only aspartame and citrus flavoring. The results revealed that carb + essential amino acid supplementation enhances muscular and hormonal adaptations to a greater extent than either carbs or essential amino acids consumed independently. Specifically, carb + essential amino acid ingestion demonstrated the greatest relative increase in type I muscle fiber cross-sectional area. Changes in type II muscle fibers exhibited a similar trend.

In addition, it's very likely that chronic reductions in the exercise-induced cortisol response associated with post-exercise carb-amino acid ingestion also positively impact the skeletal muscle hypertrophic adaptation to resistance training via reductions in hormone-mediated protein degradation.

You Can Have Your Protein Shake & Drink It, Too!

Contrary to some beliefs, higher protein intake has no adverse effects on healthy kidneys, fluid status, or bone in otherwise healthy individuals. In fact, proteins appears to have positive effects on bone health, as they increase circulating insulin-like growth factor I (IGF-1), which plays an important role in bone formation. For example, Ballard and co-workers reported that a protein supplement during a strength and conditioning program led to an increase in blood concentrations of IGF-I in those subjects compared with the concentrations in a group of persons who also trained, but consumed an isocaloric carb supplement. Also, serum bone alkaline phosphatase concentrations increased over time and tended to be higher in the protein group than in the carb group, indicating increased bone formation.

In addition, IGF-I plays a critical role in development, growth, repair and maintenance of skeletal muscle. Thus, IGF-I may partially explain why many strength-power athletes (especially bodybuilders) feel that a very high protein intake is beneficial for skeletal muscle hypertrophy. Indeed, studies indicate increased positive nitrogen balance when protein intake is increased; however, more research is clearly needed before the mystery of protein requirements in those attempting to increase muscle mass is settled.

Traditionally, the term "protein requirement" has meant the amount of dietary protein that must be consumed to provide the amino acids needed for the synthesis of those proteins irreversibly catabolized in the course of the body's metabolism. It should be noted, however, that strength-power athletes don't care about the minimum amount of protein necessary to sustain normal body functions. Rather, they are interested in maximal gains in muscle mass and/or strength. Other potential benefits of higher protein intake should be considered as well.

Summing Up

The studies reviewed in this chapter clearly indicate that nutritional mixtures containing protein hydrolysates, added leucine and high-glycemic carbs strongly augment insulin secretion, compared with the high-glycemic carbs-only trial. When short-term and transient post-exercise hyperinsulinemia is supported by a proper protein hydrolysate and leucine ingestion-induced hyperaminoacidemia, a net protein deposition in muscle should occur in conjunction with appropriate resistance training. This should lead to optimal increased skeletal muscle hypertrophy (gains) and strength increases. From a supplement standpoint, a quality protein hydrolysate/carb/leucine drink taken post exercise may represent the single most effective supplement for promoting extreme muscle enhancement. The science is impressive and the real-world results achieved by high level competitive bodybuilders is even more compelling. The key here, is of course, being sure to take a high quality protein hydrolysate supplement within an hour of exercise for maximum results.

THE EXTREME DIET

Up to this point, you've read my general strategies and philosophies that provide the backbone of the extreme muscle enhancement nutritional program. Now it's time to take that knowledge and assemble it all into a sample diet — what one might eat and supplement with during a typical mass-gaining day.

Just remember that the following doesn't necessarily apply to you personally. The example day presented here is meant to provide you with a sensible framework of reference in terms of how one might put my nutritional concepts together. You can use it as a blueprint to construct your own meal plan; you should develop your own starting point, based on your current situation and your goals, and track your progress meticulously. By determining what calorie levels and food choices work for you over time, you can create a rock-solid diagram to fuel years of muscle growth.

You'll notice that in some places, specific amounts of foods aren't given. As they would rightfully vary widely from person-to-person, it's better to simply provide the "what" as far as what you should be eating; the "how much" is dependent on your current bodyweight, your goal bodyweight, and whether you're a hardgainer looking to add mass, an endomorph looking to cut up, or someone somewhere in between.

The Extreme Muscle Enhancement Diet: A Sample Day

Breakfast, 7 a.m.
3 scrambled eggs with 2 slices of cheese
1 cup of plain oatmeal
1 cup of tomatoes, cucumbers and chives mixed with oil/vinegar or
1 cup of peas and carrots mixture
2–3 8-oz. glasses of water
Supplements: Zinc/copper, calcium, magnesium, essential fatty acids (EFAs)

Mid-Morning Snack, 9:30 a.m.
1/2 cup almonds and/or macadamia nuts
Supplements: Basic protein shake or meal replacement shake, EFAs

Pre-Workout, 10:30 a.m.
Supplements: Creatine, arginine-alpha-ketoglutarate (A-AKG),
niacin/B-vitamins, phosphorus

Workout, 11 a.m.
Water or hypotonic hydration drink during the workout

Post-Workout, 12 noon
1–2 glasses of water or hypotonic hydration drink
Supplements: Whey protein isolate or protein hydrolysate drink, branched-chain
amino acids (BCAAs), EFAs, conjugated linoleic acid (CLA)

Lunch, 1 p.m.
Large serving tuna salad
or large plate of sashimi
or large grilled chicken breast
2–3 cups mixed green salad with tomatoes, cucumbers, and dressing or
2–3 cups steamed broccoli or 2–3 cups of mixed vegetables with 2 Tbsp.
salad dressing, 2–3 glasses of water

Mid-Afternoon Snack, 3:30 p.m.
Supplements: Basic protein shake or meal replacement shake,
EFAs, calcium, antioxidants

Dinner, 5:30 p.m.
Ribeye steak
Creamed or steamed spinach
Mixed green salad
2–3 glasses of water

Last Meal, 8 p.m.
Supplements: Basic protein shake,
ornithine-alpha-ketoglutarate (O-AKG), glutamine, zinc/copper, magnesium

Troubleshooting Tips

Even in the best of scenarios, when you've done most everything correctly from a nutritional standpoint and all things are supposed to be going your way, you can still get derailed by three basic dietary quandaries that plague bodybuilders. But once you know about them and how to get around them, you will be able to stay on course without losing ground. Here they are:

1) When the Diet Becomes Monotonous

Dietary monotony is something that nearly every compliant dieter runs into, whether you're a male bodybuilder trying to get huge and ripped or a woman with five kids trying to lose the saddlebags. Adhering to the structure of a diet can become boring, repetitive and drive you crazy enough to want to throw in the towel altogether.

The bodybuilder is particularly prone to this, but for a rather interesting reason. Unlike the popular dieter who gets tired of the caloric deprivation, the bodybuilder tends to get fed up with the regularity of proper meal cadence combined with the overall sameness of the foods and the inherent required preparation. This can become so subtly annoying that you don't even see it coming until it creeps up on you one day. You wake up in the morning and despite your training going great, you just can't stomach the idea of marching through another day of food and supplements. But you're afraid that if you don't, you'll lose what you've gained.

That's when it really gets twisted, as eventually, if allowed to continue, your efforts will shift from being driven by passion to being driven by fear. You'll either give up or join the ranks of countless over-obsessed lost souls, becoming a permanent glutton for punishment as you live in fear that if a forkful of chocolate cake ever touches your lips, you'll spontaneously implode and see everything you've worked for disappear.

Luckily, there's an easy way to avoid dietary monotony. While I've discussed the idea of the rare structured fast to avoid catabolic backlash and the idea of not forcing your body to eat protein when the idea sickens you, another answer to overcoming dietary monotony is to allow yourself a "cheat meal" every couple of weeks. Of course, if you don't put in at least two good weeks of healthy anti-catabolic dieting combined with hard training, you don't deserve a cheat meal. Assuming you have put in the requisite consistency, though, it's time to let loose and be human, not super-human.

Homemade chocolate chip cookies, pepperoni pizza, fudge brownies and pancakes drowned in butter and syrup are just a sampling of some of my personal out-of-this-world cheat favorites. Judging by my choices, I'm convinced there is a fatso inside of me just dying to get out! The trick is not to feel bad about sugar, saturated fat, chemicals or processing for this meal. Just eat, enjoy and jump back on track right after that. Be worry-free. It won't ruin things. In fact, it'll help. You'll be amazed how the psychological lift of having that one little cheat meal every couple of weeks renews your commitment to healthy dieting for lean muscle mass.

2) When You Gain Fat Faster Than Muscle

Sometimes you might be doing everything right from a dietary standpoint, yet you seem to be gaining fat at the same or faster clip than you're gaining muscle. Even though you may have gone back and re-assessed your somatotype and attempted to make some adjustments based on these considerations, you still feel like you're slipping.

When this happens, usually your body, while anabolic, is too "lipogenic" (fat producing). The mistake most bodybuilders make at this point is to zero their carbohydrate intake and sacrifice their fiber-based carbohydrates in order to counter this effect. Instead of losing more fat, the result is that they then lose even more anabolic steam, watching as their muscles flatten out and their lifting poundages in the gym drop. They're left feeling smaller and fatter, unable to figure out where they went wrong.

For years I've had a rather unique trick to get around this problem. I wish I could say I thought of it, but like most great discoveries, it was something I found quite accidentally. It took a few years to refine and figure out, as I tried it with a few bodybuilders I was working with. The idea is this: When you've made no great errors in your diet, yet lipogenesis seems to be outpacing anabolism with a disturbing regularity, the answer is to ingest raw vegetables.

Rather then eliminating the fiber-based carbohydrates you have been eating, take them and, in roughly the same amounts, eat them raw for two weeks. I'm not certain exactly why it works, but I theorize it has to do with certain enzymes or cofactors that are heat sensitive and only survive in the raw state. The results are astounding.

As an aside, I'm occasionally asked why one shouldn't eat all vegetables raw all the time. I suppose you could, but then you get into both digestive and dietary monotony issues in terms of how long you could put up with it. Furthermore, there may just as easily be heat-activated enzymes or cofactors in veggies that are also important for the body. So overall, cooking vegetables is still a good thing.

3) When Dietary Supplements Stop Working

Our body will get used to anything we do continuously; it's just part of being human. In some cases, this is a good thing because it's an adaptive response that helps our bodies acclimate to that which we are exposed to in our environment. But in some cases this built-in mechanism works against us.

I first started thinking about this concept as a physician covering intensive care and coronary care units in the hospital. We used to admit certain patients after they had a heart attack and put them on intravenous nitroglycerin to reduce their chest pain. Some of the more severe and seemingly intractable patients that couldn't turn the proverbial corner could stay on continuous nitroglycerin for days. This was bad for them because, as their bodies acclimated to the drug (a situation called tachyphylaxis), steadily increasing doses were necessary just to keep the same chest pain at bay. I also saw this tachyphylaxis later on in my private practice among my elderly patients with Parkinson's disease, whose steadily escalating need for higher doses of L-dopamine (a drug used to treat the disease) was a clear signal they were becoming desensitized to the positive effects of the drug.

I'm a steadfast believer that, at some level, dietary supplements are no different. The constant bombardment of our system with the same orally-ingested supplements renders the stimulus therapeutically weakened or even ineffective. You relentlessly keep pounding your system with a substance until it no longer responds to it, or at the very least the response is dramatically weakened.

The way to avoid what I call the "supplement burnout" that plagues bodybuilders is pretty simple. Remember we are talking about dietary supplements, which are unlike the drugs and the patient conditions I've mentioned. You have to first overcome the psychological dependence by realizing that you aren't going to fall apart if you stop taking your supplements for a little while. In fact, they will work that much better after a break.

After being on a dietary supplement for a couple of months, take a week or two to cleanse the supplement from your system before starting up again. In my experience, you'll avoid suffering from the law of diminishing returns, and you'll be back on track with your body in a full state of responsiveness.

EXTREME TRAINING

TRAINING FOR SIZE

Many that meditate and do yoga are said to be on the path to self-awareness and personal growth. In fact, the practice of meditation and yoga has grown so popular that the very mention of either brings forth the notion of togetherness, peace and knowing oneself. While all that may be true (I've done my share of meditation and yoga and I'm certainly a fan), what irks me is that no one ever mentions the bodybuilder in the same light. Despite its growing popularity, the negative perceptions of bodybuilding haven't changed. Many people think we're all idiotic, narcissistic, shallow, clumsy meatheads.

Of course, our sport does attract this element. Those jackasses have a quick and obnoxious rise in the sport, driven by drugs and arrogance, but what invariably follows is a cataclysmic fizzle. They get sick from over-abusing anabolic drugs, or they're irrevocably injured from ego-training too heavy, or they become wrapped up in hard street drugs, or they simply run out of money and end up living out of their car or on a friend's sofa, all washed up. It's not a pretty story, but I've seen it countless times. Guys like this burn out and leave the sport. But it's not the sport of bodybuilding that does it to them. It is the lack of balance that does them in. These are not the true bodybuilders, however — not by a long shot.

The true bodybuilders are those that make bodybuilding a permanent facet of their lives. Looking good in public is no doubt a desirable benefit, but the ones that love the very act of training are the ones I'm talking about. Arnold Schwarzenegger announced after retiring from the sport in 1980 that, while leaving competition behind, he would never stop bodybuilding as long as he lived. Frank Zane told me how he would always find a way to train because it was too important to him. The late, great Steve Reeves loved to describe to me how he rigged up his barn so that even in his 70s he could still find ways to etch his physique. Even Joe Weider himself still works out, and he's in his 80s.

Perhaps the ageless pro bodybuilder, Albert Beckles, summed it up best for me. I'll never forget a conversation we had on a street corner in New York City shortly after he won the Night of Champions, beating guys in their 20s while in his mid-50s! I asked him how long he was going to keep training. He said, "Until they nail me in the box." That says it all.

To me, these guys (and so many like them of lesser known names but equally big hearts) are the enlightened gurus of the sport. These are the masters. They're the ones that have invited bodybuilding into their lives to stay. They're the ones that can't ever seem to walk away from the touch of cold steel.

But the greater point is that these masters know their bodies. They're remarkably self-aware. We call bodybuilding a sport, but it's really more of an art form and a way of life. The ones that have toiled for decades in the gym, bringing up their rear deltoids, adding sweep to their thighs, or training their biceps for a peak, have a unique understanding of the artistic side of the equation. Although in its purest form, it's akin to meditation and yoga, by attending to the detail of every muscle, bodybuilding is a unique path to enlightenment and self-awareness unlike any other.

Perhaps this enlightenment stems from the humbling experience of finding one's limits by failing, persevering and ultimately succeeding. There are few experiences as physically complete as bodybuilding training. You pretty much have to train everything. It is like painting a picture or tending a garden. Everything needs attention at some point. Miss a detail and you fail your personal mission of self-improvement. Some aspects need more attention then others. The ones that are keen to this are the best the art has to offer.

Bodybuilding is a cerebral game of discipline and self-control. Smart bodybuilding requires one to overcome the compunction to put all of one's energy into working on the strongest body parts, while leaving the weakest body parts behind. Training weak body parts and bringing them up is frustrating. Weak parts can't handle as much weight, often don't pump as well as strong body parts, and are temperamental or immune to soreness. Many a too-small biceps has broken many a big man.

Then you have the weight, staring back at you like a golf ball, waiting, ready to be hit, a humbling and quiet game devoid of reflexive action. You must be thoughtful and the flame of desire must be inside burning somewhere. Otherwise you're wasting your time. These are the necessary prerequisites for extreme muscle enhancement training. It's a path of self-learning where you must discover what works for you.

Myostatin-Inhibition Techniques

To begin with, you must understand that, while training takes place in the gym, the actual anabolic tissue repair and building process takes place outside the gym. Once a good workout is completed, all efforts must be focused on diet, supplements and rest. However, the hard training you do is the catalyst — all that growth isn't spurred unless you do the correct things in your training to start the anabolic engines within you.

You'll recall that the sequence of amino acids called myostatin is the greatest single catabolic limiter of muscle growth. When muscles are trained and broken down in a workout, healing and building must begin immediately thereafter for proper repair and muscle growth to occur. Myostatin controls and regulates this process in a genetically predetermined pattern. That's why most guys who are either never aware of, or never figure out how to influence this factor just never seem to grow no matter how hard they train or for however many years.

Research proves that bodybuilding training itself does in fact influence plasma levels of myostatin. Getting your rear to the gym and sticking to a routine is an important fundamental prerequisite to muscle growth. But having a thorough understanding of how to train and the techniques you must employ in order to control the untoward effects of your myostatin is the most effective way to achieve extreme muscle enhancement.

The less myostatin you have in circulation, the less it can be taken up by the muscle cells, and the less of an inhibitory effect it'll have on muscle growth. For example, in sedentary individuals, I would say a 10 percent increase in myostatin correlates to about a five-pound loss of muscle.

When trying to conceptualize the role of myostatin, just remember the story of the Belgian blue bull. This animal is born without the gene to produce the protein for myostatin. Thus, they're considered "myostatin null" (a scientific way of saying that they were born missing myostatin and remain that way their whole lives), and can basically sit out in the fields doing nothing and still pack on muscle mass. Interestingly, these animals live just as long as normal bulls, yet are much stronger.

On the human front, did you ever wonder why some professional bodybuilders just end up much bigger then others, despite both groups training hard, remaining steadfast about their diets, and in many cases abusing anabolic drugs? Well the answer is that, no matter what they do and other things being equal, the bodybuilders with the lowest amount of myostatin in their systems will by far be the biggest.

We know that myostatin levels are lower after weight training. Myostatin down-regulates in order to offset the fact that muscle is being attacked with the catabolic process of weight training. This down-regulation spurs the subsequent anabolic process needed to repair the muscle. When training is challenging enough for the muscle, this anabolic process instigated by a drop in myostatin not only serves to repair muscles but also increases their size in anticipation of having to suffer through another similar workload.

The greater the level in the workout of what I call "intelligent intensity," the more you lower your myostatin. This makes sense because if myostatin were high and you were killing yourself in the gym at the same time, you would have dual catabolic processes occurring at the same time. You would have no balance; the muscles would be heavily attacked and broken down by the training session, yet they couldn't be adequately repaired due to the high levels of circulating myostatin.

As stated, a decrease in myostatin while training is to be expected. The problem is that this downturn in myostatin is oftentimes not vigorous enough to be clinically significant and pave the way for really generous anabolic muscle gains. Small decreases in myostatin will result in only small changes in muscle mass. However, know that when the downturn in myostatin as a result of your training session isn't clinically significant, it's almost invariably the result of a poor training effort or training mistakes.

On the other hand, large decreases in myostatin result in large improvements in muscle mass. Research published out of New Zealand in 2004 tells us that bodybuilding subjects were exercised in such a way that they experienced a 20 percent decrease in myostatin. This resulted in a 30 percent increase in strength and a 12 percent increase in muscle cross section in only 10 weeks.

Practical knowledge plus the corresponding clinical research findings give us a clue how to train to significantly reduce myostatin and subsequently maximize our gains. First and foremost are concepts that deal with training input. Though they're largely common sense, it always amazes me how often I see these principles ignored even when an experienced bodybuilder knows better. Egomania, competitive showing off, and attempting to do the most weight squash our best efforts at mass building. Of course, on the other extreme, poor commitment and lack of focus are also factors that screw up our training and hamper our battle against myostatin.

Regardless of how you manage to stumble into the gym and over to a stack of weights, if you're just relocating steel and not feeling the pain of the muscle being trained, odds are you're not getting maximal myostatin suppression. Guys like this might as well give up lifting and get jobs as movers. At least then they'll still get a workout and finally put their weight belts to good use.

The moral of the story is this — you get out what you put in, with the caution that in bodybuilding it's about quality above quantity. Therein lies some general necessities:

- *Choose free weights more often then machines.* Free weights are tougher then machines because machines are easier on muscles. A machine balances the weight for you, whereas with free weights, extra muscles are called into play throughout your body for stabilization. Anything that makes life more difficult for the muscles being trained will do a better job at suppressing myostatin.

- *Use strict form.* You'll discover it's much more difficult to achieve training intensity when you're taking advantage of momentum to swing the weight up, thus missing muscle fibers along the way. Also pay attention to the pace of the repetitions by not stopping and resting between each. Again, the muscle must be maximally taxed in order to be forced to grow and have low myostatin levels working for you in the process. The set must be as difficult as possible. Muscles should not be unloaded throughout the set by a lazy lockout, a pause or a moment of relaxation during the set.

- *Nail down a consistent schedule.* The right split offers a regular training frequency while balancing your need to rest. Nutrition and lifestyle modifications can influence your overall catabolic state, but your workout offers you the single greatest moment to decrease your plasma myostatin level. If you don't train often enough, myostatin will always be working against you; your basal myostatin levels will remain too high to achieve massive muscle growth. However, don't overdo it either. If you annihilate your muscles while not resting enough, your myostatin levels may increase in the face of stress hormones like cortisol and the adrenergic hormones. That's why, when you see guys who train for several hours day after day, despite all that work, they actually start to lose size! It's akin to taking a job that pays you $50 a day but costs you $100 a day in cab fare just to get there. Figuring out frequency versus rest can be a difficult balance to strike. One method to consider is spending less total time in the gym during any one session, and just training with a little more frequency. There is nothing wrong with training five or even six days a week in some cases, provided your sessions are brief and intense.

I'm not going to kid you. Working out the way I describe is not for the faint of heart. It takes desire, courage and blood-and-guts motivation to get an extreme physique. Most guys can't hack it for more than a couple of workouts. They quit. But if you're one of those special individuals that has what it takes to persevere and properly apply these principles in a confluent manner, the results will amaze you by spurring muscle growth like you've never seen before.

Morph Code

As with your diet, your training must at times be modified to your somatotype for you to achieve optimal results. Not everyone is built the same way and all bodies aren't created equal. For example, Phil was a classmate in college who, while athletic, never really touched a weight before he met me. He quickly became interested in weight training when he saw that it was a part of my daily routine for a number of years, had long been a regular and enjoyable facet of my life, and whose results were self evident in my physique. Being that we studied together (both of us were pre-med), mirroring one another's activities just seemed like the natural thing to do. Together we fell into a Spartan routine of doing little else but studying insanely hard and training insanely hard.

He was under the early naïve impression that he would never end up gaining as much muscle as I had. However, having a few years of competitive bodybuilding and know-how under my belt, I immediately recognized his potential and knew how mistaken he was. Phil had a great deal going for him, but he didn't believe me at the time when I told him this. The fact was that, in addition to being a few inches taller then me, he was bigger boned, had a naturally rugged build, and his wrists, ankles and other joints were noticeably thicker then mine, signifying good mass-building potential. He had the classic mesomorph physique, no question about it.

In only the first year of training with me, he went from 170 to 215 pounds. That's 45 pounds total, of which I'd have to say at least 30 pounds were pure muscle! He did have the advantage of my experience in doing workouts alongside me and eating what I ate. We trained like animals and sat around studying to be doctors; it was a nutty existence, but one we were both eccentric enough to commit ourselves to. The following year also was impressive, as he grew to about 235 pounds, eventually passing me by in his development.

Had Phil started with a more ectomorphic physique as I had, he likely would have gained about 10–20 pounds less of lean mass. At the other extreme, if he had the larger and often pear-shaped endomorphic-type build to start with, I might have expected the same or even greater gain in absolute weight, but a higher percentage may have been comprised of fat.

The type of body you have influences the amount and quality of how much muscle you're able to put on. Though many experts have tossed out this somatotype criteria as being outdated, I actually still find it quite useful as a start in estimating how much muscle growth potential an individual has programmed in his genetics.

We rarely see pure ectomorph, mesomorph or endomorph builds, though I can think of a few popular examples to help you visualize and get the hang of typing physiques you see. In boxing, Mike Tyson has a fairly pure mesomorphic build, whereas Larry Holmes, though very physical, still displayed a classic endomorphic physique. In basketball, Kobe Bryant is very much an ectomorph, whereas Shaquille O'Neal, though very tall, is mesomorphic.

In contrast to these pure examples, I usually find people tend to display a mix of types. The way to classify physiques using somatotype is with their primary type listed first and secondary listed second. Here are some examples to help you get a feel for this; Evander Holyfield was probably meso-ecto (60/40), while George Foreman was meso-endo (60/40). Michael Jordan was ecto-meso (80/20), while Charles Barkley was probably an endo-meso (55/45).

In professional bodybuilding, where drugs radically influence physiques, these somatotypes are very magnified and you get a mix of visual results. For example, Ronnie Coleman has a nearly pure mesomorphic physique with just a touch of endomorphic quality (90/10), which is partially what helped him get so damn big. Look carefully and you see a trace of endomorph in Ronnie's build: His shoulders, while incredibly thick, aren't super wide; he's not pear shaped, but does have massive glutes; and, while certainly not wide in the waist, it's not exactly small, and his midsection has never been totally ripped. On the opposite extreme, Dexter Jackson is a classic meso-ecto (60/40). Looking back on bodybuilding's past, Arnold was probably a meso-endo (70/30), while Frank Zane was ectomorphic with a smaller mesomorphic component (65/35).

What's the perfect body type to begin with? To me, a very mesomorphic build with a slight touch of ectomorphic quality is the best — a 90/10, with Flex Wheeler being perhaps the ultimate example. The ectomorphic quality gives the classic mesomorph phenotype a little better shape and allows them to lose fat easier. On the other hand, too much ectomorphic quality and you've got problems gaining mass.

Another solid example would be the meso-ecto (80/20) build of former Mr. Olympia Lee Haney. He had all the big bones and mass of a classic mesomorph, but with some degree of ectomorph quality as evidenced by his narrow waist, small joints and super-wide shoulders. I'm not sure he'd ever beat Ronnie head-to-head, but certainly by somatotype standards Haney had a superior structure, albeit not as big. But again, the meso-ecto (90/10) would be theoretically the absolute best. We simply have not seen too many physiques like this in professional bodybuilding, which is a reason Wheeler was often considered in a class by himself.

Recalling the somatotype descriptions I gave earlier, take a moment and assess your own physique, remembering you will likely lie in between two with more of one than the other. Then try it with the builds of other people. You'll soon see how well this system works.

Gain Plan

If you're training regularly, going the natural route and doing all the right things, exactly how much quality weight should you expect to gain every year? This is obviously a popular question. The easy answer is that there really is no easy answer, but hang with me here and we'll be able to make some assumptions.

Though body type is a good genetic indicator of how much lean mass you can expect to pack on in a year of hard training, countless other factors influence your annual end result. Few have perfect bodybuilding lifestyles where they can do nothing but train and recover adequately. In real life, most of us have to go to work. A couple of late nights at the office or a little overtime may be all it takes to throw a consistent routine out of whack. The stress of personal relationships alone is enough to make you thankful to even get on a treadmill, let alone fit in the perfect biceps routine.

Some days you just go with the flow and take what you can get, if you can make it to the gym at all. A fast-paced life makes you miss meals or eat the not-so-good things. Holidays get in the way. Vacations are fun but usually don't mesh well with iron pumping, since most people just want to rest when they finally get time off. Then there is the illness and injury factor. All it takes is a bad bout with the flu or a spasm in your lower back to cause you to lose days or weeks of training. More serious illness or injury can result in a longer hiatus.

So, while perfect years of training aren't easy to come by, by correctly identifying your somatotype and going with the seven basic assumptions of your year below, at least you can get some idea of how much quality weight you could expect to gain. The assumptions are as follows:

1. *You maintain a level of strict, intense weight training.*
2. *You don't miss workouts, and you don't overtrain.*
3. *You suffer no prolonged illness or injuries, and keep your stress levels low.*
4. *Your body fat percentage remains relatively unchanged or slightly decreases.*
5. *Your diet is high in protein and healthy fats and low in carbohydrates, with optimal supplementation.*
6. *You don't take any performance-enhancing drugs.*
7. *You're a male of average height, 5'7"–5'11". (Obviously, height isn't a variable you control, but in order to create useful recommendations that apply to most individuals, I restricted my analysis to this range.)*

Achieving even half of assumptions 1–6 is a victory in and of itself. But assuming they're satisfied and that you've nailed down your somatotype correctly, you can get at least some idea of what your minimal average annual muscle-mass gains should be by using the following table:

Estimated Minimal Annual Muscle Gain

(Based on body type; figures are listed in pounds)

	Beginner 0 years training	Intermediate 1–3 years training	Advanced 3–6 years training	Master More than 6 years training
18–25 years old	Ecto–11 Meso–13 Endo–16	Ecto–8 Meso–10 Endo–12	Ecto–5 Meso–7 Endo–8	Ecto–3 Meso–5 Endo–6
26–35 years old	Ecto–9 Meso–12 Endo–13	Ecto–7 Meso–8 Endo–9	Ecto–5 Meso–6 Endo–7	Ecto–2 Meso–4 Endo–5
36–45 years old	Ecto–6 Meso–7 Endo–8	Ecto–5 Meso–6 Endo–7	Ecto–3 Meso–4 Endo–5	Ecto–1 Meso–2 Endo–2
Over 45 years old	Ecto–3 Meso–4 Endo–5	Ecto–2 Meso–3 Endo–4	Ecto–1 Meso–2 Endo–2	Ecto–<1 Meso–<2 Endo–<2

Finally, keep in mind that these are only general guidelines. Even though you might be strictly following the assumptions, poor genetics and/or environmental influences may result in lesser gains. At worst, if you think you are meeting all the assumptions and doing everything right yet still not making the minimal numbers I indicate, then you're doing something seriously wrong and you need to look carefully at how you might be screwing up.

My hope is that you can be one of the lucky ones to advance beyond these general assumptions. Paying close attention to your body's signals is a good way to accomplish this. Working with an experienced and successful mentor also can help. Either way, you can condense what would otherwise be years of training into months and shatter these numbers. My former training partner Phil did it, going far above and beyond this chart in his first few years, and you can too.

Advice For The Ectomorph

This, and the two following sections give a brief rundown of training advice for each of the three body types.

Ideal Rep Range: **6–8 per set**
An ectomorph's muscles are lean and of high quality, but dense and stubborn

to grow in response to resistance training. He generally favors slightly higher reps in a range of 10–15 since he gets a deep burn training this way, a burn he doesn't get in lower-rep ranges. Nevertheless, for mass gains, he'll ultimately respond better to lower repetitions on the order of 6–8. Falling into that comfort zone of higher reps simply won't lead to big size gains.

On the other hand, after a few years of training, he may want to experiment with high reps for his weaker body parts. Likely, those muscle fibers are so dense, they're virtually unresponsive to anything short of a repetition overload. You really have to feel your way instinctively as you gain experience.

Very low repetitions (1–3) do absolutely nothing for the physique of the ectomorph, other then create joint pain, so don't waste your time. While an ectomorph can build considerable strength in this range, I never see a good strength-to-muscle mass correlation; in other words, when the mesomorph or endomorph get stronger, you almost always see this reflecting in a visible increase in muscle size, whereas in an ectomorph you don't.

Training Load: 5–8 sets per body part

One of an ectomorph's best assets is that he isn't as prone to overtraining. In other words, his muscles recover faster. This may have to do with a better muscle density as defined by the ratio of muscle to fat. As a result, decreasing the total number of sets per body part (5–8), yet shortening the interval of days rested (3–5) before hitting that body part again to take advantage of this quick recovery, can prod overall mass development.

Use of Overload Techniques: Rarely

Forced reps, where a spotter helps you through extra reps when you fail on your own, or negatives, when a spotter lifts the weight for you and you lower it as slowly as you can, should be used sparingly, or the ectomorphic body easily plateaus and becomes unresponsive. Although he may have dense muscles and thus be less prone to overtraining in terms of training frequency, the same doesn't always hold true with regard to overloading sets. Again, more frequent training with fewer sets seems to be the key.

But don't misinterpret what I'm saying. An ectomorph's training intensity must be very high without going past failure. Don't confuse training to failure and using forced reps or negatives with training intensity. After all, someone could easily fail yet hardly have given much overall effort! I see it every day in the gym. Guys fail and need help with reps, but to me they're cruising and haven't dug down deep enough. The more experience you get, the easier it becomes to up your intensity without needing someone to peel the weight off of your chest.

Cardio: **Yes, With Caution**

Cardio tends to feel very good for the ectomorph. If you have this kind of build and want to tighten up, cardio is an easy way to do it. Unfortunately, a hair too much and you'll start losing mass, and it's tough for the ectomorph to detect exactly when they've overdone it. Cardio is a bad idea for an ectomorph with weak legs who wants to build mass.

Advice For The Mesomorph

The classic mesomorph has the dream physique to build quality muscle. Here you'll find some specific guidance to lead the way.

Ideal Rep Range: **8–12 per set**

A mesomorph should train at a mid-range of repetitions (8–12), as he responds beautifully in this range. Occasional shock sessions with radically low (2–3) or high reps (15, 25, or more) can result in accelerated mass gains, provided those workouts aren't done to a point of overtraining.

Training Load: **8–12 sets per body part**

Though the mesomorph grows more easily than the ectomorph, he's much more prone to overtraining when the rest interval between workouts is too short. It's almost as if a mesomorph's muscle has the perfect density to shock, then leave it alone and watch it grow. A moderate number of sets per body part (8–12) followed by an ample interval of rest days (7–10) before hitting that body part again seems to stimulate the most growth. For a lot of mesomorphs, the most difficult obstacle is to convince them that, provided they're pouring on the workout intensity, they'll truly grow optimally by training each body part no more than once per week.

Use of Overload Techniques: **Occasionally**

Training to failure or using forced reps is an important tool for the mesomorph, provided they're done sparingly. They should be done at the tail end of the workout and only on the last few sets of a given exercise.

Cardio: **High-intensity bouts**

Cardio works well for the mesomorph and can help keep the thick physique reasonably trim yet still large. As with weight training, high intensity and low duration tends to work best. Loafing through an hour of cardio isn't going to cut it. Instead, he should put in 20–30 minutes with a very high intensity, 1–3 times per week. He also responds better to challenging forms of cardio, such as a treadmill at an incline or a StepMill®; it does wonders for his build and may actually help add muscle mass.

Advice For The Endomorph

Perhaps the most challenging of the physique types, the endomorph has to put in a sustained and high-energy effort in the gym to earn results.

Ideal Rep Range: **10–15 per set**
The endomorph tends not to feel a muscle burn when bodybuilding as easily as do the ectomorphs or mesomorphs. Instead of a deep muscle burn, he tends to hit the wall and have instant fatigue, where he can't push the weight anymore. It's almost as if, while he has a truckload of push power, he lacks muscular staying power. I theorize that this is because his muscles are large and less dense, with a considerable amount of fat intercalated throughout his muscles. Also, the endomorph is the fattest of the somatotypes, meaning he'll respond best to a higher rep range (10–15) in order to appreciably refine his physique and build quality. Occasional bouts of very low repetitions (1–3) feel great to the endomorph, if such sessions dominate his training landscape, he'll end up lacking physique quality in the form of density and muscle shape.

Again, getting someone to do what is best for his physique and not what his physique is comfortable doing is always the challenge. This is most critical to overcome for an endomorph because he has the greatest degree of structural flaws among the three body types. Doing resistance training that feeds into his strength just gives you a bigger, more shapeless endomorph.

Training Load: **8–12 sets per body part**
An endomorph has so much mass potential that he doesn't have to worry too much about overtraining. The total number of sets per body part for the endomorph should be about the same as the mesomorph (8–12), while the interval of days rested before hitting that body part again should be similar to the ectomorph (3–5).

Use of Overload Techniques: **Almost never**
Though they certainly can handle it in the short run, training close to failure but not quite reaching it is good for the endomorph, but training to failure or using forced reps or negatives really has to be avoided. Otherwise, excessive soreness will limit his ability to hit the gym as often as he should.

Cardio: **As often as 5 times per week**
Lots of cardio at moderate duration and intensity are the rule. The endomorph is the one body type in which cardio is the most important. Using the treadmill on an incline or using a recumbent bike with a moderate resistance for 30–40 minutes as frequently as five times each week is an example of what I might recommend.

Knowing Thyself

As beginners, most people just mimic what the more experienced people do around them. That's how we learn. Countless guys experienced in the iron game learned their trade from some guy back in high school that looked pretty big at the time and seemed like he knew what he was talking about. This is fine and certainly par for the course in the early years.

Later on, having a consistent training partner is great for motivation, but you always have to ask yourself — are you following your routine, or his? Professional bodybuilders usually do their own routines, and only occasionally hook up with other bodybuilders at their level simply for fun and a bit of additional motivation. If he does have a steady day-to-day training partner, it's usually a guy of lower caliber who's just trying to hang with the pro and see if some of his mojo rubs off. I've seen it coast to coast a million times.

But after a year or two, if you're still following someone else's routine and not doing specifically what you need for your own body, you're making a huge error. You must define and follow a routine that feeds appropriately into the limitations and strengths of your somatotype. It comes down to one old saying: "Know thyself." Once you gain the experience you need following some other guy's routine, train on your own and find your stride. Do what works for you. Think about your body type and how you need to train (and diet) to improve your inherent weaknesses. That should be the basis of your bodybuilding goals.

The Split Is Born

In the old days, there weren't too many structured regimens. Just push it or pull it, lift it and move it. But eventually our dusty little cult of bodybuilding emerged from the dark corners and innovations changed the game. Visionaries like Joe Weider, Vince Gironda, Siggy Klein, Dan Lurie and Bert Goodrich developed the early principles and modern bodybuilding was born.

Complete training — training the whole body rather than just a few assorted parts — seemed to be the first major concept to come forth. Sessions in the gym, however, were still arduously long, lasting many hours, because the sense that "more is better" still prevailed. Few lifters took any days off, hitting the same body part as much as three or even four times per week! These hardcore guys lived in the gym and were hopelessly overtrained.

I recall talking to some of the old timers who told me if they got sore from an exercise they actually believed in getting back into the gym and working through it! Many viewed soreness as a sign of weakness and lack of condition. For bodybuilding, we now know that soreness is a key sign that a muscle hasn't recovered from a previous workout and shouldn't be trained yet.

But steadily, a more sensible system of routines was emerging. The idea of splitting up body parts into to different days was the next breakthrough. We were out of the dark ages and the evolution of our sport through modernizing training techniques had begun.

About 25 years ago, bodybuilding became increasingly popular and gyms proliferated across the country. And hardcore training was not limited to the most famous of the bunch, Gold's Gym, Venice Beach, in Southern California. On the East Coast, you had Mid-City Gym in New York City, Body World in South Philadelphia, and Big Daddy's in Massachusetts. I've trained at all of them, and some are still great haunts.

The next revolution in training was the frequency of workouts. Finally, bodybuilders realized they required more rest between workouts, because they weren't growing while suffering injuries at a steady clip. Interestingly, the man who I consider the father of modern bodybuilding, Joe Weider, knew this fact much earlier than most, but not enough people listened. Once it caught on, the 3-on-1-off training routine was born.

The idea was simple — cover your entire body over the course of three days, take a day off, and repeat the sequence. Guys were now looking for ways they could get more rest, the first sign that intensity as a training factor was catching on in earnest. Even with this improvement, though, training sessions of 3–4 hours were not unusual, as sessions invariably involved at least two large body parts and 1–2 small ones.

The typical progression of weights was the straight pyramid — the idea here being to gradually increase the weight with each set while decreasing the reps. That principle is still the most widely used today. Forced repetitions became popular, as did negatives.

The guys were finally stacking on big muscle, but it wasn't just the training that was doing it. Drug abuse also became the norm. Surviving these marathon workouts and hard training almost necessitated the substance abuse just to survive the harm they were dishing out to their bodies. Guys on the sauce were growing. Guys without that artificial edge were still hopelessly overtrained or riddled with injuries trying to keep pace.

Interestingly, another facet that suffered in the early days of heavy beatings and endless training sessions was diet. The pure number of hours committed to training actually interfered with high-frequency feedings. Training so long with too few quality calories appropriately spaced throughout the day mitigated their gains and instead helped them develop bad eating habits. They would gorge themselves post-workout with a huge compensatory calorie dump driven by starvation.

About 15 years ago, we really started figuring things out. Guys like Mike Mentzer began promoting low-frequency, high-intensity, short-duration training. Meanwhile, splits lengthened. Instead of 3-on, 1-off, it gradually became 4-on, 1-off, 5-on-1-off, and 5-on, 2-off. Ultimately the idea of training each body part only once each week came into vogue.

Guys began shortening their sessions to 40 minutes to an hour. They were hitting only one body part, or one large and one small body part, per session. Everyone was getting smarter and realizing that the gym is the only place where you attack the muscle, but your growth takes place outside of it.

The style within the splits also advanced as guys worked on variations of "push-pull" routines. The idea here was to not just arbitrarily throw different body parts into different days, but instead to match up opposing body parts or body parts that worked synergistically (i.e., chest and back, or shoulders and triceps). Changes like this were hardly subtle by any stretch of the imagination. In fact, the idea of developing a sensibility within the split was perhaps the next big leap forward in the evolution of bodybuilding, fueled by increasing levels of training intensity. They learned that they could train hard, or they could train long, but they couldn't do both.

Planning Your Routine

Your routine is your schedule, your bible. Without the right one, you have no road map and growth is simply impossible. For example, when to go back and hit the same body part again can be the most challenging to gauge. Undershoot the mark and you overtrain. Overshoot the mark and you don't get enough stimulation.

But if there is one rule in all of this to know which way to lean, it's that you'd much rather wait a little too long before training a body part again rather then not waiting long enough. This is because, while everyone is in a big rush to pack on muscle mass, there is no greater sin than overtraining. Once you reach a state of overtraining, it's tough to escape because the habituation of training so much makes it virtually impossible to have the sense to pull away and fully recover.

Meanwhile, we're creatures of habit and we like routines, but getting stuck on one routine all the time is a limiting factor preventing us from gaining maximum muscle. A routine is a good thing as long as it's working, but nothing will work forever. That's why you not only need to find a good balance and a good regimen to begin with, but you then need to be constantly monitoring yourself and your progress in order to make tweaks. It's called trial and error, and it's the only way you can ensure continued success. Of course, if you're advanced enough, you could always train instinctively. By that I mean just training whatever you feel like on any given day and not sticking to any set routine. But you'll need at least 20 years of training under your belt and a superb knowledge and understanding of your own body to pull it off successfully.

Now, with those words of wisdom, we can delve into the myriad structures available to you in constructing your workout. Here are several that span the extremes of the good, bad, and ugly, along with a typical example of each:

Option 1: 3-on, 1-off

Honestly, I hate this routine, but it became so popular back in the 1980s, I have to confess that I was stuck on it for at least a couple of years. Too much is done in one day, and the frequency with which you have to hit a body part again precludes building to any appreciable level of intensity without overtraining. For a beginner it's okay, but after that, it's moronic.

Day 1	Day 2	Day 3	Day 4
Quads	Chest	Shoulders	Off
Hamstrings	Back	Triceps	
Calves	Traps	Biceps	
Abs			

Option 2: 4-on, 1-off

This is a small step up in terms of rest from 3-on, 1-off, but you'll find yourself back in the gym prematurely in my opinion. In this routine, the only way you keep from overtraining due to frequency is by under-training in terms of intensity, but then you won't grow much. If you try it, make sure it's during a time when you're well rested and can get plenty of good food, because there isn't much room for phoning in a crappy, half-baked training session and still expecting to grow.

Day 1	Day 2	Day 3	Day 4	Day 5
Quads	Chest	Back	Triceps	Off
Hamstrings	Shoulders	Traps	Biceps	
Calves			Abs	

Option 3: 2-on, 1-off/2-on, 2-off

This was really a major evolutionary step in the late 1980s as someone figured out we all needed a bit more rest. In particular, this routine allows two consecutive days of rest each week, three total. Your weakest body part should be trained coming off those two rest days, since you can give it a strong dose of intensity, a concept known as "priority training." Incidentally, if your development is somewhat even and you don't feel you need to prioritize a specific part, start with legs, which take the most effort to properly train (as you're collectively hinged at the hip, knees and ankles in compound fashion).

Day 1	Day 2	Day 3	Day 4	Day 5	Day 6	Day 7
Legs	Shoulders	Off	Back	Chest	Off	Off
Abs	Triceps		Traps	Biceps		

Option 4: 6-Day Cycle
This is almost the same as the 2-on, 1-off/2-on, 2-off routine but doesn't give you weekends off. You basically get through the sixth day and repeat the cycle. This type of routine was popularized by six-time Mr. Olympia champ Dorian Yates.

Day 1	Day 2	Day 3	Day 4	Day 5	Day 6
Legs	Shoulders	Off	Back	Chest	Off
Abs	Triceps		Traps	Biceps	

Option 5: 3-on, 1-off/2-on, 1-off
Similar to the 2-on, 1-off/2-on, 2-off, but a bit better in my opinion for those that need more leg development, as it breaks legs out across three different days. This allows you to focus more on the three main areas (quads, hams, calves) for growth.

Day 1	Day 2	Day 3	Day 4	Day 5	Day 6	Day 7
Quads	Chest	Back	Off	Shoulders	Traps	Off
Abs	Triceps	Hams		Calves	Biceps	

Option 6: 7-Day Push-Pull
Dividing up your routine into pulling and pushing motions grew in popularity in the early 1990s. It represents a terrific sensibility — by training synergistic muscles together, such as chest and triceps, or back and biceps, you help quell the possibility of overtraining. Think about it this way; you can't help but use your biceps during your back routine, as the bi's engage in any pulling motion, so if you put the two parts together on one training day, biceps are attacked less frequently overall.

(Another variety of push-pull exists, where you train opposing muscles together, such as back and chest, triceps and biceps, and quads and hams — but for this example, I provide the synergistic approach).

Day 1	Day 2	Day 3	Day 4	Day 5	Day 6	Day 7
Quads	Chest	Back	Shoulders	Hamstrings	Off	Off
Calves	Triceps	Biceps	Traps	Abs		

Option 7: 10-Day Split

Here you'll cover your whole body over a 10-day period, with ample rest built in. It's a phenomenal routine if you're truly committed to an unwavering training intensity; if you half-step a session, it won't be coming around again for a while. For those who want to focus maximum effort on each body part while spending less time each day in the gym, this routine might be the perfect fit.

Day 1	Day 2	Day 3	Day 4	Day 5	Day 6	Day 7	Day 8	Day 9-10
Quads	Shoulders	Off	Back	Hams	Off	Chest	Triceps	Off
	Abs		Traps	Calves			Biceps	

The Wrap On Routines

In addition to what's presented in this chapter, many other routines can be formulated and modifications made; your options are seemingly endless. Some professionals even do double splits, which require going to the gym twice per day — only feasible if your entire existence is built around sleeping, eating and training, but nevertheless it's an example. Feel free to pair body parts in new innovative ways, and you'll soon learn what clicks for you and what doesn't.

THE EXTREME TRAINING PRINCIPLES

As I previously mentioned, no one "perfect" training program exists, nor does every workout affect everyone the same way. That said, we do have some road signs that provide clues as how to best train for gains. Our brethren who walked the walk before us discovered them; we just need to lift our heads, open our eyes and spot them.

These signs — or principles as I call them — can point the way and save you tremendous time and heartache, if you heed them in your quest for an extreme physique.

Principle No. 1: Let Free Weights Lead The Way

Let's get the most basic rule absolutely straight right off the bat. The most efficient way to train is by using free weights. No machines, no matter how good they look or supposedly function, even remotely compare to the benefits of barbells and dumbbells. I'd sooner take a $30 set of those old cement-filled plastic weights and the rickety bench I had when I was 13 years old than $500,000 worth of the latest and greatest machines. I'm not kidding.

Resistance training typically involves machines, free weights (dumbbells and barbells), bodyweight exercises, or a combination of the three. Although machines work well enough for beginners, those with injuries or people with physical limitations, machines can never give you extreme physique results by themselves. With machines, you have a lot less to think about compared to free weights, and therein lies the problem. With machines, the weight is already in the down position prior to exerting force. Unlike free weights, the weight is balanced and glides on a trestle for you, lending control to the motion throughout its course. This takes away the stability control required of multiple muscle groups — with free weights you must control the bar, balance the weight, and move it smoothly through a range of motion, which overall is a much higher order of demand on your body.

In addition, free weights give you more potential range of motion. Machines can only give the muscle as much stretch and range as is allowed by the confines of their design. I'm a proponent of flexibility and, while I feel that stretching should be a regular occurrence, it's much less of an issue when you're training with free weights and using maximum ranges of motion.

By the way, this isn't just some weird bias of mine, it's the truth. In the crazy world outside bodybuilding you'll find perhaps hundreds of different religions, political philosophies and ways of doing things. Yet cutting across all that, across different countries, and even cutting through time, hardcore bodybuilders everywhere in the world have always been clear on one thing — we all know and accept that you can't get to the summit of physique perfection without free weights.

With that said, you can and should supplement your workout with some machines now and then; they aren't completely without merit. But beyond occupying a small percentage of your routine and strictly to round things out, your near-complete focus should be on free weights.

The age-old wisdom that you get out what you put in holds true when it comes to free weights. If you want to master them, it'll take many worthwhile years. At the other extreme, if you want to master a machine you can do it in an instant. Here's how — sit down and push. Understand the difference?

Principle No. 2: You Need Intensity For Immensity

Fifty-plus years ago, bodybuilding was a subculture that sprung from Muscle Beach in Santa Monica, California. While at that time they cared about the aesthetic side of muscle growth, the main emphasis was on building the strength to do physical stunts. To see what I mean firsthand, pick up the book *Remembering Muscle Beach* by Harold Zinkin, a terrific pictorial remembrance of bodybuilding's roots. Masses would flock out to Muscle Beach, which was located in front of what is now Shutters Hotel in Santa Monica, to witness a show of strength and stunts that would last all day in the hot sun. Handstands, human pyramids, one-arm lifts, jumps, tosses and tumbling all entertained our post-war forefathers. While you could find some stunning exceptions, most of the builds back then were very top-heavy, since few did much in the way of leg training. Most were smooth, or even fat by today's standard. Big hammy biceps and a meaty chest were in.

The pervading training sentiment was that the more time you put into weight training, the better. Many of those routines were a combination of maximum-poundage weightlifting tricks and quasi-gymnastic physical stunts, with little or no focus on shaping particular muscles or ratcheting up the training intensity. Men were doing things like one-arm overhead barbell lifts or working with kettlebells, doing tricks that required skill and effort, but which didn't necessarily equate to muscle size and definition.

Then guys like Steve Reeves came along. While he did some tricks and stunts in his earliest days (I understand from his contemporaries that rings were a specialty of his), his main focus was on the aesthetics of his physique. He was the first guy in my opinion that, while still in his prime, really trained not just for mass, but with the intensity required for a complete physique. He was an absolute stickler for balance and symmetry. I remember him telling me shortly before he passed away how he felt that, in some ways, these aspects were even more important then mass. When you have the elements of proportion and balanced development, he reasoned, you look so much better next to someone who just trains for strength and ends up fat with an uneven mix of body parts. That's likely why Hollywood loved him and he is still so awe-inspiring on film. While small by today's standard, he was amazingly complete for his time.

Reeves ushered in the earliest wave of men training strictly for muscular development and with some tangible intensity. His ilk and brethren cared less about what they could do with the weight, and more about what the weight could do for them.

When looking back at bodybuilding, we find a critical turning point when Arnold Schwarzenegger came along. Joe Weider was responsible for not only bringing Arnold to America, but also for shaping much of the way he approached bodybuilding. Arnold was the first guy to prove the theories, showing that full-blown training intensity will break the mold.

Sure it was refined by Mike Mentzer, taken a step further by Tom Platz and Dorian Yates, and brought to new heights by Ronnie Coleman, but in my opinion Arnold was really the first to develop the modern concept that training intensity was directly proportionate to the immensity of his physique. According to the old-school iron pumpers I've interviewed, Arnold was the first to fearlessly push beyond the pain barrier in an intense, self-sacrificing way. When Arnold wanted to put on slabs of quality muscle, he needed several training partners, because he'd burn through any one of them if they tried to swing his whole routine week-in and week-out. His training sessions were as legendary as his physique.

Learn from our bodybuilding past. The more time you spend in the gym and the more sets you do, the more likely it is that you're simply not working hard enough. Intensity doesn't just mean going to failure or doing forced repetitions either. The mere act of doing those hardly means you've worked hard. Instead it means getting deep — deeper then you've ever reached and exploding out all your energy in the last repetitions of your sets. If the intensity isn't there, you'll never build an extreme physique. If you want to be immense, fear of muscular pain isn't an option and must be overcome.

Principle No. 3: Perfect Your Form

To create muscle, you must feel it. If you don't feel the muscle contract and relax within each rep, you're not getting the prerequisite stimulation. You must train with the strictest of form. That's not to say that with enough overload, sloppy form can't build muscle. I've actually seen a few fairly good physiques over the years built with a great deal of sweat and hard work but poor form. But these were guys with unbelievable genetics, and still their physiques could have been that much better had those individuals paid proper attention to form.

For me, one example sticks out. His name was Mark, but we all knew him as Cheat Mark. To this very day I've never seen a guy employ worse form. He cheated on everything. He'd cheat so much on his bench press it actually hurt to watch. With his feet on the ground, back arched and hips way off the bench he'd let the barbell career down to his chest and bounce back up with rib-cracking impact. He'd cheat so much on the lat pulldown that you couldn't walk behind him while doing it because his head might swing down and bump you in the knees. On squats he used to wrap his knees so tightly he had to be helped up.

Even so, he managed to build a little bit of muscle and actually had a somewhat respectable build. I attribute that to his hard work and intensity. But he was missing a ton of body parts, with pole-thin arms and no hamstrings or calves. Shortly after his pathetic attempt at a local bodybuilding show, where his flaws became apparent even to him, he finally succumbed to injuries and disappeared.

Throwing weight around and inviting momentum causes the weight to work you, so to speak, instead of you working the weight. That was Cheat Mark's problem. Apart from skipping a great deal of muscle fiber, sloppy form also unnecessarily invites injury. You'll find almost invariably that as long as you stick with strict form and always control of the weight even in failure, you'll never have a serious injury.

In our pursuit, ego gets in the way. A bounce here, a swing there, a little more weight goes up. It's a tough temptation to resist. Invariably you'll find yourself caught up in the moment with training partners for some odd reason, and you'll get sucked into throwing that extra plate on and loosening up your form for a few extra repetitions. The trick is to make this temporary mania the exception and not the norm. Finding the intensity to throw on extra plates is nice and exactly what you should do, but never at the expense of proper form.

Principle No. 4: Keep The Pace

Often overlooked is the concept of maintaining the proper pace within your reps. I see guys all too often who come to the gym with regularity and push themselves hard, but not make gains simply because they pause too long between repetitions. The idea of pausing between the repetitions results from a combination of wanting to preserve your strength for an elongated workout and possibly a fear of the weight and your ability to control it.

Indulging that habit is a big mistake. The reason you're in the gym is to build muscle, not test yourself. Leave that to the powerlifters. Preserving energy by taking long pauses does nothing more then unload the muscle and reduce the amount of intensity it's subjected to. Your goal should be exactly the opposite. Your aim should be to make the situation as pressurized as possible for the muscle you're training. Muscular hypertrophy (growth) won't occur unless the muscle is subjected to a stress beyond what can be regulated or beyond that which it has become accustomed. Resting between reps goes completely against the logic of intensity and load.

Instead, do your reps smooth and rhythmically with a machine-like cadence. Don't pause to take a few breaths and gather more energy. That's not your mission. Your mission is to blast the muscle and you can't do that by unloading the muscle with a pause. It takes some getting used to, but after a while you will. If you have always trained with a pause and you're now trying to get rid of it, you may experience a short-term drop in strength. But therein proves the point that in fact you're weaker and smaller then you should be because of this unloading.

You need not worry about repetition cadence interfering with peak contraction of the muscle. Slowing the movement down at the top in order to squeeze the muscle hard is an active process, so I don't consider that poor rep cadence. This is a far cry from going to the top of a rep and passively stalling for rest.

As with many rules in life, there's an exception: During the heights of an intense set I'll allow a bodybuilder to compose himself mid-set and take a breath. While this does require a pause, I only allow it if the intensity is at a fever pitch, and only on some of the large-scale leg and back motions like squats or bent-over barbell rows. It's very short and is never followed by only a single repetition. For example, while working with one pro, we regularly utilized what I called a "mini-set" on the final set. On squats, the last set was so brutal that he would virtually have to pause or he'd collapse. So I would let him. Amazingly, he regularly worked his way up to 545 pounds for 10 reps with no belt or wraps. I'd have him do six reps, take a moment to breathe, followed by two and a short pause, and then two insanely painful reps, going all the way down to a deep squat. His legs got absolutely huge.

Your rep pace is contingent on the idea of working through each exercise, building up to a heavy weight for an ultra-intense set, and leaving it at that. Regardless of whether you do a straight pyramid of steadily increasing weight and decreasing reps, or a series of plateau sets for volume, training with one heavy set at the end, keep the pace steady, going for broke on the last set.

Principle No. 5: Stimulate, Don't Annihilate

You need to push your limits to develop a monster physique, yet you still have to know your limits. When you're in the throes of your workout, you must give all you've got and leave every last effort on that gym floor. But at the same time, the law of diminishing returns is ever-present. Though Arnold started a training revolution honored by other Mr. Olympia's to follow, much havoc would be wreaked along the way in the form of countless bodybuilders attempting to surpass his efforts. It became a training norm in the late 1970s and the 1980s to go well beyond failure, with forced reps, negatives, tri-sets (three exercises back-to-back), and even giant (four-in-a-row) sets. Double-split routines spread the madness to two balls-to-the-wall sessions per day. The results? Bodybuilders and weekend warriors were getting injured by the truckload. I still see countless guys from this brief era with chronic lower back problems, herniated discs, degenerative shoulders, tendonitis…you name it.

One amazing Mr. O rose above this fray. Eight-time winner of the Sandow trophy, Lee Haney took Arnold's super-intense training motor and added advanced-level gears to it. He represented the coming of yet another revolution of training philosophy. The quality of Olympia physiques that came along in the immediate wake of Arnold, while certainly better then what came before, never really surpassed The Oak. But when Haney arrived, the game was elevated. Haney figured out that you can't train so insanely hard that you extend beyond the point of being able to read your body. He told me more then once, "Stimulate, don't annihilate."

For Lee, that meant putting in a flesh-tearing workout, but stopping right before he pushed things too far. It was amazing to watch him train and spot him. People used to call him a weak bodybuilder because he never worked with colossal weight. But he was a master, sheer poetry in motion. He was smart beyond his era. As a result, his physique grew beyond that which we had seen before and well beyond Arnold's. He had achieved the next evolution by adding some modulation to Arnold's all-out techniques. In my opinion, Lee's results were so extraordinary that at his best, his physique wasn't truly surpassed until Ronnie Coleman's 287 pounds of pure freak show in the 2003

Olympia ushered in yet another age.

Understand that, while intensity is a necessary prerequisite, you have to still listen to the signals of your body. In other words, push to the point of true failure once past your warm-ups and into your working sets, but be careful reaching beyond that point. An occasional forced repetition is okay. But make this the exception. Learn from Lee; he knew when to stop. Don't do multiple forced reps or negatives because, unless your body is riddled with anabolic steroids, you won't be able to recover fast enough between routines on a regular basis to do much growing.

Also, I don't care if you're all-natural or a steroid abuser, the rule still holds that if you're spending more than an hour at any one time working out, you're likely overtrained. The best trainer I know of that follows this principle to the max is my old friend and fixture of Venice Beach, Mike Ryan. His routines are efficient and to the point. That's why he has trained so many high-profile clients. He gets you in and out with no screwing around. Mike and I used to sit back and marvel at some of the Muscle Beach morons in Gold's Gym that would come in and train for hours. We'd be able to get to the gym, train, shower, bullshit with the girls and go eat all the while these idiots were still slaving away. The take-home message is that keeping your sessions to an hour or less is perhaps the single best thing you can do to keep your body from getting annihilated and overtrained.

Another good tidbit of advice is to avoid overusing weightlifting belts, wraps, straps, chalk, and other such paraphernalia unless absolutely necessary. Relying too much on all this crap turns them from tools into crutches you can't do without. You start acting like a powerlifter, caring more about the numbers. I stopped using this stuff many years ago and only wish I stopped sooner. You tend to train too heavy and end up losing the feel of the contracting muscle in favor of moving heavy objects. As a result, your potential to overtrain (and get seriously injured) rises exponentially.

Principle No. 6: When In Doubt, Chill Out

Knowing when you're about to do too many sets for a body part and knowing how much rest to get between workouts can be tricky, but you have to know how to do this or else you'll overtrain and never grow. It's tough to resist the twisted compunction that more is better. There you are in the gym with a great pump, sweat pouring like a faucet. Your muscles are bulging, your veins are popping; you feel like you're about to blast right out of your skin. Then it happens. You get caught up in the moment and do one set too many. You pop like a water balloon, and there you are flat as a pancake wondering what the hell you did wrong.

The same thing happens with workout frequency. You had a memorable chest routine the other day where you had a great pump and stopped short of overdoing it. Everything was perfect. In fact, it went so well that you can't wait to hit chest again, and you're back in the gym prematurely trying to squeeze out another chest routine. Now your pump is nowhere to be found, and you're weaker than your little sister. You don't have to worry about flattening out, at least, because you can't even get any blood into your body parts in the first place. The bullet has left the gun and is headed straight for your head. The self-inflicted wound is a bodybuilding near-suicide.

Let's start with knowing when you've done enough reps. Obviously, you must do a certain number of reps with rest in between (i.e., these are sets) in order to stimulate muscle mass. That's why you can't just come in the gym and do one thick-headed set of 50 reps to failure and call it a workout. This is not to say that such a one-set workout is not a good shock every now and then, but just that you can't build a routine of consistent muscle growth at an extreme level with this approach. The limiting factor probably has a great deal to do with coaxing blood flow into the muscle for maximum effort. This takes brief intermissions, if you will, to allow the vasculature of the deep muscles to dilate and engorge the muscle. It simply doesn't happen efficiently with one set.

As a side note, the late, great Mike Mentzer, whom I liked very much, placed the idea of one-set-to-failure as the centerpiece of his heavy-duty theories. But honestly, every time I saw him train, he wasn't working out this way and he certainly didn't build his physique on the one-set principle. Nevertheless, an occasional session or period of training this way purely applied by an experienced bodybuilder can have its place; just don't try and apply it too early in your bodybuilding career or you'll be disappointed.

Here are a few general considerations about stimulating the muscle while stopping short of annihilation. Larger body parts like chest, shoulders and hamstrings respond well to repetitions as low as six. Small- to medium-size muscles like triceps, biceps and traps favor moderate repetitions around eight. Complex body parts like back and quads seem to respond better to slightly higher repetitions of at least 10. Dense muscles like abdominals and calves respond to the highest range of 15 or more. (You have to tailor this around what your own individual body, and for that matter somatotype, responds to.)

When it comes to the number of sets you're doing, you have to be careful not to overload as well. Too many sets invariably will lead to overtraining. Though the total number of sets needed varies from body part to body part and person to person, there are some finer points that apply across the board. In particular, pay attention to fatigue. If the muscle is shot, stop training it. Don't beat it beyond recovery. If you've failed on the last repetition of a set and you've got at least a few sets behind you, it might be a good time to stop. Also pay attention to your pump. I've observed that it's not helpful and actually counterproductive to train beyond maximum pump. Try to abort training before the first sign of deflation.

Training frequency (i.e., how often you should hit a given body part) is perhaps the most intricate variable to figure out, yet the easiest way to enter overtraining if you blow it. As a steadfast dictum that always applies, never train a body part that feels sore. If sore, it's simply not recovered yet. Training it again too soon will flush away any possibility of muscle hypertrophy and will make it that much tougher to stimulate the next time you train it. Watch the mirror and learn the look of your muscles when they're full. You'll find that the muscle usually fills out about a day or two after any palpable soreness disappears. You'll notice that when they're full, they feel supple yet not mushy to the touch. That's when you know you're ready to go at it again.

Soreness is a good barometer with which to measure whether you hit the muscle hard enough, but not all your body parts will respond this way. For those that don't, focus on the quality of the pump during the routine and not how spent and sore the muscle feels in the days that follow. If this is the case, don't get sucked back into hitting the body part again too soon. That's always a killer and one of the toughest things to resist in bodybuilding, because when you don't feel the muscle blown away, you'll feel like you didn't do enough. Most every bodybuilder is guilty of this at some point or another; the trick is to fight it into your head that just because a body part isn't sore doesn't mean that it doesn't need the same recovery time.

One of my old training partners, Carlos, figured out a clever way to contend by purposely having us miss at least one body part every cycle. That way we were fairly certain we weren't overtrained, at least as far as training frequency was concerned. Of course, almost any approach you take will dim in comparison to simply getting adequate rest in the form of sleep (covered in more detail in the next principle).

Professional bodybuilder and actor Roland Kickinger made an interesting point several years ago while we were training in his Southern California home gym. He said there's really no such thing as overtraining, only getting too little rest. It's kind of true and profound. Joe Weider knew this as well, and preached it years before Roland and I were even born!

Principle No. 7: Get Your Zzzzzzz's

Rest, in particular sleep, is vital to successful muscle building. During sleep cortisol levels balance and surges of growth hormone occur. Too little sleep, and no matter how perfect you might be training or diet-wise, you'll never heap on the muscle. During waking hours, our bodies are focused on our external environment and dealing with all those things that we're exposed to in the course of a day. These include everything from work stresses to relationship issues, physical training, and even food intake. On the other extreme, sleep is the chance our bodies have to focus on the internal environment and heal us from the inside. Sleep rejuvenates us and makes us whole again.

Insufficient sleep leaves one a physical, mental and emotional wreck. I recall vividly the days of medical residency. In those years it was a prerequisite to become an expert at minimal-to-no-sleep on many a night. Through force of will we had to learn how to tough out being sleep deprived for 24 hours or more. Short little power naps were often the key, but with these you had to be careful when you took them. I remember witnessing one female resident colleague after 24-plus hours on-call try to close her eyes while standing! During rounds in the intensive care unit, while the attending physician was in the middle of talking, she just folded up and collapsed to the floor. I also remember seeing one of my male interns, who was so tired and not yet used to the grueling hours, literally slump over and fall asleep in the middle of interviewing a patient.

While medical residents learn to adapt to minimal sleep and simply train themselves to operate at a reasonably high level of proficiency while sleep-deprived, this certainly in no way reflects an optimal state of being. Whether you're a medical resident, a bodybuilder, or anyone else, too little sleep is bad. If you don't get enough sleep, the catabolic processes in your body take over. Muscle mass is the first to be lost. As cortisol levels climb, fat is suddenly easily stored (recall principles of starvation alert). As adrenergic, speed-like hormones begin to rule your body out of necessity, muscle is incinerated. Irritability and even distractibility soon arise. Total testosterone levels suffer, resulting in not only a loss in lean muscle mass, but a plummeting libido, marked with erectile dysfunction or simply sexual disinterest.

Sleep requirements vary from person to person, but suffice to say that everyone needs some degree of deep sleep. While handy in helping you through everything from medical residency to late Saturday nights partying, naps just don't cut it in the long run. Deep healing and rebuilding sleep is a requirement for the bodybuilder seeking extreme muscle enhancement. This type of sleep is also called Rapid Eye Movement (REM) sleep. It's the deepest form of sleep and is signified by delta waves on an electroencephalogram (EEG). The reason the term REM is used is because you can actually see the eyes rapidly moving under the eyelids of a person during this phase. This phase signifies the hallmark of healing and reparative sleep.

The speed with which you pass through the earlier, lighter phases of sleep dictates how fast you'll arrive at REM. Some people get into REM fairly rapidly after falling asleep, while others require hours to get very deep sleep. In general, this variability from person to person will dictate how much total sleep a person needs. In my experience, if you're a hard-training average bodybuilder and you're going all-out in the gym, chances are you need at least seven hours of continuous — uninterrupted — sleep each night. (Obviously, if you're interrupted during REM sleep, recovery suffers.)

Given the importance of sleep, you may come to a point where your diet and rest can't keep pace with a very intense workload. As soon as that happens, you quickly become overtrained. The more you do, the worse it gets, because there are no such things as magic foods or supplements that counterbalance the damage to your body during intense periods of training in substitution of sleep. No question, you have to put in the work to get the results, yet you also must be aware when you aren't sleeping enough. Listen to your body and dial back your routine temporarily, or stay out of the gym until you can get back on track and recompose your rest pattern.

Downtime is not a bad thing. In fact, it's essential. But it's no coincidence that most bodybuilders are overtrained. After all, you wouldn't be a bodybuilder if you hated the gym. Guys that don't like to train and are just in it for the beach body never last for long. Their flame burns out rather quickly. Instead, it's the guys with the passion for lifting and the burning desire to train who are the most committed, and thus the most prone to overtraining. These are the dudes that usually get into trouble with rest. They need sleep.

Drugs help some, but in many cases they're counterproductive. The category of benzodiazepines, which includes drugs like Valium™ and Xanax®, is fine if prescribed to counter a heavy component of anxiety. But even then, it shouldn't be relied upon too heavily. Though definitely able to knock you out, when overused, these drugs actually end up suppressing the amount of REM sleep you get. This results in poor recovery for the bodybuilder because deep, restful sleep is an absolute prerequisite for big muscle growth. I tend to be partial to simple sleep consistency achieved naturally, without drugs. While I'm not a fan of snoozing it up for more then eight hours, getting less then seven takes its toll.

Principle No. 8: Adjust For Your Age

As you pass the age of 35, some of the rules of the game change. At this point and thereafter, your body won't respond to resistance training the way it did when you were 25. You've got to train smarter because you have much less room for error. You won't have the same ability to recover between workouts like you did in your younger days, no matter how much sleep you get. But here is the catch — too much rest and infrequent workouts decondition the body. This is because when you get older, the act of getting in the gym and training is actually both healthy and therapeutic. As my good friend and one of my old training partners Gregg Bertsch likes to say, "Motion is lotion."

As a result, the routine for the 35-plus bodybuilder should consist of almost daily training with only occasional days off, but sessions should be shorter and more diverse. Your attention should gradually become more centered less on how you look and more on what you can do with your body. Training only one body part each workout while incorporating more cardio and functional compound movements works best. While it may take as much as two weeks to cover all your individual body parts, remember that the focus as you get older is practicality, durability and maintenance, not insane growth. Whereas this might be too much rest for the younger bodybuilder between sessions for a particular body part, it offers both the necessary rest and training diversity needed for the older bodybuilder.

It's important for the older bodybuilder to understand that, even with the assistance of drugs, you simply can't get a whole lot bigger in the years ahead. Most of the growing your body is capable of will be behind you. What you can hope to do is train smart enough to keep what you've built, grow as much as your body will allow you to, and carve each muscle, crafting density, quality and muscle maturity.

Principle No. 9: Harness The Power Of The Pose

I remember a revelatory moment with Joe Weider, sitting front row center at the prejudging for the Night of Champions in New York. Joe, disappointed with some of the competitors' lack of hard muscularity and poor posing mechanics, wanted to drive a point home to me about the significance of flexing muscles hard.

What I've always loved about Joe is that he has a passion for our sport and wouldn't hesitate to go to great demonstrative lengths to get his point across. In that spirit, right then and there, he told me to flex my biceps! I have to admit, I felt a little squirrelly at the order. I mean, I'm with The Godfather himself, none other than the spiritual leader and guru of modern bodybuilding, and he's telling me to throw down a pose in my seat! I felt like a nut job, but despite my trepidation, as discreetly as I could, I slumped forward a bit, brought my fists against my chest and began to flex my biceps.

He then leaned toward me and told me to flex harder. I squeezed down, now feeling a pretty strong torque. But that wasn't enough for Joe. He got real close to my face and screamed at me, "Squeeze 'em harder!" I went ahead and locked in as hard as I could stand it. It must have looked bizarre to those behind us — there I was, doubled over, writhing in pain in my seat next to "the man" in the middle of a bodybuilding show.

Of course, at that point I didn't give a crap what people thought because my biceps were honestly hurting, like a really deep pump. As if that wasn't enough, he leaned over and grabbed my left arm with both hands and tried to dig his fingers into my biceps, while at the same time demanding that I squeeze even harder. By then, I thought my biceps were going to rip and I honestly broke a sweat because I thought that if I were to relax for even a second, his fingers would drive right down into my arm. That's just what he wanted me to think.

There we were, the two of us looking like we should have been carried out in straight jackets, when he started counting: "One-one-thousand, two-one-thousand, three-one-thousand." By the time he got to 10, he let go of my arm, told me to relax and leaned back in his seat. It hurt so much when the blood rushed back I thought he took a biceps muscle with him. He just smiled, laughed a bit at me and said, "You see what I mean? Guys think flexing isn't a workout. They think it's a waste of time. Well, they're wrong and they don't do it nearly enough!"

He went on to tell me about the lost art; about how bodybuilders of yore would spend hours posing and flexing, not in a narcissistic intoxication, but to properly assess their physiques and actually improve the quality of what they were looking at. The point Joe was trying to illustrate was something he had told me before: Too many of today's bodybuilders don't flex their muscles hard enough. Nowadays, it's all about training and few see the value in posing, whereas in the days of Arnold, Ed Corney, Steve Reeves and other legends, posing and muscle flexing was an integral part of building a quality physique. In fact, when guys with good builds like Bertil Fox started showing up on stage with obviously no interest in posing and probably no homework done on showing their physiques, it became an all too common trait of mediocrity among competitors.

Posing wasn't just for showtime. You'd see guys in Gold's posing, comparing themselves to one another, seeing what areas needed to be improved and flexing for more detail, density and striations. Yet, somehow, hard muscle flexing and intense posing got tossed out of bodybuilding along with the raw-egg drinks the Barbarian Brothers used to suck down and those wide-side posing trunks Arnold used to sport for his photo shoots.

Flexing is one of the best ways to carry a weak body part past a training plateau or to improve the quality of a body part that already has reasonable size. Try it yourself. Choose a part that's weak on you, one that continues to be weak despite training religiously for months or years. Set aside some additional time after you train that muscle to start posing it in a focused and committed fashion. Don't worry about what happens to your pump, either. If you get more pumped from flexing, it may be a sign that you weren't contracting the muscle enough during training. If you flatten out, the muscle may need to adapt to the added stress of the posing sessions in addition to the resistance training it's being subjected to.

Also, don't pay too much mind if this added posing session gives you more soreness or less soreness in the days that follow. Either way, don't attempt to read into or interpret the subtleties of the various responses your body might have in the short term, as you do with your more responsive body parts, because the bottom line is that it probably doesn't matter much. After all, again, you're not dealing with a strong body part that responds easily to training. Rather, we're talking about a lagging area that you haven't been able to figure out up to this moment. So, what's the point of overanalyzing now? Just shut up and flex hard.

Joe Weider was the first guy I know of who recognized how this same principle applied to training. He authored his "Peak Contraction Principle" many years ago so that you could easily apply hard flexing and posing from the static model to the kinetic training model and realize additional benefits. The idea is to give a hard squeeze to the muscle you're training at the fully-contracted position of each repetition.

It sounds easy enough, but a clarification is necessary when applying this pure principle to heavy pressing movements when you don't fully understand it. The issue is joint lockout, which many incorrectly perceive is necessary for flexing at the top of a move. As a result, cutting most pressing movements a little short and going right through each repetition without stopping has become commonplace. I actually think this is a correct move by most bodybuilders and a good general recommendation for safe overall mass building. In fact, it's the way I train most of the time, since it provides my muscles with the best of what I call "continuous kinetic resistive stimulation."

Continuous kinetic resistive stimulation — a fancy name for the aforementioned rep cadence of Principle No. 4 —shouldn't be incorrectly thought of as being impossible to do along with incorporating peak contraction. Together they can be thought of as "focused kinetic peak contraction." The idea here is that it's a fallacy to think you have to completely lock out your joints, resulting in potential harm, in order to achieve a maximal contraction. If you pay attention to the tracking of the weight and the flexing of the muscle, maximum contraction can actually be achieved with only about a 95 percent lockout! Try it and you'll see. It's amazing, but whether we're talking about shoulders, triceps or quads, you don't need to fully extend the joint and expose yourself to injury to get a full contraction.

Of course, for the more experienced bodybuilder with more lean mass, it'll be easier to feel what I'm talking about versus the thinner bodybuilder with less muscle mass and fewer years of training. Nevertheless, the principle applies evenly to both scenarios. Once the weight is at the top of the rep, slow down to a near stop just long enough to fully flex the muscle without a long pause, then immediately resume the repetition path, tracking the weight without any rest or unloading. If done correctly, you'll probably have to come down a bit on your weights, since it's so much harder than you might think.

You'll find that the real mitigating factor in training like this is the mental effort it takes. When you go through a full routine just once using this notion of focused kinetic peak contraction, merely remembering the degree of intense pain associated with "the squeeze" is enough to make you want to take a pass on another workout like that for a while. Done right, it feels like you dug so deep into the muscle that it's contracting right from the bone! It's that intense.

But don't let that dissuade you from trying. Remember that breaking a frozen muscle out of the dark tundra and back onto the sunny path of growth takes a superhuman effort. Don't kid yourself. Defying genetics and reaching for hardcore improvements won't happen below the pain barrier. When it comes to improving your overall physique by leaps and bounds in a short period, or dramatically improving a stubborn body part, you reap what you sow. In this case, you put in an occasional painful workout practicing my brand of focused kinetic peak contraction and follow up a few workouts with some intense posing, and you earn an improved physique that's more complete, harder, more striated and denser then ever! Sounds like a bargain to me.

Principle No. 10: Do Cardio — Correctly

Many natural bodybuilders still subscribe to the age-old belief that if you do cardio, you'll lose mass. And actually, when measured by the traditional way most people do their cardio, this wisdom tends to hold true. However, I have a better way, a somewhat unconventional method you can use that'll enhance your pump, counter catabolism and help you build (yes, build) mass.

Customarily cardio has come to mean endless mind-numbing sessions on the treadmill, using TV headsets or an MP3 player to counter the excruciating monotony. Go into any gym around the country and you'll see rows of equipment taken by clone-drones going about it in this dazed-and-confused fashion, all with the same misguided notion that somehow they're doing it right.

When cardio is performed in this way, there's no "right" answer, but certainly the worst piece of equipment is the ever-popular treadmill. People claim they run on the treadmill, but for the most part, they're doing no more than plodding along at a clip just slightly above a snail's pace on a flat surface. Having never really pushed their bodies or used much of an incline, most of these walkers don't mount much of a challenge to their cardiovascular system or their fat stores. Some don't even sweat! Sad but true, a quick tour of the cardio room the next time you're at the gym will confirm that the fattest, most out-of-shape people tend to comprise the majority of treadmill users.

As I see it, the main limitation is that these machines dial down to an unchallenging level way too easily, while lulling you into a false sense of hopefulness by feeding you worthless information on how many calories you're supposedly burning. Basically people just watch the digital readout (along with those televisions hanging from the ceiling) in hopes that they can last long enough to burn off that soda and slice of pepperoni pizza they slapped on their hips last night, or just long enough to incinerate the donut they had at breakfast. But what they never realize is that they're playing a game they won't win because, unless they're so exercise-starved that virtually any form of activity will yield results, they won't make much headway in the sense of appreciable fat burning.

If one really looks at the numbers and the potential of countering average dietary indiscretions, one would have to spend literally half the day on the treadmill. For example, an individual doing the average fast walk on the treadmill at 4 miles per hour on a flat surface will burn about 360 calories an hour, according to a digital readout on most any popular machine. Based on that rate, you have to spend the better part of three hours on the treadmill to burn off a slice of pepperoni pizza, a large soda and a glazed donut (over 900 calories total) just to draw even with your baseline!

To go further and actually burn off this same number of calories beyond that sample intake in an attempt to lose some weight, you would need to double up to six hours. Ask yourself, how many people do you know that really could spend six hours on a treadmill every day? The answer is none. Then ask yourself how many people you know that could easily slip and blow their diet by having soda, pizza and a donut. The answer here is practically everyone.

When a bodybuilder hoping to gain muscle, shed fat and not lose their quads tries to do cardio the popular way, the results can be disappointing, to say the least. Bodybuilders are amazing sources of real-life clinical information on what actually occurs in the body. Through trial and error, we learn things long before the medical or scientific community ever stumbles upon the answers. The same is true when it comes to cardio. For justifiable reasons, many bodybuilders have largely avoided cardio altogether, and here's why.

Bodybuilders have a much higher lean-mass to fat-mass ratio. We constantly fight with our bodies to force muscular growth. We can thus be accused of forcing our bodies to take on an unnatural or unintended state. Our bodies battle back by making it difficult to increase lean mass and decrease fat beyond a certain threshold. (This is the mechanism of "homeostasis," which I originally touched on in Chapter 1; it's a Latin term describing primordial programming of the body to want to remain in a steady state, thereby limiting significant swings of muscle growth or fat loss.)

If too little food comes in, or one has too little rest, or one engages in too much activity, the body responds by losing muscle mass and hoarding fat. This is why so many of the more serious bodybuilders take in 5–10 small meals each day, nap regularly, and struggle to avoid overtraining. For the same reason, they avoid cardio. What they've found is that cardio done in the long-duration way described above systemically overtrains the body and decreases muscle growth overall, while specifically overtraining the legs.

The more profound question for bodybuilders is, have we missed something here? Is it worth finding a way to do cardio? My answer is yes to both questions. In addition to cardio making us healthier, we simply become more functional by exerting our bodies in this way. Few things are more disgusting then a 275-pound bodybuilder who can't walk up five steps without getting winded. What's the point in having all that mass if you can't do anything with it?

Bodybuilding lore like, "Take the elevator or you'll burn muscle!" has infected our psyche. Other weird thoughts include, "Don't dance with your girlfriend or else you might overwork your calves," or "Keep shifting your grocery sacks from one arm to the other, or you'll overtrain your biceps and traps." I've heard and thought it all.

Bottom line: Cardio is healthy to do because it helps to make the body more durable and fit. Moreover, cardio, when done correctly, can actually serve to build and improve muscle mass! Yes, I'm serious. How? Cardio increases the peripheral circulation, which fuels your muscle pump. If the circulation is poor, the pump is poor.

Recovery is also circulation-dependent. As lactic acid builds up, the muscle becomes warm and stretched. After that, it becomes sore as an inflammatory process sets in to repair the damage. This process intimately depends on efficient circulation, as better circulation enhances your post-exertion recovery. Just look at how much more vascular your whole body is after intense cardio.

Finally, cardio done the right way burns fat, but not by counterbalancing calories taken in, which is the fallacy of standard cardio approaches. Instead the principle works by stimulating the metabolism, thereby allowing your body to burn more fat throughout the day, even when you aren't in the gym.

Now, if you're sold, the right way to do cardio is twofold:

1. *Take into account the timing of meals versus when you do your cardio throughout the day. The popular model says it doesn't matter, as long as your burn rate matches or exceeds your ingestion over a 24-hour period. I say it does matter, because research tells us that a calorie is not just a calorie, and that the more calories you have later in the day, the less likely you are to lose weight, simply because your overall activity levels decrease as the day progresses. As such, if you do cardio early and then back-load all your calories into the evening, the cardio you did that morning may have little or no impact. On the other hand, front-loading your food earlier in the day and then doing cardio sometime after your last*

meal, with little or no calories afterwards, can yield dramatic results.

2. *Stick to short-duration, high-intensity interval training. Instead of a steady-state, even pace over the course of 30–60 minutes or more, condense your activity into 20–25 minutes max and rev up your workload within that time. Interval training is marked by periods of a slow pace interspersed with all-out sprints. For instance, a 30:30 interval is 30 seconds of a slower pace followed by 30 seconds of a full-bore run, alternated for the duration of the workout. You can also do other intervals like a 30:60, a 60:60, or a 60:90. One simple trick is to use the timer clock on the machine to run a 15-second sprint every minute — every time the clock hits 45 seconds, you go like hell until the next minute begins. Surround your intervals with a five-minute warm-up at a steady, easy pace to start and a five-minute cool down at the same easy pace to finish. Depending on your goals, you can include a cardio session in your weekly split anywhere from twice to 4–5 times per week (on the lower end if you're in mass mode, on the higher end if you're after a full-on ripped physique).*

Ten To Grow On

There you have them, the Extreme Training Principles. Consider yourself armed for the next phase, your body part by body part plan, which will serve as your blueprint for your time spent lifting, pushing, pulling and willing your muscles onward to incredible heights.

CHEST

Precise exercise recommendations that will work for you specifically are virtually impossible to make, especially in a forum such as this that's geared to speak to a mass audience. As I've pointed out, everyone is different in a multitude of ways; bodybuilding is a sport and endeavor that, at the end of the day, you have to find your own way in. Trial and error coupled with the wisdom of time will reveal the exact way you should travel.

However, despite our differences, I do believe that nearly everyone can benefit from the universal philosophies outlined in this text, including the 10 Anti-Catabolic and 10 Extreme Training Principles. As well, this book would not be complete if I didn't provide details about training particular body parts, and some basic routines for each to provide you with a sample framework.

First, a caution: If the sample workouts I've provided seem like they're a bit light on volume, then you're probably either chronically overtrained, habitually going too light on your sets, or using sloppy form.

Don't be thrown off by the regimens of professional bodybuilders that weigh 300 pounds off-season and are juiced to the gills. You can't train like that and expect to grow. The routines I provide have plenty of volume for the other 99.9 percent of the population. If you sandbag during these workouts and only put forth a half-hearted effort, they'll pass by in a blink and you'll feel like you've done nothing. On the other hand, if you approach each with a singleness of purpose, a serious commitment to flawless form, and unbridled intensity, you'll see blazing results.

Approach The Bench

As I'll talk about in the "Quadriceps" chapter, I consider the squat to be the most beneficial exercise you can do for your lower body. In that vein, I'd say the flat-bench barbell press is almost the equivalent of squats, but for the upper body.

The bench press adds beef to the chest area, but it also helps you bulk up your arms, shoulders and back. Though not quite as critical to the upper body as squats are to the legs, you should still make sure the bench finds a way into your routine with some regularity. You won't be sorry.

Benching was once a common foundation of chest workouts, which is a main reason behind the stronger, thicker, more complete pectorals of the earlier generations. Back then, we would never think of avoiding the bench press — we believed that if you didn't bench, you didn't train your chest!

Today among the new crop of bodybuilders, it's a different story. While incredible shoulder development and huge backs are smattered through the pro ranks, weak pecs are a dime a dozen. Chest exercises have become far less basic and much too "cute," with all these new funky presses and gimmicky machines, and it's led to the demise of the massive chests of yesteryear.

Don't follow in the footsteps of those who shy away from the bench. Here's how to perform it correctly:

- Although I prefer that more experienced lifters put their feet up on the bench (as I'll explain later on in the "Tips" section), starting with your feet flat on the floor is fine until you get accustomed to the movement.
- With your head, shoulders and glutes flat on the bench, grasp the bar with an overhand, thumbs-wrapped grip. Some lifters use a "thumbless" grip (i.e., all fingers, including the thumb, on the same side of the bar), but I don't advise it at first because of the dangers of the bar slipping off your palm. As you gain experience, if you feel more comfortable with this grip, go for it.
- Move the bar off of the racks and position it over your chest. Your elbows should be fully extended but not locked out.
- Let the bar descend slowly and under complete control — keep in mind my benching motto, "The lower you go, the slower you go."
- Touch the bar lightly to your chest, no lower than just under the line of your nipples.
- Briskly accelerate the bar back to the top position, pushing into full elbow extension without locking out the elbows completely.

Benching activates a number of muscles, primarily the pectoralis major and pectoralis minor. However, there is considerable synergistic involvement of the anterior deltoids and triceps. This accounts for the great upper body stimulation that this movement provides. In fact, legend Vince Gironda swore that the bench press was more of a shoulder movement than a chest movement. Of course, he was wrong from a purely physiological standpoint, but his underlying suggestion that shoulders are heavily recruited, is still well taken. The higher you touch the bar above the line of your nipples and close to your neck, the less pectoral and more anterior delt you target.

In addition, modern kinesiology tells us that the bench press also stimulates the serratus anterior, biceps brachii and shoulder girdle abductors. As a result, one can easily appreciate the profound core benefit of this motion when done correctly.

Follow Your Inclination

Although flat benching forms the core of most top-notch chest routines, it's often done second, after an incline press. In terms of producing aesthetic pectoral development, emphasizing incline pressing in this priority fashion pays off.

Incline presses stress the upper chest region. For most people, the upper chest is smaller and less muscular than the bulkier mid- and lower-chest region; it's stubborn and needs a special focus. Going even further, the outer edge of the upper chest (the chest/delt tie-in) is often uncooperative as well. The fix? An exercise like the dumbbell incline press, which exerts tremendous focus on the tie-in area (because of the longer range of motion), and pounds the upper chest directly. Follow these instructions:

- Set an adjustable incline bench press slightly steeper than 45 degrees — I tend to favor this more extreme angle with dumbbells as opposed to barbells because it focuses the stimulation right onto the tie-in area, a benefit not as pronounced when at a lower angle.
- The starting position is the same as for the flat-bench press, but the dumbbells will be over your upper chest instead of your mid-chest. Grasp two dumbbells with an overhand, thumbs-wrapped grip, lie back and hoist both weights to an extended-arm position.
- Keeping your elbows stacked directly under your wrists and your forearms perpendicular to the floor, begin a controlled descent. Touch your anterior deltoids or outer chest with the inside edge of the dumbbells at the bottom.
- From there, power the weights upward to a non-locked elbow extension.

Expanding The Rib Cage

Although the back shares the load in this exercise, the dumbbell pullover can be a very strong addition to a chest routine if you're just starting out. Though I do not make it a regular part of the routines I recommend, it must be discussed because it's such an effective expander of the entire rib cage. This movement has tremendous utility because it seems to add breadth and depth to the entire torso. It also establishes flexibility and strength deep in your shoulder joints in arms-overhead positions, both qualities that protect the shoulders from injury.

- Lie across the center of a flat bench in the opposite direction to its length (i.e. at a 90-degree angle to the direction of the bench). Your body should be in a "bridge" position, your upper back flat on the bench, your feet flat on the floor, and your glutes as close to your heels as possible.
- Have someone hand you a single dumbbell in a vertical direction. Grasp it with a stacked hands-flat grip, both hands on the inside face of the dumbbell's top end, fingers overlapping each other (your fingers should form a triangle around the bar).
- Obtain complete control over the dumbbell in an overhead position with your elbows extended, arms at a 90-degree angle to the floor.
- Slowly reach back and stretch the dumbbell over and behind your head, keeping your elbows slightly bent but extended away from your head. Attempt to reach the floor with the bottom edge of the dumbbell if possible before returning to the start.

As your rib cage strengthens and expands, the stretch will be deeper and more profound. This is one of the few moves where you don't have to accelerate through the pressing phase, as I so often emphasize with other exercises. Instead, employ a slow, steady and consistent speed through both the stretch and contraction.

Besides the pectoralis (major and minor) and latissimus dorsi, the intercostals, obliques and serratus anterior are also stimulated. In some cases, it's far better to incorporate it as part of your back routine as a finisher.

Just know that, while you should reap the benefits of this rib cage expander early in your training years, as you gain experience over time, pullovers tend to lose their luster and become surprisingly ineffective at improving your physique. So don't fall into the trap of making a lifelong habit of doing them. Instead, be objective about pullovers and be sure that they're really doing the job. If you honestly find they're no longer effective, leave them behind in favor of more beneficial exercises worthy of your advanced status.

The Routines

The following are sound examples of chest routines, but don't get caught up in the specific poundages or repetitions I list. They're only included to paint the picture of a typical progression. Instead, work with weights you can handle, and that challenge you — in no way should the numbers here be interpreted as any sort of benchmark or even an average. You must only work with weights that you can safely handle.

Also, under "sets" is the number of the set for each exercise, not the total number of sets you do. For instance, in Beginner Chest Workout No. 1, you'll see the flat-bench barbell press leads off. For Set 1, you'll do 12 reps at 135 pounds. For Set 2, you'll do 10 reps of 155 pounds. On your third set, you'll do eight reps of 185 pounds, and so on. (This format will continue throughout the body part chapters.) Also note that when I use the term Beginner in this context, I'm not talking about someone who never touched a weight before, just someone with less experience.

Beginner Chest Workout No. 1: This is an efficient, rock-solid routine for beginning bodybuilders and athletes to build a foundation of mass and strength across the chest region. It's a very basic routine and thus essential for guys starting out. Yet it's so effective that even the most advanced bodybuilders still return to this routine now and then.

Exercise	Set	Reps	Weight (lbs)
Flat-Bench Barbell Press	1	12	135
	2	10	155
	3	8	185
	4	4–6	225
Incline Barbell Press	1	12	135
	2	10	155
	3	8	185

Intermediate Chest Workout No. 2: This is still a mass builder, but is tailored a little more for the developing bodybuilder than the novice or starting strength athlete. It places incline first and thus places more emphasis on the upper chest, which is an aesthetic concern more than a power-related necessity.

Exercise	Set	Reps	Weight
Incline Barbell Press	1	12	135
	2	10	185
	3	8	205
	4	6	225
	5	6	225

Exercise	Set	Reps	Weight
Flat-Bench Barbell Press	1	10	135
	2	10	185
	3	8	225
	4	6	250
	5	12	225

Advanced Chest Workout No. 3: Here's an advanced all-out assault on your upper and inner pecs. It's highly challenging.

Exercise	Set	Reps	Weight
Incline Barbell Press	1	15	135
	2	10	185
	3	8	225
	4	8	225
	5	6	250
Incline Dumbbell Press	1	10	160 (80-lb. dumbbells)
	2	10	200
	3	10	220
	4	8–10	240

Exercise	Set	Reps	Weight
Flat-Bench Barbell Press	1	10	135
(to the neck/clavicles)	2	10	185
	3	10	185

Wrap-Up: Top 10 Chest-Training Tips

1. Warm up your shoulder joints thoroughly.

Any serious chest workout will stress the shoulder joints. To guard against injuries to your muscles, tendons and ligaments, take extra care to do a complete warm-up. Rotate your arms through all planes of motion prior to your first warm-up set. Before you even get into the sets and weights listed in the workouts in this chapter, do a few sets of presses with only the barbell, 15–30 reps apiece. Take 2, 3, 4, or however many light sets you need to feel like the blood is pumping and your muscles are loose. This creates a smooth transition to your heavy resistance training, gently nudging your body into the work you want to do, and much preferred to loading up the bar, jumping in and risking a nasty pull or tear.

2. Concentrate on inclines.

As I said earlier, the flat-bench press is the king, but for aesthetic reasons, you should do inclines first in your routine. A weak upper chest is exponentially more common than an underdeveloped mid- and lower-chest region, so you should hit the weakest area while you're freshest and thus have the most strength to devote to it. A long-term commitment to such prioritization should eventually bring the upper region up to par, giving you a nice, rounded and proportional set of pecs overall.

3. Put your feet up when benching.

Here's a great tip, especially if your chest is stubborn. When you master benching with your feet off the floor, your development will really take off. By lifting your feet and resting them on the edge of the bench, your lower back flattens, giving you an angle in your press that better hits the middle and upper chest versus the lower pecs. This is in sharp contrast to benching with your feet on the floor, which necessitates a slight arch in your lower back; in that case, the motion is shortened as your torso approximates a decline-like position. Benching with your feet up is the true measure of chest strength. If you can get past the ego blow of having to work with a slightly lower weight, the payoff is phenomenal. And with enough dedication, your weights do eventually increase significantly as you build real pectoral mass and strength. However, before diving headfirst into this practice, please learn to bench first with your feet on the floor. Putting the feet up is an advanced technique, and you want to build a base first before trying something that, if not attempted correctly, can lead to injury.

4. Skip the declines.

For 99 percent of bodybuilders, the decline press is nothing more than an ego boost for those who can't press very much weight on the flat or incline bench. You usually can handle a lot more on a decline because, once you get the hang of it, the motion is easier — because of the angle of your body, the bar has a shorter distance to travel. If you concentrate too much on decline pressing, your lower chest tends to grow disproportionately to your upper chest, especially because the lower portion tends to be less stubborn. Subsequently, a little stimulation goes a long way. The result is sloping, breast-like development, far from what I'd call aesthetic on a male physique. As such, training this area should be avoided in almost every case.

5. Bench pressing is essential.

It's the equivalent of squats, but for the upper body. In my experience, not only does the bench press add piles of beef to the chest area, but it also helps you bulk up the entire upper body (arms, shoulders and back). It used to be the foundation of chest workouts in the "old" days. That's why I think chest development was actually better in the bygone era of the likes of Arnold and

Franco. Back then, we would never think of avoiding the bench press. Today's world of bodybuilding is a different story. While I see incredible shoulder development and huge backs, weak pectorals are a dime a dozen. I think the reason for this is that chest exercises have become far less basic and much too "cute." With all these new funky presses and machine gimmicks, it's no wonder I rarely see the chest development of yesteryear.

Also, doing a bench press with a high strike to either the neck or clavicles is a favorite method of mine. Just be sure you warm the shoulders up thoroughly and don't do it if you can't take the pain. You'll have to reduce the weight considerably, but the deep pump it produces by forcing a maximal stretch across the pecs is extraordinary. By the way, I never do bench to the neck/clavicle area as my first motion. It's always done second or as a finisher. But however you bench, just be sure bench pressing is part of your routine. You won't be sorry. Not only is it the best way to build a big chest, but the upper body power it gives you is unparalleled.

6. Move through a full range of motion.

Partial reps for the chest are simply crazy. The pectorals must be trained through a full range of motion, not only for building muscle, but also for the health of the shoulder joint. Cutting into your range is an amateurish mistake of the lowest order — get the benefits of a full stretch and extension on every set.

7. Maintain a slow and controlled descent.

It's pretty scary to see some inexperienced lifter bouncing a heavy barbell off of his chest. Trying to take advantage of momentum to break through a sticking point and get a higher bench total is a sure path to injury. Building a thick and powerful chest is contingent upon a controlled negative, or eccentric, motion. Remember that mantra, "The lower you go, the slower you go." If it helps you develop a cadence, try counting to four on the eccentric portion of every pressing rep in your workout — one-one-thousand, two-one-thousand, three-one-thousand, four-one-thousand, touch down lightly and then push the weight back up.

8. Watch your width.

Employing an excessively wide grip on barbell exercises can sacrifice chest development, as it de-emphasizes the chest and over-emphasizes the shoulders. You'll find a lot of modern-day bodybuilders with big shoulders but relatively unimpressive chests inadvertently favoring a wider grip; for them, it's like taking the path of least resistance. A wider grip also radically changes the range of motion and subsequently exposes the shoulder to potential injury. Instead, I favor a moderate grip, just outside shoulder width. This allows for maximal chest stimulation and minimal risk.

9. Keep a tight grip on the bar.

Don't let the bar shift loosely in your hands. Focusing the power of your pectorals on hoisting a loaded barbell requires a firm and consistent grip. A weak grip prevents your power from being directly translated to the bar — your force has no focus. By using a tight grip, you'll even find you're slightly stronger, perhaps even by 5–10 pounds on a particular lift, which isn't a bad thing at all as you strive for constant improvements.

10. Favor free weights over machines.

Don't kid yourself; you'll never build a massive, powerful chest on a machine. The resistance is already balanced for you, making the movement far less challenging. As a result, no matter how hard you work (i.e., failure, forced reps, negatives, etc.), you'll never duplicate the technical demands of free weights. Remember, the innate superiority of free weights over machines lies in the fact that free weights require proper form, balance, control, coordination, concentration, consistency and attention to detail.

BACK

Ask a men's-clothing tailor, and he'll tell you that a man with a 10-inch difference between his chest and waist circumference, or "drop" as it's known, has a significant V-taper. But let me tell you, in the world of bodybuilding, such an average disparity in those two numbers doesn't even come close to your potential. And for that, you can thank your back. I'll explain.

Back in college, shortly after my competitive years in bodybuilding, I finally visited a tailor. I was wearing baggy clothes at the time (you know, a Gold's Gym shirt and a pair of my old buddy Snake's Dedication Bodywear Baggies. Hey, that was stylin' then). At any rate, I suggested he completely cut a suit for me instead of trying to fit me off the rack in a 54 jacket with Ralph Kramden pants to match.

But he was a cocky, salty old dog and insisted that fitting me wouldn't be a problem. He claimed, "I've got all sizes," and "I fit all the football players." I emphasized that I was a bodybuilder and not a football player — after all, the average football player, although big on top and bottom, has a relatively wide waist, so all they have to do is buy oversized clothes off the rack with minimal tailoring. Even so, he insisted on taking my measurements.

We stepped behind a screen and as my bags hit the floor, so did his chin. This old guy cracked me up. He said, "What the hell did you do to yourself, kid?" At 5'9" I was a chiseled 216 pounds with a 29-inch waist. My drop was about 25 inches from chest to waist, two-and-a-half times the tailor standard for big taper.

How did I get such a dramatic V? Having a small waist is appealing and creates the beginnings of a taper on the order and magnitude of what a tailor recognizes as impressive. But when it comes to creating an awe-inspiring drop, it's all about one pursuit — building a thick, wide back.

One of the few things that I did correctly early in my bodybuilding career was to focus my back training on width. As a result, in a surprisingly short amount of time, I built one hell of a back. I was known for having almost disproportionate width and thickness across my upper rear torso, which helped me tremendously in competition. Furthermore, although my contest years are far behind me, my lats still carry noticeable size and thickness — something most people find a little odd on a practicing physician, but I get a kick out of it anyway.

Pull Your Weight

Don't kid yourself with the 90 million different back motions I see people getting nowhere doing. Even lat pulldowns (also called pulldowns to the front), while useful in some cases, won't build width like pull-ups. Instead, these other motions are supplementary and should be done as an addition, with pulls forming the basis of your back routine.

I first got into doing pull-ups purely by chance. I came across a rock climber in the gym one day and, because I was a lot heavier, I challenged myself to try and keep up with him, since all he did was pull-ups. Needless to say, the following few days produced the most dramatic soreness I had ever experienced across my upper lats.

I stayed with pulls, repeating the workout several times over the subsequent weeks. Suddenly, I had huge lats! No kidding. People couldn't believe it. In retrospect, I view the hundreds of back workouts I had done prior to that experience to have been a waste of time. Since then, I have yet to stray from making pulls the foundation of my back routine.

Here's how to do them for optimal gain:
- Jump up and take a just-outside-shoulder-width grip on a pull-up bar, palms facing forward. During my early training years for a short time I made the mistake of listening to too much hype. Although my back development was progressing just fine, I heard that the wider your grip, the wider your lats will grow. I tried it. As my pump flattened and my development came to a halt, I realized that the wider my grip, the shorter the range of motion. Also, a wide grip exposes the shoulder to injury. (At the other extreme, a grip that's too narrow unnecessarily overemphasizes the arms, thus cutting down on the stimulation your back receives; this is why chin-ups, with their close, palms-facing grip, is considered more of a biceps than a back exercise.)
- Stay directly under the bar as you pull your chin up toward the level of

the bar. Don't swing — such extracurricular movement takes away from the directness with which you tax the upper lats. Swinging will instigate contribution of muscles like the rear delts, chest and arms. Instead, a good tip is to look straight up at the bar.

- With each rep, attempt to touch your chin to the bottom of the bar. Don't try to get your chin over it. It's not worth it. Likely, you'd have to break form and swing out or move your head too much to accomplish this position. Instead, stay in form. Just gently touch your chin to the bottom of the bar, ease back down, and feel the burn.

Since you're handling your own bodyweight, you can't get the true benefit by simply doing a few sets of pull ups and moving on to another motion. Instead, you need to do a few more sets than you would need on weighted exercises.

Finally, try not to chase after fatigue, but let it find you. In other words, don't shoot for failure by the second set. For example, if at most you can do 12 consecutive pull-ups, rather than doing two sets of 10 (meaning you'll invariably fail on the second set), do 4–6 sets of six reps. You'll still fail by the final set, but a higher overall volume of reps will stimulate more growth.

Row To Grow

Pull-ups build the width; rowing motions give you thickness. A row, such as a bent-over barbell row, T-bar row or one-arm dumbbell row, work your back from the inside out, punishing those strong cords of muscle that make up your mid- and upper back.

All three of the rows I just mentioned are solid, but for purposes of explanation, let me walk you through a bent-over row:

- With your eyes forward, lower back arched and glutes out, bend at the hips and grasp a barbell with a shoulder-width, overhand grip. The bar should be an inch or so off of the floor in the bottom position, your elbows straight.
- Keeping your knees soft (unlocked), drive your elbows back toward the ceiling as you bring the bar to your abdomen. As the bar rises, your shoulder blades should move toward each other.
- Once the bar touches your torso, reverse the motion. Don't let the weight touch down between reps, and don't ever lose the protective arch in your lower back — tighten your core for the duration of the set.

Cable Guy

You've heard me rant about the inherent value of free weights over machines.

In back training, however, you'll find some exceptions. Machines such as the cable row can be very helpful. Such exercises provide an opportunity to load the muscle throughout the range of motion, providing even resistance at all points of a rep, a condition the back responds to rather well.

Just keep in mind that I'm not a big advocate of pulldowns as a width builder. If you can do a chin-up, you should. All the lat pulldowns in the world won't substitute. Only rely on them if your strength doesn't allow you to do meaningful repetitions on pull-ups, or for some occasional added variation within your routine. With that said, let's walk through the seated row:

- Sit at the seated row station and grasp a hammer-grip handle with both hands.
- At the start and for the duration of the move, keep your knees slightly bent, torso upright, abs tight and low back slightly arched.
- Pull the handle toward your lower abdomen, keeping your arms close to the sides of your body, bringing your scapulae together at the end. The rowing motion should come from the upper back, not the arms or lower back.
- Slowly allow your arms to extend to return the handles to the starting position, without leaning forward at the finish.

The Routines

The back is a highly muscular area and generally can take a bit more volume then most other areas of the body. But you have to work up to it.

Beginner Back Workout No. 1: Pull-ups are everything when it comes to width, and width is the most important aspect of back development, so this routine starts with this exercise. In fact, nearly every back routine I recommend begins with some form of pull-up.

Exercise	Set	Reps	Weight (pounds)
Pull-Up	1	10	Bodyweight
	2	10	Bodyweight
	3	8-10	Bodyweight
Bent-Over Barbell Row	1	15	95
	2	12	135
	3	10	185

Exercise	Set	Reps	Weight (pounds)
Seated Cable Row	1	15	130
	2	15	150

Intermediate Back Workout No. 2: While pull-ups are still the mainstay, with a little experience under your belt, the back routine must become a little tougher and more sophisticated as it incorporates lengthening movements.

Exercise	Set	Reps	Weight (pounds)
Pull-Up	1	10	Bodyweight
	2	10	Bodyweight
	3	10	Bodyweight
	4	8-10	Bodyweight
Seated Cable Row	1	12	130
	2	10	150
	3	10	160
	4	8	180
One-Arm Dumbbell Row	1	12	140 (70-pound dumbbells)
	2	10	180

Advanced Back Workout No. 3: A good advanced routine will place a balanced emphasis on building thickness and depth in addition to width and lengthening.

Exercise	Set	Reps	Weight
Pull-Up	1	10	Bodyweight
	2	10	Bodyweight
	3	10	Bodyweight
	4	10	Bodyweight
Seated Cable Row	1	12	160
	2	10	190
	3	8-10	220
T-Bar Row	1	12	90
	2	10	135
	3	10	180
One-Arm Dumbbell Row	1	12	180 (90-pound dumbbells)
	2	10	220

Wrap-Up: Top 5 Back-Training Tips

1. Know all of your T-bar options.

The T-bar can be done in a variety of ways, some of which are better than others. You can use a special plate-loaded T-bar apparatus, where you stand on a platform and grasp handles attached to a long bar running between your legs. A second kind of T-bar apparatus includes a chest rest, but these aren't ideal, as the pressure put on your chest when pulling heavy weight impairs breathing during the set. Or, you can do T-bars the old-fashioned way, by securing the unloaded end of a barbell in a corner, loading plates on the other side, straddling the bar, taking a hand-over-hand grip and rowing.

2. Try a counterbalanced pull-up machine to work your way up to the real deal if necessary.

Counterbalanced pull-up machines are excellent tools for beginners and those who are overweight. Beginning bodybuilders often lack the strength to execute a proper pull-up, while people carrying extra fat have more to pull than they can necessarily handle. The counterbalanced machines help in either scenario, giving you the boost you need to gain strength. Just don't get complacent and fall back on these machines as a permanent solution. It's like training wheels — it's nice for learning, but you don't want this crutch your whole life! With consistency and commitment, steadfastly work toward less and less of a counterbalancing weight, until you reach the day when you can complete pull-up sets on your own, no assistance necessary.

3. Stretch between sets.

A good tip I picked up from a training partner is to stretch between sets. It worked well for him, so I incorporated between-set stretching into my routine and saw an immediate response. However, don't overdo it, as I believe too much stretching could potentially inhibit your growth. As a rule of thumb, I leave stretching for later, as something I do between the last few sets of my back routine. Two good stretches to try: Relax your back and hold an arms-straight dead-hang position on a pull-up bar for a 10-count; or grasp a sturdy object, such as the frame of a machine or cable station, and lean away from the fixed object to stretch out your lats for a 10-count.

4. Use but don't abuse straps.

Although I'm the first to admit that the use of wrist straps is too commonplace in gyms today, with pull-ups and other heavy pulling exercises, it may be necessary, at least until you build enough strength to go without them. When completing a significant number of sets and reps, your grip will likely fail before you reach full fatigue in your back muscles. Wraps will help you pursue lat and mid-back failure without your forearms acting as a limiting factor.

5. Don't rely on a training belt.

Only a few back exercises may necessitate a belt. One such motion is the bent-over barbell row, where a belt tends to help support the lower back and keep the hips from shifting. Other than that, keep belt use to a minimum. You'll hardly ever need to use one if your form is strict and proper. All too often I see lifters strap on their belts for everything, practically wearing them to bed. Unfortunately, this practice will decondition the lower back over time, making it weak and susceptible to injury.

SHOULDERS

Wide shoulders signify power. A massive shoulder span represents an advantage in the animal kingdom when battling for dominance, thwarting aggressive advances of other males during fights, and impressing the opposite sex for mating selection. Humans are no different. Big shoulders on a man inspire fear and a dose of respect from other men, and attract the female of the species as well.

Properly training the deltoids for that coveted width can be tricky. For functional purposes, the overhead press is the basic tool of choice, but total reliance on this move overdevelops the front head of the delts while leaving the rear portion of the muscle lagging behind. For perfect bodybuilding-type symmetry, movements in multiple planes are required, so that the middle and rear heads of the delts can receive stimulation and keep pace with the front. Physique artisans do require some form of overhead press as a foundation, but should pay ample attention to lateral raises and bent-over lateral raises to achieve a properly sculpted, wide set of shoulders.

Press To Impress

An overhead press must be a balanced effort between brute force and targeted execution. Sometimes, even seasoned bodybuilders push too quickly through the contraction phase, inviting the chest and triceps to get into the act. To combat this unwanted activity, you must harness the power within your delts by concentrating on each of them firing to bring your arms overhead. Squeeze the delts, and the bar goes up.

For presses, you have a group of four winners to choose from: The standing or seated barbell press, or the standing or seated dumbbell press. You can use them almost interchangeably to anchor a delt routine. Here's how you would do a seated barbell press:

- Sit on a military bench, feet firmly planted on the floor. Reach up and take a grip just outside shoulder width on the bar.
- Unrack the bar to an arms overhead position, elbows straight.
- Lower the bar down to your clavicles, keeping your elbows and wrists stacked directly beneath the bar.
- From the bottom, drive the bar back up to the top, stopping just short of elbow lockout before beginning the next rep.

Lateral Motion

With perhaps the exception of Markus Ruhl at the 2004 Mr. Olympia, the biggest set of shoulders I've ever seen belong to my old training partner Gregg Valentino. I actually saw him once with arms at his sides balance a full glass of water on his front delt! When his shoulders were at their largest, he was almost exclusively doing lateral raises. Gregg recognized early on that the shoulder is a joint with a great deal of angles, and finding the ones that gave him the greatest pump was most important. It was instinctive training at its most pure.

The lesson to learn is not to do a lateral-only regimen. Instead, it's an indication that a) the lateral raise may not involve moving tons of weight but it's still a strong weapon, and b) you need to be smart and read your body's signals to work this, the most perplexing and complicated joint in the body.

When doing dumbbell lateral raises, go at them with intensity. Work hard when performing this motion. All too many times I see inexperienced lifters think they're training hard, but they're reaching failure because the weight they're using is too heavy, not because of muscular fatigue. Pick a weight that provides a burn, and just lets you barely get to the final reps of the set with good form. A trick I use with the more advanced lifters is to find the proper weight for laterals and stick with it for multiple sets, letting the fatigue and burn catch up to them. This is in sharp contrast to pressing motions, where I'm considerably more aggressive in terms of advancing the weight with each set.

When doing a dumbbell lateral, follow these steps:

- Stand with your knees slightly bent, abs contracted and feet shoulder-width apart. Hold a set of dumbbells, one at each side of your thighs, your palms facing each other.
- Raise your arms up and out to your sides in an arc, stopping when they're parallel to the floor. It helps to think about "leading with your elbows" to

make sure your elbows stay high and the workload remains on the middle delts. Throughout the exercise, your elbows will remain straight, but not locked — the movement should be generated in your shoulders, not your arms.

- Lower the dumbbells under control. For an intense burn, don't let the dumbbells come all the way down to your sides; instead, go right into the next rep as soon as they reach a point 1–2 inches away from your body.

Don't forget bent-over lateral raises. In these, you bend about 90 degrees at the hips and, keeping your back flat as a board to protect the lower back, raise the dumbbells straight out to your sides. These will isolate the hard-to-reach rear delts. Most people's rear delts are stragglers in development as compared to the side and front heads, so you may even want to consider doing bent-over laterals first in your routine while they play catch up.

In addition, you could do barbell or dumbbell front raises, which work the front head. For most, this is overkill, as a regimen of chest and shoulder presses will develop the front delts enough. The only practical application for the front raise is on the rare occasions when someone's front delts lag in development, or you're a competitive bodybuilder, in which case every muscle needs attention to maximize size, symmetry and proportion.

The Routines

As stated in previous chapters, the workouts that follow serve only as examples. The weights and reps are only samples, so stay within your personal limits.

Beginner Shoulder Workout No. 1: Covering all the bases, this deceptively simple regimen produces extraordinary results.

Exercise	Set	Reps	Weight (pounds)
Seated Front Barbell Press	1	20	45 (Olympic bar)
	2	15	95
	3	10	105
	4	10	105
	5	8	125
Dumbbell Side Lateral Raise	1	20	30 (15-pound dumbbells)
	2	15	40
	3	15	50

Intermediate Shoulder Workout No. 2: Once some basic mass and strength is obtained, a more complex intermediate routine will add dimension and shape to your shoulders. The routine leads off with barbell front press, something you don't see too much of in the gym these days (but should). At this level, introduction of rear delt training is a must.

Exercise	Set	Reps	Weight
Seated Barbell Front Press	1	15	45 (Olympic bar)
	2	12	95
	3	10	135
	4	10	155
	5	8-10	185
Dumbbell Side Lateral Raise	1	15	40 (20-pound dumbbells)
	2	15	50
	3	12	60
Reverse Pec-Deck Machine	1	15	50
	2	15	70

Advanced Shoulder Workout No. 3: At this level, the shoulders must be trained from a number of different angles. A combination of movements should be chosen that cap the delts symmetrically around the shoulder. Full, round, yet striated delts are what you are looking for.

Exercise	Set	Reps	Weight
Seated Dumbbell Press	1	15	80 (40-pound dumbbells)
	2	12	120
	3	10	160
	4	8	200
	5	6-8	220
Cable Side Lateral Raise	1	20	30
(one arm at a time)	2	15	40
	3	15	50
Cable Front Lateral Raise	1	12	50
(one arm at a time)	2	10	60
	3	10	70
Exercise	**Set**	**Reps**	**Weight**
Bent-Over Dumbbell Lateral Raise	1	20	50 (25-pound dumbbells)
	21	5	60

Wrap-Up: Top 10 Shoulder-Training Tips

1. Warm up thoroughly.

The importance of stretching and rotating your shoulders through all planes of motion prior to a challenging workout cannot be emphasized enough. Not only will this help to prevent injury, but in my experience, a supple and flexible shoulder tends to respond better to resistance training.

2. Use both dumbbell and barbell work when pressing.

Although I incorporate the overhead barbell press as a foundation to most of the shoulder routines I design, dumbbell work is excellent in terms of rounding the deltoids. Perhaps this is due to the range of motion, which is longer and more exaggerated, leading to deeper fiber stimulation in the shoulder. A caution though for both dumbbell and barbell presses — despite what you see in the photos in muscle mags, don't go overboard piling on the weight. Excess poundage only exposes the delicate rotator cuff to potential injury, with little added benefit for the delts. Form is where the burn is born, not weight.

3. Skip the behind-the-neck presses.

Experts have argued both ways on this move — that it's dangerous and puts your spine at risk, and that it's safe if used correctly. I do think it can be used safely, but you have to be extremely careful, and have a competent spotter that will watch your form and will correct you when you stray. Because such help is hard to find, err on the side of caution and stick with presses to the front. They both work essentially the same, so why take the chance?

4. Concentrate on lowering the weight slowly.

The lowering of the weight, or eccentric motion, should be strict and slow. Controlling the weight on the way down forces the deep muscle fibers to work and allows you to get more out of the motion. The old Nautilus adage of "two seconds to lower, one second to lift" is still quite applicable to this day and certainly applies to shoulder free-weight movements.

5. Take advantage of cables.

Like the cable-based movements I spoke about for the back, cables do have a place in a shoulder routine. Cable lateral raises, bent-over raises, and front raises are outstanding in terms of the continuous tension they put on the delts. Unlike dumbbells, which exert resistive force in the direction of gravity, cable motions can be positioned in such a way that resistive force is always opposite the direction which the deltoid is contracting. Also, because you do cable raises one arm at a time, all your concentration is on that one head (a trick you can also use with dumbbells, of course, but here that benefit is inherent in the exercise).

6. Vary your wrist position when doing lateral raises.
Slight variations in wrist position can dramatically alter the feel you get in the area of the middle delt (a region of the shoulder where development is key to achieving width). By turning the wrists either upward or downward for your set, the degree to which you will feel what I call a "capping" of your side deltoids will change. Experiment, and with time you'll find the position that digs the deepest into your delts.

7. Pair your raises into a compound set.
To change up a workout and add a bit of efficiency if your time is at a minimum, do your raises as compound sets. For instance, do 10 reps of lateral raises, followed immediately by 10 reps of bent-over lateral raises. Front, side and rear-delt raises all can be combined easily together, as dumbbells or cables are easy to switch from weight to weight.

8. Flex your delts hard at the end of each set.
I've found that one of the quickest ways to achieve sculpted and striated delts is to strongly contract them between sets. Stretch your arms out to your sides with your hands a little higher than the level of your elbows, keeping your shoulders back and chest elevated. Proceed to squeeze your deltoids. This maximum contraction should be achieved with minimal movement of the arms; it's a matter of concentration.

9. Avoid overtraining the deltoids.
Too many sets in a workout (i.e. extending toward 20 sets or more), or hitting shoulders with too much frequency over the course of a week, are the surest ways to limit development and predispose yourself to injury. As a rule of thumb, any natural weightlifter who trains his shoulders more than twice a week is likely overdoing it. If your intensity is high enough, training shoulders once each week is more than adequate.

10. If you cheat, take a seat.
If you find you consistently bounce at your knees and use momentum to your advantage to lift the dumbbells during raises, start doing them seated. With a short-back chair or a flat bench, you can do front, side or rear lateral raises (for the latter, bend at the hips so your chest is over your lap, feet firmly on the floor in front of you).

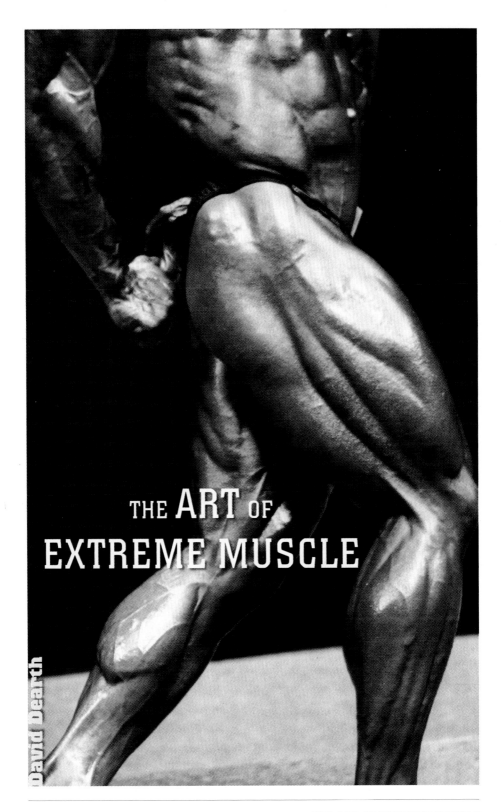

THE ART OF EXTREME MUSCLE

David Dearth

Ron Coleman

"**A**t 5'11" and nearly 300 lbs, no one in the competitive arena has even approached the mind-blowing combination of mass and cuts displayed by Ronnie Coleman. The reigning king of bodybuilding, he's the thickest and arguably the strongest bodybuilder I have ever seen. Not only does Ronnie move heavy weight, but he does so in impeccable form. I'm talking about monster weight for major repetitions. For example, does 315 lbs on behind-the-neck-seated-shoulder-press for 20 repetitions sound impressive?"

EXTREME MUSCLE ENHANCEMENT – 2nd Edition

Flex Wheeler

"In my opinion, Flex Wheeler had the most flawless physique I've ever seen. With small joints yet huge muscle, he displayed a physique that was simply awe inspiring. Just look at how large each of his muscles were and how they tapered down dramatically into small insertions on his joints. Even though he never won a Mr. Olympia, Flex was the envy of fellow competitors throughout the 1990s. Had he been bigger and more ripped, he may have enjoyed greater competitive success, nonetheless, his physique still lacked nothing and his shape was about as perfect as it gets."

Lee Priest

13

"**L**ee Priest displayed a physique with amazing thickness, proving that a shorter man can sometimes beat the giants if he gets really extreme. Lee has been in bodybuilding since his teenage years. As a fixture on the competitive scene for years, Lee is a regular at trade shows and a super nice guy. For Lee, though, he may never again break through for a big win, but remains a fan favorite. **"**

Andreas Munzer

"Though not blessed with great shape or lines, Andreas Munzer made up for his genetic limits with unearthly cuts. He literally re-defined what it meant to be shredded. No professional bodybuilder in history ever reached as far as Andreas did to achieve a ripped condition. His abdominals, serratus, obliques, and intercostals were not only fully carved, but actually cross-striated. He redefined near zero body fat to the point that such condition actually seems unattainable today. **"**

THE ART OF EXTREME MUSCLE

Jay Cutler

" **A**ttention to aesthetics by carefully choosing what muscles you prioritize and how you train them is critical to bringing out the best visual representation your physique has to offer. The physique of Jay Cutler reminds us that the best extreme physiques not only display mass and cuts, but also shape, symmetry, and proportions. "

EXTREME MUSCLE ENHANCEMENT — 2nd Edition

Paul Dillet

"**V**enice Beach regular Paul Dillet gained bodybuilding fame for showing up at competitions displaying an amazing show of huge mass. He had an almost disturbing degree of freaky vascularity, to the point that it almost hurt him in competition by eroding his aesthetics. Even so, he was always a monster force to be reckoned with."

Victor Martinez

"**O**nly a few bodybuilders in history had what the great Austrian Oak Arnold displayed—a physique that looked spectacular from every angle. Victor Martinez is perhaps the only present day bodybuilder with this gift of visual completeness. Victor still needs to gain about 20 lbs more lean mass to measure up to the big boys to really be a competitive threat at the big dance. But if he keeps putting on the beef and shows up ripped, look out."

EXTREME MUSCLE ENHANCEMENT – 2nd Edition

Dave Palumbo

Dave Palumbo stays in top shape all year around. This allows him to get freakishly ripped at contest time, displaying a rare degree of separations and vascularity. Though not the most aesthetic physique, for a guy who comes into the nationals bigger and more ripped every year, I am baffled why he has still been deprived of a professional card. His consistent improvement and crazy cuts are legendary among both amateurs and professionals alike.

"**W**ithout a doubt, the bodybuilding competition is the highest level of physique development. It's one thing to frequent the gym and build some beach muscle, but it's another thing entirely to enter a competition and stand side by side against others. Though I do applaud everyone who joins our fine sport of bodybuilding, I reserve deepest respect for those who have stepped on stage and had a respectable showing, at any level.*"

EXTREME MUSCLE ENHANCEMENT — 2nd Edition

Markus Ruhl

Intensity when training is absolutely critical to packing on thick chords of muscle. You won't reach your true potential for hugeness without being able and willing to reach down deep in your gut and find the intensity to train through the pain. Super massive German powerhouse Markus Ruhl is a perfect example of how true hard-core training builds real hard-core mass. Though he may never be a legitimate threat to win the Mr. Olympia competition because of a wide waist and a blocky shape, it is awesome to see him thunder onstage with mass on top of mass. ⟩⟩

Ahmad Haidar

"**T**he abdominal region is the center of the body and the eye is naturally drawn to that area first. Thus well-defined abdominal development is critical to a visually impressive physique. Professional bodybuilder Haidar built a phenomenal physique all-around, but is best known for his chiseled abdominal region. He managed to build his mind-blowing washboard without thickening his waist. As a result, he's hard to beat in competition even when he is not 100%."

EXTREME MUSCLE ENHANCEMENT — 2nd Edition

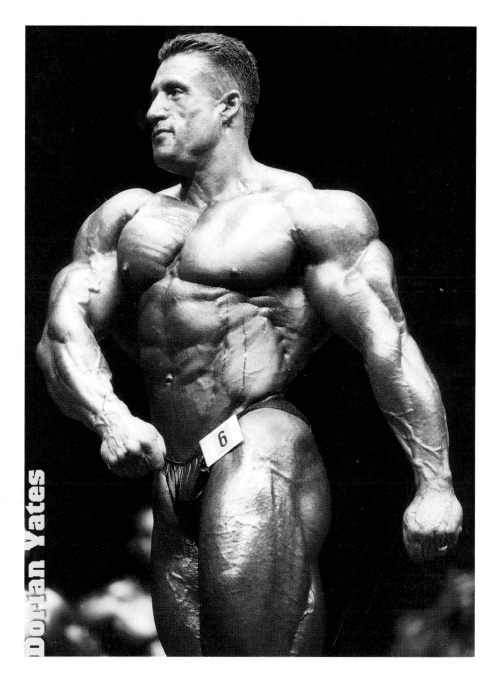

Dorian Yates

"**M**any believe the physique of Dorian Yates was the most complete Mr. Olympia of all time. He was the first Mr. Olympia to display a massive 260 lbs plus ripped physique with fully proportioned muscles from head to toe. Even though I think Lee Haney was a better bodybuilder and Mr. Olympia, Yates was more physically complete. He had the best calves of any Mr. Olympia in history."

Dorian Yates

EXTREME MUSCLE ENHANCEMENT – 2nd Edition

TRAPS

The trapezius is that awesome muscle that jumps off your shoulders and up the sides of your neck. When thick enough, it's not only majestic, but intimidating as well. I recall watching the professional wrestler Hawk from the Road Warriors tag team simply blow my mind with his nutty traps. They were huge and, though the rest of his musculature wasn't nearly at the same level, it was that one body part he had that just made your jaw drop. As a bodybuilder, you require that kind of size in your traps, or your shoulders will look weak no matter how big they are — also, needless to say, a skinny neck does nothing for your physique.

While they can get huge, the traps honestly don't move much, so training them doesn't involve a great deal of variety. The upper traps just pull up and down, while the middle of the traps retract and rotate the scapulae. That means one thing: It's shrug time.

Art Of The Shrug

Once upon a time, most everyone rotated the shoulder as they shrugged in a misguided effort to better work the traps. Now, however, we've learned the best way is the simplest way, as described here for the barbell shrug:

- Grasp a barbell with an overhand, shoulder-width grip.
- Maintaining the natural arch in your lower back, and with your knees loose, take the barbell from the supports and hold it in front of your thighs, traps stretched.
- Bring the bar up by moving your delt caps straight up. In order to get a full range of motion, it helps to think of trying to touch your ears with your

shoulders — impossible, yes, but the act of trying will help you get to the fully-contracted position.

- Lower the bar directly back down to a full traps stretch, and repeat.
- Throughout, make sure to not bend your elbows as you lift. If you bend your elbows, it's a sign you're going too heavy. This is a trap exercise, so make those muscles carry the load, not your arms!

The only real variation with a barbell is doing them in front of the body or behind the back (the latter originally popularized by Lee Haney). You can also shrug on a Smith machine, where you can solely focus on the contraction up and down without the need for stabilization, or you can do them with dumbbells.

The Routines

Using whichever routine corresponds to your level of experience, give your traps the attention they deserve with one of the elementary but highly effective regimens below.

Beginner Traps Workout No. 1: This traps routine only requires one exercise, but you have to blast it hard.

Exercise	Set	Reps	Weight (pounds)
Barbell Shrug	1	15	135
	2	15	185
	3	12	225
	4	10	275
	5	10	275
	6	8-10	315

Intermediate Traps Workout No. 2: Traps can also be effectively trained with dumbbells. Though I find they don't do as much for mass and height of the traps, they'll do wonders for your density and muscularity.

Exercise	Set	Reps	Weight
Barbell Shrug	1	15	135
	2	15	225
	3	12	275
	4	10	315
Dumbbell Shrug	1	15	100 (50-pound dumbbells)
	2	15	120
	3	12	140

Advanced Traps Workout No. 3: Doing shrugs behind the back is one of the best tips I ever got for advanced traps training, and it was given to me personally by Big Lee Haney himself. My only modification is to do it as a finishing motion on the Smith machine. This little extra stability gives me maximum height and contraction.

Exercise	Set	Reps	Weight
Barbell Shrug	1	15	135
	2	15	225
	3	12	315
	4	10	405
Smith-Machine Shrug	1	15	135
(behind the back)	2	15	185
	3	12	205
	4	12	205

Wrap-Up: Top 10 Traps-Training Tips

1. Don't neglect your traps.

Bodybuilders and athletes often avoid this body part altogether or relegate it to a "throw in" once a week for a few sets at the end of another workout. Perhaps it's because, unlike a big chest or muscular arms, traps aren't an aesthetically "in your face" body part; maybe people don't view traps as functionally important. Whatever the reasoning, it's decidedly false. The traps support and encase the posterior aspect of the shoulder joint and help to stabilize the neck. They're also aesthetically vital; without them, a physique totally lacks the dominating power a bodybuilder needs. If you're ever in a bodybuilding contest in which I'm a judge, I'd crucify you for lacking traps!

2. You'll find the proof in the pull.

The essence of getting your traps to "sit-up" on your shoulders is the incorporation of a heavy pull. Look at powerlifters and Olympic weightlifters, who both use tremendously heavy pulling motions in their workouts. They demonstrate the thickest traps development of any athletic discipline. Don't kid yourself into thinking you can get away with a workout that doesn't incorporate significant weight. Slow, peak contraction of the traps with moderate to light weight is good for a little pump and for maintaining tone, but to really build thick traps, you have to hoist some ball-busting poundage at one point or another. For this, do your heaviest sets of barbell shrugs with lifting straps — that way, you can put the impetus to fail squarely across your traps, and not on the forearms.

3. Don't rely heavily on lifting straps.

Your heaviest sets of barbell shrugs — yes to straps. Other shrugging exercises — no to straps. Often in a noble and single-minded purpose to develop traps, we rely too heavily on straps, wraps or hooks in an effort to keep the weights heavy. The reason for this is that the forearms are really the limiting factor, as they give out way before you ever get to weights that your traps balk on. Wrist straps take the weight off the forearm and provide the grip for you. I believe that straps and similar devices are generally good and necessary for optimal mass and development. However, I would restrict my use of straps to heavy barbell shrugs, and not get into the habit of using them on every trap set. They are simply not necessary for other trap movements, especially dumbbell shrugs. This way, your forearms will stay strong and well conditioned. Also, interestingly, when I rely too heavily on straps, I actually lose some density and muscularity across my upper back and arms. Perhaps it's due to the intensity it takes to bear down and hold onto the weight, but in any case, don't spoil yourself with straps. Save them for the heavy stuff.

4. Try barbell shrugs behind your back.

Functionally speaking, traps are more of a back muscle than a shoulder muscle. These muscles start at the base of the skull, travel out to the edge of the shoulder, and run all the way down the center of the back along the spine. Knowing these "origins and insertions" of the muscle reveals the optimum way to functionally achieve muscular contraction. Given what we know about the anatomical location of these muscles, the center portion of these muscles is best contracted when shrugging a barbell from behind the back. Lee Haney, who had some of the most mind-blowing traps I ever saw, put it in brutally simple terms: "Your traps are located behind you, so that's where the bar should be — behind you." So, try barbell shrugging behind your back. Be patient, as the path of the bar takes a little getting used to, especially if you're accustomed to conventional barbell shrugs in front of your thighs.

5. Train traps with the back or alone on a separate day.

Bodybuilders like former Mr. Olympia Dorian Yates prefer to couple traps training with shoulders to get the best results. However, although everyone is different and you have to experiment to find what works for you, in most cases traps development is best coupled with back training. This again has to do with the origin and insertion of the muscles of the trapezius. Their location makes them more of a back muscle that's designed to lift the shoulder girdle. Hence, coupling traps training with the back is a kinesiologically sensible thing to do. Every now and then I also like to bomb traps on a separate day as a primary body part. This allows me to really concentrate and give them the attention they deserve, as I would with any other body part.

6. Don't overdevelop your traps.

It sounds odd for me to say, especially after I just got through telling you how neglected traps training is. Nonetheless, you do have to be careful that, once your traps start growing, they don't overdevelop. The reason for this is largely aesthetic, since I've never heard of large, muscular traps leading to functional limitations. When shoulder development and back width can't keep pace with overdeveloped traps, your shoulders take on a sloping, narrow look. If this happens, lay off traps training for a while until your proportions return, and know that, unlike the rest of us mortals, you're blessed with responsive traps that should not be over-stimulated.

7. Shrug straight up and down with no shoulder rolling.

I still see some misguided souls shrugging weight up and rolling their shoulders from front to back or back to front, and then down. This is an archaic way of trap training that fails to yield significant results. The true gospel of traps involves no shoulder rolling. Too many secondary accessory muscles are used in a shoulder roll, making such kinetics virtually worthless outside the area of therapy and rehabilitation. In my own 20 years of experience, I started out ignorant and made the same dumb mistake. Luckily, before too long, I found that shoulder rolling with the intensity and weight necessary to build traps can actually irritate the shoulder joint and cervical spine. Here's a perfect example of where the "K.I.S.S." rule works best — "Keep It Simple, Stupid." Straight up and down, it's as basic as that.

8. Don't be afraid of high reps.

Like the muscles of the calves and abs, the trapezius muscle is dense and responds favorably to high repetitions. Although some bodybuilders find they get adequate stimulation from reps as low as six, most stay in the range of 10 or higher. In fact, for stubborn traps, I like to push up to a repetition scheme as high as 50 or more! Don't be afraid of experimenting with a higher scheme and seeing how you respond, especially if your traps are stubborn. Traps are not like chest or triceps, for example, which tend to flatten out with too many reps.

9. Use dumbbells to get a good squeeze on shrugs.

Peak contraction of the traps tends to work better if you use dumbbells. The barbell pulls both hands down in front (or back). This is great for the most important pulling aspect of traps development and stimulation for mass, but tends to be disadvantageous for holding the traps in a contracted position at the top of the shrug. One would want such a contraction to add density, striations and detail to the traps. As such, I tend to reserve such peak contraction movements for more advanced physique artisans who already display a bit of mass in this area. If you fall into this category and are looking to benefit from such peak contraction, use dumbbells as opposed to the barbell. This allows each arm to turn slightly around the side of the thigh as the weight tracks up the body. In so doing, the arms are not locked into the same set range of motion as with the barbell. The result of allowing the arms a bit more latitude in terms of freedom of independent motion gives the traps a chance to fully contract at the top position. At the apex, squeeze the traps hard and hold for a count of one.

10. Try bent-over barbell front raises.

As I've mentioned, the traps muscle runs all the way down the mid-back (at the 12th thoracic vertebrae, for those interested in the exact location), so the bulk of the muscle isn't the visibly obvious portion above the shoulders. Most of the muscle is below that level. As a result, although heavy barbell shrugs seem to take care of this region just fine if done properly, the lower bulk of the trap may be underdeveloped. If you wish, you can hit this area effectively by doing bent-over barbell front raises. Start by bending forward over a flat roman chair, your chest and upper abs resting on the bench, your arms hanging over one side, your feet firmly on the floor on the other. Grasp a light barbell with an overhand, shoulder-width grip and raise it from the floor up in an arc directly out in front of you. Stop when the bar ends up even with the level of your back. You won't believe the great contraction you get in the meat of the traps. Just remember not to go too heavy; it's a finishing motion, so easy does it.

TRICEPS

It seems like every male wants massive arms. Big guns are the rage. For many men, stretching the sleeves on a T-shirt is the quintessential signal that one weight trains. And many of those men overlook the number one thing that could give them the size they covet.

The answer is triceps training. Although building great biceps muscles is important, too often the triceps are ignored in deference to excessive biceps bombing. Unfortunately, most people are unaware of the difference in contribution of each muscle to arm size. The triceps muscles are composed of three heads (with the prefix "tri" meaning three), while the biceps muscles only have two heads (with the prefix "bi" meaning two). The triceps occupy about three-fifths of the upper arm. As a result, building muscular arms means focusing more efforts on the tri's.

The Crush

For big-time triceps, once you reach an intermediate stage, the first move you must become proficient at is lying barbell triceps extensions. They are also known as skull crushers. You'll need a spot for this one.

- Place a straight barbell on the lower-rung safety arms of a flat-bench-press station.
- Lie down on the bench at a point where your butt drops off the end of the

bench, while your lower back is flat against the bench.

- Reach back and grab the bar with a few inches of space between your hands. Have your spotter grab the bar evenly outside your grip and help you with a lift-off.
- Once the barbell is stabilized and under your control at a 90-degree angle from the flat bench, slowly bend your elbows and lower the bar behind your head to the point that your knuckles touch the bench pad.
- Make every attempt to keep your elbows from flaring out to the sides.
- Once your knuckles reach the bench, extend your arms briskly back to the upright position.

Start with a light weight (just the bar) and work your way up gradually. You can go heavy, down to a repetition range as low as six if that's appropriate for you. Just be careful. With a good spotter, you'll be okay pushing your limits on this exercise. If you have a bad spot, well … that's why they're called skull crushers!

Rediscovering A Gem

One forgotten weapon in the grand arsenal of effective triceps exercises is the dumbbell incline triceps extension. This is a beautiful mass builder that I never see performed anymore. Yet every time I do them, someone approaches me, curious and eager to learn how to do it themselves — especially after seeing the triceps pump I get from it.

- Start by raising an adjustable incline bench to about 60 degrees. I've always liked to stand up and lean back on the bench and not sit on the seat. Also, if the design of the bench allows, putting your feet on the front legs of the bench helps for stabilization.
- With a dumbbell in each hand (remember to start light and gradually work your way up), lie back against the bench, with your head over the top edge.
- Begin by gripping in the center of each dumbbell and pressing them overhead, palms facing each other (all you should see in the mirror is the circular end of each dumbbell).
- Keeping your elbows in tight and not letting them flare out to your sides, slowly lower the dumbbells simultaneously behind your head.
- When your elbows reach 90-degree angles, reverse to the extended position.

Like skull crushers, with a spot you can work pretty heavy on this. You'll see more growth if you concentrate on achieving a full range of motion, lowering the dumbbells as far down as possible behind your head, and staying in a rep range up to at least 10 per set.

The Routines

With these routines, you'll be on your way in your crusade for big guns.

Beginners Triceps Workout No. 1: This routine utilizes two of the most basic movements to set the foundation and begin to develop the triceps.

Exercise	Set	Reps	Weight (pounds)
Lying Triceps Extension (EZ curl)	1	15	55
	2	12	75
	3	10	95
	4	10	95
Cable Pressdown	1	12	60
	2	10	70
	3	10	80

Intermediate Triceps Workout No. 2: This is a basic and fundamental mass builder that leads off with lying extensions, i.e. skull crushers. Use a straight bar and bring it all the way down to where the top of your head contacts the bench. Be sure to not work sloppy. Skull crushers tempt even the best to break form, which can result in a lack of significant growth or even injury.

Exercise	Set	Reps	Weight (pounds)
Lying Triceps Extension (barbell)	1	20	45 (unweighted Olympic bar)
	2	15	85
	3	12	105
	4	10	125
One-Arm Overhead Extension*	1	15	40 (20-pound dumbbells)
	2	10	60
	3	10	70
	4	10	80

* This exercise is performed standing or seated on a short-back bench. Do reps one arm at a time, moving the dumbbell between an arm-straight-overhead position to an elbow-bent position, the dumbbell directly behind your head.

Advanced Triceps Workout No. 3: This advanced all-dumbbell regimen puts a premium on form, and doesn't let a slightly underdeveloped triceps get away with not doing its fair share of the work. The one-arm dumbbell extension helps the triceps to really pop out from the upper arm.

Exercise	Set	Reps	Weight (pounds)
Dumbbell Incline Extension	1	15	50 (25-pound dumbbells)
	2	12	70
	3	12	80
	4	10	90
	5	10	110
One-Arm Overhead Extension	1	15	50 (25-pound dumbbells)
	2	10	60
	3	10	70
	4	8-10	80
	5	15	50

Wrap-Up: Top 10 Triceps-Training Tips:

1. Warm up your triceps thoroughly before you start training them hard.
Abruptly starting your triceps routine is the road to ruin. What might begin with mild elbow pain can rapidly progress to a debilitating injury that makes almost any triceps motion nearly impossible to execute. If you find it helps, you can ease your way into the heavier, basic motions with cable pressdowns leading off your routine. I prefer the straight bar for pressdowns in the meat of the workout, but as a warm-up, I prefer a V-bar because it's more forgiving on the elbows. You only need about two warm-up sets of 15–25 reps with a very sub-maximal weight, then you're ready to go.

2. Stick with the basics.
Barbell skull crushers and cable pressdowns are the two basic triceps moves, in my mind. Dips and close-grip bench presses also are considered by many to be fundamental, but I haven't seen the proof in the results when solely concentrating on them as the core of a triceps workout. Instead, I prefer using those as an addition to or sometimes as a substitution for one of the basics. This way, you achieve variation without sacrificing long-term results.

3. Train the angles.
Slight variations in wrist position change the training angle dramatically and promote triceps stimulation. Unlike biceps training, where small adjustments of the wrist can virtually disengage contraction, variations in wrist position while training triceps actually spur growth and add muscularity. Choose movements that challenge your triceps with a variety of wrist positions.

4. Never slam your elbows into the locked position.

As with a poor warm-up, sloppy form can be injurious. In particular, slamming your elbows into the locked position is one of the most common examples of poor form that can easily lead to injury. You should still be explosive and press hard to the top of a rep, but only to a 95 percent lockout. Recall that you don't need to lock your elbows completely to achieve maximum contraction. On the contrary and quite surprising to many, maximum extension of the elbow joint actually results in a slight relaxation of the triceps muscles and even a looseness or "laxity" in the joint.

5. Don't overdo cable pressdowns.

While pressdowns are a stellar core motion, oftentimes they're done in excess and at the sacrifice of other important movements. They tend to primarily hit the outside head of the triceps. Unfortunately, this outer head is really the easiest part of the triceps to develop. As a result, beyond stimulating this region, triceps pressdowns add little to the bulk and firmness of the triceps. Therefore, while working hard on the pressdown portion of your routine, also put plenty of time and energy into other exercises that develop the other heads (i.e., motions that force the arm to extend from overhead).

6. Go deep.

Few things are as pathetic to me as watching a person train using a partial range of motion. True muscular stimulation only comes from training a muscle through its full range of motion. But too often, ego gets in the way and good productive training is pushed aside in favor of a numbers game. Sorry guys, partial reps don't count. In addition, despite some who think they're being "careful" by not executing a full range of motion, partial reps are a set-up for injury. Both tendons and ligaments experience positive stimulation when stretched through a full range of motion. Such stretching improves the strength of tendons and ligaments by increasing their passive tone or "tissue turgor." Partial movements are unable to achieve this result. So, from squats to triceps extensions, the rule holds true: Work on establishing proper technique so that you can train in a full range of motion and get the most out of your efforts.

7. Finish with one-arm overhead extensions.

I'm a firm believer that the one-arm overhead dumbbell extension is the single best finishing movement for the triceps. If done correctly, I've seen it slab piles of mass onto the triceps when other motions have failed miserably. As a finishing motion after you've done your heavier, more basic work, stay in form and don't push the weight up too fast, otherwise you'll lose the feel.

8. Keep your descent slow and controlled.

As with any motion I teach, slow and controlled descent is paramount to engaging and triggering deep muscle fiber while remaining injury-free. I won't belabor this point, but the same principle holds for triceps training. Save the explosiveness for the positive movement.

9. Stay away from gimmicks and tricky movements.

In my experience, things like bars with adjustable circular rotating grips, pressing straps, cable ropes and oversized elastic tension bands never built great triceps. Although fun and interesting for occasional variation or perhaps as a rare finishing motion, these gimmicks are more for rehabilitation or sports-specific training and, unless these are your issues, they should not comprise the core of your routine. Too much energy invested in these motions is an effort in futility. No matter how hard you train using these techniques, by themselves they won't give you impressive results.

10. Squeeze and flex the triceps as hard as possible between sets.

This will add granite hardness to the back of your arms. A lot of the density I achieved early in my bodybuilding career can be traced to this technique. Squeeze your triceps between sets of the last exercise in your routine for a continuous 10 seconds, progressively increasing the intensity of the squeeze each second before finally relaxing at the end.

14 BICEPS

When I think back on the years of pro bodybuilding, some unforgettable images stand out. Arnold's front double biceps pose. Larry Scott's patented "two arms out" pose. Robby Robinson's sweeping single biceps pose. These hazy remembrances still blow me away, even by today's standards.

Why don't we have the same undying images today? The answer is that somehow we forgot what made them so indomitable — big guns! Champions of the past knew the power of biceps and triceps. Think about it: No matter how big your arms ever get, they just keep making you look more impressive.

The heroes of yesteryear didn't have a lot of today's state-of-the-art equipment, but they still found a way to train for maximum development. Things may have been a bit Jurassic comparatively speaking, but as far as arm training is concerned, I think our methods were still far better than what I see today.

If you want big arms, you need to keep one fact in mind — arms respond best to plain, basic movements. For biceps, the basics boil down to two classics, standing barbell curls and seated dumbbell curls.

Stand & Deliver

A few years back I was at Gold's Gym in Venice, California, training at my old stomping ground and shooting the breeze with some current professional bodybuilders. One in particular (who shall remain nameless, of course) has just about every body part in freakish proportion, except arms.

He told me how hard he's been training his biceps, yet how frustrated he was. He asked me for some feedback. After watching his routine, I was appalled at the absence of any simple solid mass-building motion. He was jumping around like a chicken without a head, from one piece of equipment to another. Cables, machines — I was ready for him to slip in a Jane Fonda video and start doing curls with an elastic band!

Anyway, the answer to all this effort in futility was to re-introduce him to standing barbell curls. I told him to make them the focus of his routine. And as it worked for him, so shall it work for you — its value is priceless in regards to the benefits it provides the bi's. This is how you do it:

- With your feet shoulder-width apart and a slight bend in the knees, grab the bar just outside shoulder width with an underhand grip.
- Start your curl from the fully-extended elbow position.
- Shift your elbows slightly forward and in front of your body as you begin your curl. I teach bodybuilders to begin the curl in the straight-arm position and initiate the motion by rotating the entire arm forward. The move should be slight, but just enough to keep the elbows from shifting back. After this slight forward motion of the arms, begin to flex the elbow and contract the biceps. (Don't bring your arms forward too much, or the front deltoid gets involved and excessively assists in raising the weight.)
- As you reach the top of the motion, squeeze your biceps and slowly lower the bar back down to the starting position.

Dumbbell Curling

The other classic exercise is the seated dumbbell curl, which puts equal stress squarely on each arm. Modern-day bodybuilders like Shawn Ray have used it to jump-start stubborn biceps with great success.

For these, some people twist their wrists from a palms-facing to a palms-up position at the top, but this action disengages the biceps at some points of the motion. Also, you may see these done alternating one arm at a time, but this allows for leaning into the motion, which invites momentum. Instead, perform it as follows:

- On a seated bench, begin with dumbbells in each hand and arms fully extended at your sides. Your back and shoulders should be against the back pad of the bench and your chest should be raised up.
- Turn your wrists forward (or "supinate" them, as it's technically called) and keep them this way throughout.
- Curl both dumbbells simultaneously toward your shoulders, then reverse.
- Don't pause at the top of your curls; keep the dumbbells moving through the entire range of motion.

The Routines

Of these routines, one is not necessarily better then the other. They all contain movements that can be effective at virtually any level of training; biceps take some tooling around to figure out what works best. Be aware that often times some of the simplest routines are often the best.

Beginner Biceps Workout No. 1: This basic routine focuses most on mass and strength building and least on cuts and striations. It's a necessary beginning.

Exercise	Set	Reps	Weight
Standing Barbell Curl	1	15	45 (unweighted Olympic bar)
	2	12	65
	3	10	75
	4	10	85
Standing Alternate Dumbbell Curl	1	12	60 (30-pound dumbbells)
	2	10	50
	3	10	40

Intermediate Biceps Workout No. 2: This routine includes two of the most basic muscle building powerhouses, the standing curl and the dumbbell concentration curl. Both were favorites of the great Arnold himself. While the barbell curl tends to add the mass, the concentration curl shapes and adds peak. This routine is timeless and phenomenal results will be achieved by those with all levels of experience.

Exercise	Set	Reps	Weight (pounds)
Standing Barbell Curl	1	15	45 (unweighted Olympic bar)
	2	12	65
	3	10	85
	4	10	95
	5	10	105
Dumbbell Concentration Curl	1	15	50 (25-pound (one arm at a time)*dumbbells)
	2	10	70
	3	10	70

* Sit and place your working elbow against your same-side inner thigh. Curl the dumbbell up toward your chin then lower it back to the start. They also can be done standing and bent over if you find that position comfortable.

Advanced Biceps Workout No. 3: The advanced workout should address the mass issue, but place a greater emphasis on peaking and shaping the biceps.

Exercise	Set	Reps	Weight
Seated Dumbbell Curl	1	15	50 (25-pound dumbbells)
	2	12	70
	3	10	80
	4	10	90
	5	10	90
Preacher Curl (straight bar)	1	10	85
	2	10	105
Cable Concentration Curl	1	12	50
(one arm at a time)*	2	10	60

*This is like the dumbbell concentration curl, except you use a D-handle attached to the lower pulley of a cable station. It must be done with slow, super-strict form.

Wrap-Up: Top 10 Biceps-Training Tips

1. Avoid heavy cheat curls.

Although this went out of style with bell-bottom pants, satin disco shirts, tie-dye handkerchiefs and clogs, I still occasionally see some moron loading up a barbell and swinging it up with all that might and momentum will allow. The result — a sore lower back. I've seen some idiots cheat so much, it's a wonder they don't bang the back of their heads on the ground! Unless you're trying to herniate a disc, I suggest avoiding heavy cheat curls. Today's biceps training centers around strict form for maximum growth. Stegosaurus-like detractors of my thinking quickly point to old clips of Arnold doing cheat-curls and believe that if it worked for him, then it must be good for them. Unfortunately, what they fail to realize is that Arnold had genetically fabulous arms. I don't think it would have made any difference what exercise he chose to do, or in what form. Instead, with all due respect to the main man of bodybuilding, a better champion to learn from was Lee Haney. The reason is that Big Lee, unlike Arnold, had poor arms to begin with and had to figure out how to make this genetically stubborn body part grow. His answer was strict training. Proper technique took the unimpressive arms he demonstrated in 1983 to monstrous proportions within five years. He ended up piling on biceps thickness to the point that his arms were nearly 22 inches around. (Lee was sharply criticized by some as being weak because he chose to work with more modest weights and in stricter form. But if you watched him train, you would see firsthand how hard he was working with those weights. Few bodybuilders could hoist the weights he did in the same form without dropping down the rack in a big way.) The lesson, at any rate, is to avoid heavy cheat curls. Your back and biceps will thank you.

2. Emphasize barbells and dumbbells.
All too often people waste time with painfully ridiculous motions in the guise of looking for variation. Sometimes it's almost comical to see the bizarre movements and acrobatic positions people attempt in an effort to make their biceps grow. "Exercises" like inverted decline curls or one-arm cable rows with a rope are nothing more than a circus act. I preach the basic movements for maximum development. I consider standing barbell curls, standing or seated dumbbell curls, barbell preacher curls, barbell reverse curls and one-arm dumbbell preacher curls to be the basic biceps exercises. For top-notch development, your routine should focus on the strict use of anywhere from 1–3 of these per workout, depending on your current level of experience.

3. Keep your wrists turned up when curling dumbbells.
I use this trick for professional bodybuilders that have stubborn biceps, and even those with good development that I want to take up a notch to freaky. Keeping your palms supinated while curling dumbbells will deeply stimulate the biceps. To understand this, keep in mind a little kinesiology. For example, did you know that, with your elbow bent at a 90-degree angle, you can actually contract your biceps by simply tightening a screw into a wall? Try it. This analogous outward turning action of the wrist should demonstrate to you the importance of maintaining this position while curling dumbbells in order to achieve supreme muscular contraction.

4. Experiment with bar thickness.
A thicker bar tends to stimulate forearms more during a curl, while a thinner bar tends to stimulate a stronger contraction of the biceps at the top of the curling motion. As a result, thinner barbells should "peak" your biceps better than thicker barbells. Honestly assess your area of weakness and utilize these techniques to maximize your biceps growth. Fixed-weight (racked) barbells tend to have a narrower bar thickness; Olympic bars tend to run thicker.

5. Don't be fooled by cables.
While cables are noteworthy as a finishing movement, any cable-curl motion as your first and primary exercise won't cut it. No matter how hard I have someone work on cables, and despite apparent muscular failure, I'm never completely sure when they've fatigued their biceps. Even with my own training, as I approach failure I seem to be able to use more accessory muscles

to hoist the weight — although I might do a set to apparent failure, it's more of a diffuse failure involving muscles of the forearms, shoulders and upper back. The biceps, although somewhat pumped, tend to be left relatively under-stimulated when compared with the same effort exerted on barbell or dumbbell work. As a result, I rarely, if ever, use cables in my biceps routines as a first motion. At most, I relegate it to a finisher role after I've put in honest time with the basics.

6. Always start curling from the fully-extended position.
You should never begin a curling rep with your elbows in a bent position. This shortens the range of motion and makes the exercise a great deal easier. Although you might be able to lift more in the way of poundage, you'll sacrifice a tremendous amount of muscular growth in the process. Instead, always start your curl from a fully-extended elbow position. As long as you're training with strict and controlled form, you don't need to worry about suffering a hyperextension injury.

7. Move your elbows slightly forward as you begin your curls.
When some people curl a barbell, they tend to move their elbows back behind them as they begin the upward motion. This is what we call a "drag curl," because you're dragging the bar up along your body instead of holding it out in front of you. In sports medicine, we use this motion as a way to rehabilitate a damaged rotator cuff; curling in such a way will not adequately stimulate the biceps. Like a cheat curl, you can master this bad technique to hoist some pretty impressive weight, but don't expect your biceps to do much growing. Instead, I always teach people to begin the curl in the straight-arm position and initiate the first phase of the motion not by flexing the elbow, but by shifting the entire arm forward slightly, just enough to keep the elbows from moving back. After this forward motion of the arms, begin to flex the elbow and contract the biceps.

8. Don't pause too long at the top of your curls.
The top of a curling motion, where your forearm moves directly beneath the weight, lacks resistive force. Because gravity ceases to exert an angular stress when you top out on most types of curls, you tend to lose the active contraction. As such, the lack of force loosens the muscles of the biceps in what amounts to a resting position. A good way to prevent this from occurring is to keep the bar or dumbbell moving through the entire range of motion, not allowing for any pause or deceleration at the top. This technique will put continuous stress on the biceps. By not allowing them to rest and lose contraction at the top of the motion, biceps flexion is maintained, muscular fatigue is more focused and more easily achieved, and a deeper pump is produced.

9. Tighten and flex your biceps between sets.

By flexing your biceps between sets, you enhance your pump by promoting more blood flow to the target area. In the process, you create more muscularity. In my days as a competitive bodybuilder, during my precontest biceps workouts, I would flex my biceps so hard between sets that veins would trace across my arms like a road map; the practice helped me craft tremendous arm peaks. This tightening and flexing between sets created a high degree of muscularity in my biceps to the point that nearly every fiber was permanently visible under paper-thin skin. Try this technique between sets of your last exercise.

10. Strengthen your forearms.

Forearms are the link to the biceps. Without a strong grip, how can one expect to ever dig deep and feel a significant burn in the bi's? I don't believe you can ever optimize biceps development with weak forearms. In addition, skinny forearms just don't look good. To counter bad hooks, do barbell wrist curls, reverse barbell wrist curls, or standing behind-the-back wrist curls as a finisher to your biceps workouts.

15 QUADRICEPS

From a visual standpoint, your legs make up half of your body. Obviously, come training time, your efforts should reflect this. Unless they're a genetic strength for you, you'll need to train legs, especially quadriceps, with the greatest intensity as compared to other body parts.

The quads sit on the front of your thighs, and are intricately involved in movements at the knee and hip joint. To work them efficiently, you need to go hard and heavy with compound movements that work them from both joints, such as leg presses, hack squats, and the granddaddy of them all, the barbell squat.

King Of All Exercises

Make no mistake about this: You need only understand one word when it comes to training the quads — squats. They enhance overall body power and specifically strengthen the quads, hamstrings, glutes, back, calves, and even shoulders and arms to some degree. Squats stimulate you both anaerobically and aerobically, and can even spur an anabolic hormone surge. By far, squats are the single most effective resistance motion there is and ever will be, if done correctly.

And that's really the operative phrase — done correctly. As natural and perfect a motion as it is, I seldom see the squat performed with proper form. Follow these 10 steps to ensure you're getting the most from this amazing exercise:

1. Warm-up before you squat.

The way to properly begin a squat workout is to pick a non-impact, non-ballistic, aerobic motion to start with. No running, no stretching! Stationary cycles or the elliptical are excellent choices. The point is that you want to increase your heart rate to an exercising level in a gradual fashion. Limit your activity to nothing more than a warm-up. In other words, I don't mean 45 minutes on the bike, nor half hour, nor even 15 minutes. I'm only talking about 3–5 minutes of easy pedaling; that's all it takes to power the circulation and ready your whole body for a squat routine.

In addition, as part of your warm-up, you should always do at least one set of squats with the lightest possible weight. For example, no matter how many 45-pound plates you can pile on and no matter how strong you ever get, always begin by squatting just the bar for high reps. This will serve to warm-up and stretch the knees, as well as send a signal to your body that you're about to begin.

2. Always do a full-range-of-motion squat.

There is no such thing as a "quarter" or "half" squat. If you can't do a full squat because of injury, lack of experience, or a lack of significant muscle mass needed to support the full squat position, then you shouldn't be doing it. Do leg presses or hack squats instead. Strive to consistently tolerate a full range of motion, and then advance to squats as you build more strength. It's an "all-or-none" phenomenon — a light-switch, if you will. You're either doing a full squat, or you're not squatting.

This recommendation is always met with controversy whenever it comes up in my lectures because of the residual myth that somehow full squats are bad for your knees. This is absolute nonsense. As long as you remain tight, slow and controlled at the bottom of the rep without bouncing, you risk no injury to your knees. In fact, I believe this steady, controlled stretching through a full range of motion in the deep squat position actually strengthens the knee joint, while working partial reps actually puts the knee in more jeopardy, as the joint capsule itself is strained in an effort to stop the rep short.

3. Descend slowly.

Your descent into the deep squat position should be very slow and controlled. I tell everyone I coach on squatting, "The lower you go, the slower you should go." Although true for nearly every motion, there really is no better application than the squat. A quick ballistic dropping motion is the best way to end up with a career-ending injury.

4. Create a "pocket."

As you near the bottom position, or "hole" as it's sometimes referred to, you must stay very tight in the seated position; squatters who rush, or even bounce, through this segment invariably end up with some kind of internal knee derangement. The best squatters are so slow in the pocket that it almost appears as if the motion decelerates to a stop for a microsecond prior to the concentric contraction.

Perhaps the most important fundament to keep in mind while performing a full squat is not to bounce at the bottom. Doing so will injure the knee for sure. Instead, you should have a controlled transition from negative to positive force. By creating a tight "pocket" sensation as you bury the repetition, you limit your possibility of injury.

5. Use a heel lift.

About 90 percent of people naturally lack the flexibility needed to do a full squat without a heel lift. The result is what we call a "cut" repetition. What this means is that, in order for your heels to stay in contact with the floor without the use of a lift, your center of gravity is pulled forward and your lower back comes into play to compensate. This is problematic in that it takes a significant load off the large muscles of the lower body and puts it on the less resilient structures of the spinal lumbar region. The result can be a catastrophic insult to your spinal discs.

Next time you see someone squatting in the gym without either a board or a 10-pound plate under each heel, observe — odds are they're exhibiting a classic "cut repetition" and are in desperate need of a lift. Imagine a line extending from their shoulders through their knees, and you'll be able to see how forward of center they are. Next, visualize how a heel-lift would move their center of gravity back over the meat of the quadriceps, and end up basically shifting their legs underneath the bar. In this way, the quads would do most all of the work, as is the ideal.

As an aside, keep in mind that as you gain years of training under your belt squatting in deep, strict form, you will find that your arch flexibility improves. In this case, you may find that you no longer need a lift under your heel.

6. Maintain the natural arch in your lower back.

Be sure that your back assumes a nice concavity. This puts your center of gravity over the middle of the quadriceps and focuses the weight over the column of vertebral bodies. These vertebral bodies are the densest and heaviest portion of each vertebrae. (Our spinal column is made up of vertebrae, stacked one on top of the other.) When one's lower back assumes a gentle concave curve, these bodies line up on top of one another in such a way that any force from above downward or below upward is translated safely along these relatively massive bony cylinders.

7. Never lock out your knees at the top of the rep.

With an almost mechanical fluidity, you should reach the apex of the motion without locking your knees completely. Always maintain a slight bend in the knees in the top position. This keeps pressure off the cartilage of the knee and forces the quadriceps to bear the brunt of the weight in the so called "resting position" (and done this way, it isn't much of a rest!).

8. Higher reps rule for legs.

Some body parts respond better to higher repetitions than others. Obvious ones include the calves and abdominal muscles. A more surprising body part that seems to respond better to volume is the quadriceps muscles. The advanced bodybuilders I work with train with a significantly higher repetition scheme on legs than what's standard for heavy sets. As a result, their legs are better as well. I'll credit the "Golden Eagle" Tom Platz with discovering this principle. The fact is, as heavy as he ever trained, he seldom dropped under eight reps on the squat, and he assured me that it wasn't until his famous squat challenge with Fred Hatfield that he even attempted a one-rep max. For mass, legs respond better to more reps, in the range of 10 or higher.

9. Stretch after squatting.

Flexibility is extremely important to focus on, as quite a number of injuries can be traced to poor flexibility and a limited range of motion. In general, flexibility and functionality go hand-in-hand. But for weightlifting purposes, you need to do it correctly. Recent research in the area of stretching has revealed some interesting parameters. First, it has been indicated that your flexibility is greater when you stretch after a workout as compared to before. Actually, several studies show that stretching before a lifting session can actually decrease your strength levels! Add to that the research showing no marked reduction in injury risk if you stretch before a workout, and the verdict is clear — do all of your stretching after your leg workout, not before. Before leaving the gym, dedicate about 5–10 minutes to leg-focused, quad, hip and hamstrings stretches done passively (i.e. no ballistic-type bouncing stretches, only the "reach-and-hold" type).

10. Don't start a squatting routine before you're ready.

Squats are the most technically demanding of all exercises, and although of far greater benefit than any other one move you can do in the gym, the squat can also result in the greatest harm if done improperly or in an untimely fashion. Rookie lifters are simply not ready for the squat. In fact, many lack the muscle mass and coordination necessary. You'd be surprised how many professional athletes I've worked with who weren't ready to squat the first time out and, instead, had to progress to squats in a slow and methodical fashion.

The less-experienced individual should start with the leg press and begin working this motion deeper and deeper, until full range of motion is achieved. The next step usually involves increasing the weight to a level of comfortable significance. When that significant weight is pressed through a full range of motion on repeated leg-training days, and for a significant number of sets and reps, the next step is the hack squat. There you would repeat the same gradual approach. When such form is mastered on the hack, finally you graduate to the squat.

The Routines

These regimens give you a full selection to choose from.

Beginner Quad Workout No. 1: This is an example of a very basic, fundamental leg routine for development of both early-stage mass and functionality. It can be done with either exercise being performed first. Just remember that if squats are performed first, you must go through a thorough warm-up.

Exercise	Set	Reps	Weight (pounds)
Leg Press	1	25	90*
(plate-loaded machine)	2	15	180
	3	12	270
	4	10	360
Barbell Squat	1	25	45 (unweighted Olympic bar)
	2	20	135
	3	15	185
	4	15	185

* Weight listed only counts the plates used; the starting weight (i.e. the weight of the sled) is different from machine to machine. For tracking purposes, it's better to only concern yourself with the weight you add, and not the starting poundage of each machine.

Beginner Quad Workout No. 2: This is an alternate workout to squatting. It can be used occasionally when your quads feel ready to hit but the rest of your body feels too fatigued to carry you through squats. Just don't use it too often thinking that such a routine can completely substitute for deep, strict squatting.

Exercise	Set	Reps	Weight
Leg Extension	1	25	50
	2	20	80
	3	15	120
Leg Press	1	25	180*
	2	15	270
	3	12	360
	4	10	450
	5	10	720

* Weight listed only counts the plates used; the starting weight (i.e. the weight of the sled) is different from machine to machine. For tracking purposes, it's better to only concern yourself with the weight you add, and not the starting poundage of each machine.

Intermediate Quad Workout No. 3: This is an example of a leg routine that focuses very heavily and intensely on the squat, but adds a shaping exercise to finish. When done in super-strict form, it's a quad killer.

Exercise	Set	Reps	Weight (pounds)
Barbell Squat*	1	25	45 (unweighted Olympic bar)
	2	20	135
	3	15	185
	4	12	225
	5	10	275
	6	10	315
Sissy Squat**	1	15	Bodyweight
	2	15	Bodyweight
	3	12-15	25 (holding a 25-pound plate)

* The first exercise must be preceded by a light cardio warm-up as described in the text.
** Sissy squats involve using only your bodyweight and squatting down deep without hinging at the waist; only the knees bend. To do it, hold a sturdy object, such as the frame of a machine (like the Smith) with both hands. Lie back as you bend deeply at the knees; your heels will come up off of the floor as you lower yourself. When you can go no further, reverse back to a standing position. The movement should be slow and strict, so that you feel a deep burn in your quads.

Advanced Quad Workout No. 4: Combining squats and lunges is a Ronnie Coleman favorite. His parking lot walking lunges are the stuff of legend. Just brace yourself because it's incredibly demanding to perform the entire routine in absolutely perfect form. This routine heavily stresses the quads with an added emphasis on the glutes and hamstrings.

Exercise	Set	Reps	Weight
Barbell Squat*	1	25	45 (unweighted Olympic bar)
	2	20	135
	3	12	225
	4	10	275
	5	10	315
	6	10	405
Walking Barbell Lunge**	1	10	95 (20 paces)
	2	10	105 (20 paces)
	3	10	135 (20 paces)
Leg Extension	1	25	100
	2	15-20	140

* The first exercise must be preceded by a light cardio warm-up as described in the text.

** For walking lunges, hold a barbell across your shoulders (as if you were about to squat). Step forward with your right foot as you drop your left leg toward the floor by bending both knees, making sure your right knee doesn't pass over the plane of your toes. Stop just short of your rear knee touching the ground as your front thigh comes parallel to the floor. Press yourself back up, forcing your bodyweight through the heel of your forward foot, and bring your back leg forward so it becomes the front leg. Continue walking in this lunge fashion; 20 total steps equal 10 reps.

Advanced Quad Workout No. 5: This advanced routine is particularly useful because of the emphasis it places on the outer sweeps of the thighs. Once you have some mass, it's an important session to include every now and then to be sure that your quads are shaping out nicely as they grow.

Exercise	Set	Reps	Weight
Leg Extension	1	25	80
	2	20	100

Exercise	Set	Reps	Weight
Hack Squat	1	15	90*
	2	12	180
	3	12	270
	4	10	360
	5	8-10	450
Front Squat**	1	15	45 (unweighted Olympic bar)
	2	15	135
	3	12	225
	4	10-12	275
	5	6-8	315

* Weight listed only counts the plates used; the starting weight (i.e. the weight of the sled) is different from machine to machine. For tracking purposes, it's better to only concern yourself with the weight you add, and not the starting poundage of each machine.

** The bar sits across the front of the shoulders on the upper chest; in all other ways, it's just like a regular squat.

Wrap-Up: Top 5 Quad-Training Tips

1. Train your quads with intensity.

Your quadriceps muscles represent the largest and most powerful muscle group in your body. So, unlike working the smaller muscles of the upper body, which can thrive on lower reps to grow, the quads are a different story. Dig your heels in and train all-out. Intensity must rule quad day — if you don't have the energy, rest and try again the next day. Don't settle for a half-baked effort. Go hard or go home.

2. Keep the legs under load at all times.

Never lock out your knees. This not only is bad for your joints, but also unloads the quads (i.e. takes the weight off of them) and makes the workload much easier for them. Keep the knees slightly bent at the top of each motion and don't pause between reps.

3. Wear comfortable clothing.

For a leg routine, comfortable clothing is essential to a good performance. Exaggerated movement of the knees and hips is indispensable to proper quad training. Restrictive clothing that binds or bunches, especially around the knees, not only interferes with body mechanics but can precipitate injury. Also, don't overeat before doing quads. A little food might keep your belly quiet, but too much and it will end up right next to you on the floor.

4. Recruit a good spotter or training partner.

Leg training is akin to driving your car at high speeds on an interstate. You don't do it every day, but when you do, you damn well better have a seat belt on. A spotter or training partner you trust is the proverbial seat belt. He can bail you out when the going gets a little too tough on a set, and motivate you to work harder throughout.

5. Don't train other big body parts on the same day as quads.

The sheer physical sacrifice it takes to properly train quads precludes combining these sessions with other big body parts. Something small like abs or calves may be okay, but unless you have naturally huge quads, you'll want to keep the emphasis on them and not share focus with another large muscle group. Also, allow your quads to recuperate fully between training sessions. Don't train them again if they're even remotely sore or stiff. Naturally, some sessions will be more taxing than others and will require more rest. Just listen to your body and only train your quads again when they're fully ready to be pushed.

16 HAMSTRINGS

In bodybuilding competition, few things are as impressive as a guy with huge quads taking a quarter turn and displaying a comparably large set of hamstrings. It's a total showstopper when one more quarter turn reveals massive striations from the rear.

But you may not necessarily be training for competition, so what's the glory of hamstring training for you? In addition to a complete-looking pair of legs, the hamstrings have vital functions in regards to knee-joint stability.

Dynamic stability of the knee, or the stability exhibited while moving laterally (i.e., side-to-side) or stopping and turning, is challenging because, unlike flexion movements, one can't rely solely on the strength and bulk of the quadriceps to stabilize the joint and prevent it from harm. The hamstrings must be strong enough to counterbalance the strength of the quads and be able to protect the integrity of the knee.

The best examples can be seen in the athletes and bodybuilders I've worked with over the years. The ones without knee problems didn't necessarily have the best or biggest quads, but almost invariably had well-developed hamstrings. Perhaps the most extreme example from bodybuilding would be Tom Platz. Although famed for his freaky quad development, I don't think he ever got enough recognition for his equally freaky hamstrings. To his credit, he never suffered knee problems. Later in his years he became an avid tennis player, and despite the lateral movement demands of the sport, still to my knowledge suffered no knee-joint ailments.

The Built-In Knee Brace

The first step in understanding the importance of the muscles on the back of the leg is to examine each of their respective origins and insertions. When I speak of the origin of a muscle, I'm referring to the starting point at which one end of the muscle is connected to the bone. At the other end of the muscle lies the insertion, where the opposite end inserts onto the bone. In the case of the hams, the origin and insertion of these particular muscles highlights their significance as lateral stabilizers of the knee.

Three muscles, the biceps femoris, semimembranosus and semitendinosus, constitute the hamstrings. The origin of the latter two is at the base of the pelvis, on an area of bone called the ischial tuberosity; the long head of the biceps femoris also originates at the ischial tuberosity, while the short head originates on the femur (a large leg bone). Lower down on the leg, the insertion of the biceps femoris is on the head of the fibula (a bone next to the tibia). The semimembranosus and semitendinosus insert on the tibia.

All three muscles, due to their insertion points, serve to brace the knee joint during dynamic movement. The quadriceps, whose insertion follows the patellar tendon over the front of the leg, can't help stabilize lateral movement, including stopping and twisting; it has to be the hams.

How do we effectively work these muscles? I've heard far too many bodybuilders in my time whine about how stubborn they are, how they never seem to get sore, or how there isn't very much you can do for them. Of course, they say all these things until they work with me for a session of training torment. I teach them what they're doing wrong, and, exactly how to get to their hamstrings.

The first thing to realize is that most bodybuilders, trainers and coaches promote doing a great deal of leg curls and little else to affect this area. Add to that, they usually do these curls as a finishing motion after a hard quad workout. Would it surprise you to know that the leg curl alone is a relatively ineffective way to work these muscles? By only doing leg curls, you largely neglect the meatiest portion of the muscle.

The only muscle being worked extensively by leg curls is the one that originates on the rear (posterior) part of the leg and inserts on the fibula, the short head of the biceps femoris. Unfortunately, this small muscle contributes little to the overall bulk of the hamstrings. The semitendinosus and semimembranosus are used to some degree on lying leg curls, but due to their insertion, aren't significantly engaged and working until the weight is lifted above 30 degrees.

Ham Helper

Finding an exercise that works the rest of the hamstrings requires another look at the anatomy chart, this time at the origins. The biceps femoris, as implied, has two heads, the long head of which originates on the ischial tuberosity. The semimembranosus and semitendinosus also both originate on the ischial tuberosity.

This tells us that in order to stimulate these muscles we absolutely must extend the hip. For that, you can't get any better than the Romanian deadlift.

- In a standing position, grasp a barbell with an overhand grip, hands shoulder-width apart on the bar.
- Keep a slight bend in your knees to start and throughout the move. Also, maintain the arch in your lower back by tightening your entire core.
- Making sure the bar tracks very close to your legs, bend at the hips to lower the bar down to shin level. If the bar drifts too far forward in front of you, you're risking a back injury.
- At the bottom, flex your hamstrings and glutes to bring your body back to an upright position.
- The downward motion should be slow and deliberate; the upward portion should be explosive but controlled.
- At the top, don't lean too far back or rest. Instead, rise powerfully to the upright position, then go right into another slow downward motion without hesitation.

I've found that about five sets of anywhere from 3–50 (yes, 50) repetitions, depending on your goal, works best. Avoid using a "false" grip (the powerlifting over-and-under grip). Instead, use wraps or hooks if you have to, as the false grip causes some shoulder asymmetry issues. Finally, as with any motion that flexes or extends the hip (the body's largest hinge), watch for what I call systemic draining; in essence, it's a move that's usually very taxing on your energy reserves. As with heavy squats, you may require more rest after performing Romanian deadlifts compared to other less-demanding motions.

The Routines

These workouts are built to attack your hams at both the hip and knee joint, a necessary tact for complete development.

Beginner Hamstring Workout No. 1: The simplest routine begins with lying leg curls to warm things up and only then introduces Romanian deadlifts.

Exercise	Set	Reps	Weight (pounds)
Lying Leg Curl	1	25	40
	2	20	50
	3	15	60
	4	12-15	70
Romanian Deadlift	1	20	45 (unweighted Olympic bar)
	2	15	95
	3	12	135

Intermediate Hamstrings Workout No. 2: This is my pick for one of the best hamstrings routines for overall size, strength and muscular density that you can do at nearly any level of experience. You can start doing it with only intermediate experience, yet it's a routine that can get you results over many years of training.

Exercise	Set	Reps	Weight (pounds)
Romanian Deadlift	1	20	45 (unweighted Olympic bar)
	2	15	135
	3	12	185
	4	10	225
	5	10	225
	6	8-10	275
Lying Leg Curl	1	20	50
	2	15	70
	3	15	100
	4	12-15	110

Advanced Hamstrings Workout No. 3: Due to the attention to splitting and carving the muscles, this more advanced routine should really only be done once you have achieved the mass on the posterior aspect of the thighs that you're looking for.

Exercise	Set	Reps	Weight
Romanian Deadlift	1	20	45
	2	15	135
	3	12	185
	4	10	225
	5	10	275

Exercise	Set	Reps	Weight
Lying Leg Curl	1	20	50
	2	15	80
	3	12	110
Seated Leg Curl Machine	1	15	80
	2	12	120
	3	10–12	140

Wrap-Up: Top 5 Ham-Training Tips

1. Hamstrings shouldn't be an afterthought.

Don't be one of those guys who sticks a couple of hamstrings sets at the end of a hardcore quad routine and calls it a day. Strong hams are essential to the overall look of your legs, as well as for healthy knees and optimal athletic performance. So train them with the same seriousness you give all other body parts.

2. Stretch the hams thoroughly after each workout.

Inflexible hams are a precursor to injury, while flexible hams enhance development. My favorite stretch for this area is an alternating split-stance stretch (one leg forward, one back) — from a standing position, lean forward with your hands reaching down the front leg. Hold for a count of 10, then switch legs.

3. Try combining back or traps with hams as a workout.

I've always found this coupling of body parts to be an outstanding combination. Since the upper back and traps are both stressed during the stiff-legged deadlift, they compliment each other in a therapeutic way.

4. Use both a flexed and extended foot angle when doing leg curls.

Pointing the toe either up (dorsiflexion) or down (plantar flexion) can have a profound effect on ham contraction. When my feet are pointed up, I feel a "fatter" hamstrings contraction higher on my leg. When pointed down, I feel a deeper contraction lower in my hams, along with some action in my calves.

5. Walking lunges also work your hams.

Most people think of walking lunges as a quad movement and, although that may be true, if your steps are long enough and you go down deep, you'll stimulate your hams as well. Along with Romanan deadlifts, this is one of my favorite hamstring and glute movements. Just make sure your quads are fully recovered from their workout, because they'll surely catch a bit of a beating.

CALVES

The muscles of your lower leg are specially constructed with one thing in mind — rep after rep after endless rep. Walking or running, the calves are called upon every step of the way. No wonder, then, that they're some of the densest muscle tissue we find ourselves up against when training for size.

The thick, resilient calves need a consistent, exacting pounding to grow. Light weight and endless reps aren't going to break through — your calves are built to withstand thousands of steps per day, supporting your bodyweight, so how can a few half-hearted sets of calf raises make a dent?

Like traps, you won't find a lot of variety in calf training. Your calves flex and extend the foot — you can either do this in a knees-straight position (standing calf raise, leg-press calf raise or the donkey calf raise), or in a seated, knees-bent position (the seated calf raise). Cover both options over the course of your training and you're golden.

Standing Raises

The standing calf raise activates the gastrocnemius, which makes up the bulk of your overall calf mass. When the knees are straight, the gastroc activates during foot movement.

A barbell across your shoulders or traditional standing calf-raise machine (with pads that sit across your shoulders) are best, because such a position focuses the most stress directly over the center of the calves, as opposed to other movements whose stimulation is less direct. The donkey calf raise machine and doing raises on a leg press also work, as long as you don't bend your knees during reps.

This is how to perform a standing raise:

- Stand holding a barbell balanced over your traps, or step in so your shoulders are squarely under the pads of a standing calf raise machine.
- With the balls of your feet on a raised surface, such as a step, and keeping your knees straight, lower your heels to stretch your calves as far as you can.
- Press upward on the balls of your feet as high as possible.

Seated Raises

When you bend your knees, the smaller soleus muscle takes on the majority of the workload when you flex and extend your feet. While not as critical to overall lower-leg size as the gastroc, if you want a complete physique, you need to blast them both. That's where the seated leg press comes into play, as a secondary movement to a standing exercise:

- Sit in a seated calf raise machine with your knees under the pads, or sit at the end of a flat bench and place heavy dumbbells on your thighs (flat ends against your legs).
- Place the balls of your feet on the edge of the platform or a raised surface, release the safety lock (if you're on a machine) and lower your heels to the floor until you feel a good stretch in your calves.
- Pause, then push through the balls of your feet to raise your heels as high as you can.

The Routines

Note that I see little point in distinguishing between beginner, intermediate and advanced routines when it comes to calves. Unlike other muscles, calf training is fairly straightforward and the rules don't change much from one level of experience to the next. Barring the tips I'm going to give you, either they grow or they don't. So no matter what routine you choose, in order to find out if they're going to grow or not, you have to rely on a great deal of muscular overload. It's for that reason I like doing only one exercise per workout, using multiple sets. That way you can pour all your focus and intensity into that movement, knowing that when you're done with it, your workout is complete. However, some days you need to bring the soleus into play, which is the function of the second workout option that involves two exercises.

Calf Workout No. 1: This simple routine is all about the standing calf raise, so you can smack the gastroc with all you've got.

Exercise	Set	Reps	Weight (pounds)
Standing Calf Raise*	1	15	50
	2	15	100
	3	15	200
	4	15	200
	5	12	250
	6	15	180
Seated Calf Raise	1	25	90
	2	15	140
	3	12	180

*Can be done on the Smith machine or using the regular standing calf machine.

Calf Workout No. 2: You'll give your gastroc and soleus ample attention here.

Exercise	Set	Reps	Weight
Donkey Calf-Raise Machine	1	15	50
	2	15	100
	3	15	150
	4	12	200
	5	12	250
Standing Single-Legged Calf Raise	1	25*	Bodyweight
	2	25*	Bodyweight
	3	25*	Bodyweight

* Per leg.

Wrap-Up: Top 10 Calf-Training Tips

1. Train the calves with both extremes of heavy and light weight.
Calves, especially stubborn ones, respond remarkably well to heavy-weight, overload training sessions (as much weight as you can handle while still doing about 12 reps), alternated with less frequent, lighter sessions (with reps as high as 50).

2. Make standing single-legged work part of your routine.
You don't need any added weight for this motion. Simply use a step or the edge of the spotting platform on the back of a bench and rep one foot at a time. Isolating each calf allows you to identify which calf is weaker and/or smaller and focus on equaling them out.

3. Do partial repetitions to reach failure.

Negatives and forced reps are cumbersome and unnecessary given the limitations of the range of motion. For added intensity, calves respond favorably to partial-repetition overload without easily slipping over the line into overtraining. Just be sure you complete as many reps as possible in a full range of motion before you resort to partials.

4. Stretch your calves thoroughly.

As with hamstrings, inflexible calves limit development and are a precursor to injury. Take time to stretch this area after the training session.

5. Point your feet forward.

Many used to believe that going pigeon-toed versus duck-footed developed the outside and inside of the calves, respectively. Although recent research seems to give some credence to the theory that by pointing your toes in, you slightly emphasize the lateral gastrocnemius, and turning them out, you work the medial head, the influence of these positions in my opinion is minimal. If either your inner or outer calves are lacking, try what the old guru Vince Gironda taught me for standing raises — shift your weight inside or outside by rolling your feet slightly. Give it time and you'll get the hang of it. Just keep them pointed straightforward in the process.

6. Minimize rest between sets.

The calves are thick, and to get to the deeper fibers you can't slack off. Excessive rest between sets really takes away from the effectiveness of the workout. Don't rest any longer than 30 seconds between sets, or you may "ice up" (my term for getting cold and losing your pump from too much rest).

7. Squeeze hard at the top of the repetition.

Contracting the calves hard at the top of each rep promotes muscular density and stimulates growth. Enjoy every bit of benefit by squeezing hard at the top; don't just leisurely pass through this valuable part of the set.

8. Now and then, skip the sneakers.

If the manager or gym owner where you train doesn't have a heart attack when you take off your sneakers, give it a whirl every once in a while. Training your calves without shoes gives you a different feel and can add a further dimension of intensity to your routine. Arnold himself trained in bare feet a lot, as you see in many of his black-and-white training shots.

9. Do reps in the double digits.

I consider a heavy, complete set of calves to be no less than 10 reps. Piling the weight on so much that you fall short of that is just a waste of time. Remember that calves are perhaps the densest skeletal muscle in the body, so you need to put up quite a fight to get them to respond. Striving for a higher-rep scheme while going to your strength limits is a method of attacking the problem from two sides at once.

10. Power past the burn.

When calves are done correctly, they burn. Some people terminate the set at the first onset of this sensation, while others know that just beyond that burn lies the growth zone. Don't give in when the heat's on — suck it up and continue moving through a full range of motion, all the while letting the fire build inside your calf muscles. Stop when the muscles actually give out, and not at the first sign lactic acid is kicking in.

18 ABDOMINALS

Could the proverbial washboard midsection be the single most beneficial body part to have? I think so, and many would agree. At the beach, big guns, rhinoceros quads and giant pecs manage to only turn a few heads, but the real scene-stealer is a set of chiseled abs.

Apart from abs, you could have the most incredibly developed body parts and still look like crap. On the contrary, washboard abs simply look spectacular on absolutely anybody. Amazing, isn't it? Case in point — in past summers I spent time with some friends on the beach in Hampton Bay. The women we hung out with were really into the fitness scene, but it was interesting who caught their attention. The juiced-up, bulked-out bodybuilder types would walk by and not even net a glance, their soft or distended midsections turning off the girls like a light switch. However, it was interesting to see the double-takes when this scrawny college wrestler with nothing on his frame but a killer set of abs came by.

Finding Your Abs

To burn through unwanted belly fat and reveal the diamond-hard six-pack underneath, diet plays the lead role. You can do all the ab training you want, but if you're fat, you need to lose the excess weight through a strict diet and an uptick in your cardio. (For dietary guidelines to lose body fat, refer back to Section 1 of this text.)

I should also just touch briefly on the concept of "spot reduction." Despite all the press decrying spot reduction as impossible, millions still buy into the idea, literally, by buying products built around crunch-type movements from stores and via infomercials. Hear this loud and clear — you cannot crunch your midsection body fat away. A million reps of any ab exercise won't peel away the fat. At best, it will tone and strengthen the abdominal muscles beneath the flab, but seeing the results of that hard work is a question of burning calories through cardio and dietary restriction. Having a good, simple ab routine is part of the overall equation, but this is one body part that's critically dependent on proper eating.

Quashing The Crunch

Before I tell you what movements I do use during ab workouts, let me tell you a common one I don't recommend too much of: Standard on-the-floor crunches. Five years of mixed martial arts and submission fighting taught me that crunches are not a very functional movement, because they don't require hip flexion. Furthermore, their focus is almost entirely on the upper abdomen — an area that's fairly easy to develop — as opposed to the lower abdomen — a far more stubborn area that's often neglected. So though a little bit of traditional crunches are good, building your whole ab routine around them is a big mistake.

The moves I prefer incorporate some degree of hip flexion, and target that lower-ab region. First, a modified reverse crunch — the difference from a regular crunch being that you straighten your legs on the descent, and bend your knees on the ascent, versus keeping your knees bent throughout:

- Lie on the floor with your hands at your sides. Slightly raise your heels an inch or two off of the floor, legs straight.
- Bring your knees toward your chest while allowing your knees to passively flex. Your lower back should curl slightly off of the floor.
- Straighten your legs as you lower them back down; stop them just before they touch the floor and go into your next rep.

Next, the modified reverse crunch with inward rotation:

- Lie on the floor with your arms and hands at your sides. Slightly raise your heels an inch or two off of the floor.
- Open your legs as you bring your knees toward your chest. Again, your lower back should curl slightly off of the floor.
- When you get your knees close to your chest, bring your knees and feet back together as you extend and lower your legs back down to the ground.

This should create an inward circular motion at the hips.

And finally, the modified reverse crunch with outward rotation:

- Lie on the floor with your arms and hands at your sides. Slightly raise your heels an inch or two off of the floor.
- Bring your knees up toward your chest while allowing your knees to passively flex, your lower back curling off of the floor.
- At the top of the motion, spread your knees and feet apart and out to the sides as you extend and lower them. This should create an outward circular motion at the hips.

The Routines

Both of these routines nail the lower abs (which in turn stimulates upper abs as well), with the second a more advanced option and one I prefer because it incorporates so much more of your core muscle.

Beginner Ab Workout No. 1: The simple sit-up is so often overlooked in favor of trickier movements and fancy machines. Yet, when done correctly, few other movements result in the time-tested development offered by the sit-up. You can use a sit-up board or bench, or just do them off the floor. Keep in mind that they must be done slowly and strictly while feeling the muscle contract. It should be just like training any other bodypart. It's not time to rest, slack off, or let your mind wander like so many do when they get to abs.

Exercise	Set	Reps
Sit-Up	1	15-25
	2	15-25
	3	15-25
Crunch	1	50
Straight-Leg Raise	1	50

Intermediate and Advanced Ab Workout No. 2: Here, the level of difficulty is significantly increased. The forced multidirectional flexion of the hips provides far greater functionality along with development. Make sure you move your legs in a slow and controlled fashion throughout a full range of motion.

Exercise	Set	Reps
Modified Reverse Crunch	1	15-25
	2	15-25
	3	15-25

Exercise	Set	Reps
Modified Reverse Crunch w/ Inward Leg Rotation	1	25
	2	25
	3	25
Modified Reverse Crunch w/ Outward Leg Rotation	1	25
	2	25
	3	25

Wrap-Up: Top 10 Ab-Training Tips

1. Focus on the lower abs.

Building the upper abs is relatively easy, since almost every ab motion involves a contraction of the upper region. The majority of ab exercises work the upper abs at the cost and neglect of the lower abs. Meanwhile, even exclusive training of the lower abs will still result in impressive upper-ab development.

2. Reverse crunches and reverse crunch variations are the most ideal exercises for abs.

I started doing variations of reverse crunches only in recent years, but have found them to be more effective for abdominal development then anything I've ever done. By flexing the hip and rotating the legs, you engage so much more muscle. They do so much for functional strength because they demand that you use the entire anterior core to propel the legs up and knees toward your chest. Rotating the legs both inward and outward add a critical variation. This motion holds the key to good midsection development — it stresses the bulk of the central muscle of the abdomen, called the rectus abdominis, with an emphasis on the lower area.

3. Don't rep yourself into oblivion.

Frequently, people go crazy with repetitions, doing dozens or even hundreds per set for their abs. After a certain point, you stop stimulating and start annihilating. Overuse of these muscles in such sequence can lead to overtraining and injuries like the common epigastric hernia (a tear in the tissue in the center of the abdomen that connects the two sides of the rectus abdominis called the linea alba). Granted, abs do require a slightly higher rep scheme than your average body part. However, I tend to keep my reps to 25 or less while instead increasing the level of difficulty with either added resistance (such as a dumbbell held between your feet on leg raises) or a steeper bench angle.

4. Don't twist.
While twisting motions might seem like a great way to warm up or start your abs routine, they're actually quite dangerous and of little benefit. For example, holding a stick across your back and twisting is a good way to expose the lumbar spine to disc injury (the worst is in the seated position, where your lower body is fixed, thus translating the greatest amount of torque to the lumbar region). Although I'm not opposed to slight rotations from a sit-up or crunch position to emphasize the upper obliques every once in a while, this in no way represents a "twist" to me in the true sense of the word.

5. Avoid side bends.
The abdominal muscles, like other muscles, will grow with the stimulus of resistance training. If your goal is a small waist, you don't want to overdevelop muscles that will give you a wider appearance. Unfortunately, doing dumbbell side bends with weight will do just that, stimulating the muscles of the external obliques, located in the lower outer abdominal region. When excessively stimulated by resistive training, these muscles can grow and make your waist look wide and blocky. I always cringe when I see some guy pick up a dumbbell and do side bends.

6. Squeeze and flex your abs.
One of the big mistakes you can make with abdominal training for bodybuilding purposes is not to flex the muscles as you train them. Too many people just go through the movements without squeezing hard. They view the ab session as an afterthought where they can just coast. Provide the same attention as you would any other body part you want to develop.

7. Maintain a slow descent.
As with any other exercise I teach, your descent should be slow and controlled, relative to your faster positive (concentric) motion. This is key when attempting to dig deep into the fibers of the abs and really sculpt them.

8. Don't do forced reps or negatives.
These advanced training principles may work for other body parts, but for abs it's overkill. You'll gain no added benefit to having a partner help you through forced reps or resistance-based negative ab training. Implementing such tactics will give you no edge, and is almost a surefire way to get hurt.

9. Train your abs with more intensity but less frequency.

Too often I see overzealous fitness freaks training their abs every day. They tend to forget that the abdominals are just like other muscles, in that they need rest to recuperate and improve. Although the abs can be exposed to a bit more frequency in terms of the number of times you train them in a week when compared to other body parts, training them any more than two to three times each week is excessive.

10. Whenever possible, get a partner to train abs with you.

Ab training gets a little monotonous. Because the rep scheme is higher, training frequency is greater, and you use no or very little resistance, your effort and intensity level can naturally get a little flat. I avoid this by grabbing a partner to run through my workout with me. This makes it more fun, and a healthy competition between you and your partner can boost your intensity.

SECTION III

BEYOND THE EXTREME

ANABOLIC STEROIDS

Building a big, muscular physique with low levels of body fat is a dream that becomes a reality when hard work, dieting and attention to the details of one's lifestyle are correctly factored into the equation. However, the temptation to take shortcuts is inevitable. It's human nature. We all want to get to the finish line before the next guy. Sometimes shortcuts work out for you, but sometimes they end up exerting a cost far greater then the toll of the original road you were on.

This is especially true when it comes to taking the concept of bodybuilding to its utmost levels. Bodybuilders are extremists by definition, so shortcuts don't scare them. Some of us choose to press our luck beyond the extremes of our natural boundaries by using drugs. It's just a reality of the sport.

Steroid use isn't an issue of good or bad, or right versus wrong. Nature doesn't care about that. It's just balance. Every action must have an equal and opposite reaction, as a part of the biological law. It's akin to my belief in the balance of nature, how every natural illness has a natural cure out there somewhere.

In that way, a decision to take shortcuts will have a consequence. I'm not saying that shortcuts don't sometimes work out at the time you take them. Rather, I argue that a proportionate price is always paid, whether the price is immediately evident or whether it's settled later on in life. Furthermore, the compensatory reaction for one's action is not always evident in the same physical realm. Sometimes the cost of a physical shortcut is felt in the psychological or social realm.

The harder you push life, the harder it pushes back. Whatever temporary glory they provide, shortcuts don't matter because it all evens out in the end. Balance will always be restored.

T Time

Without a doubt, the most commonly attempted shortcut in bodybuilding for extreme muscle enhancement is anabolic steroid abuse. In an effort to convey as much honest information as possible in a concise manner, I'll cover only the more common steroids.

I begin with the parent molecule of all anabolic steroids, testosterone, the defining male sex hormone. In men, about 8 milligrams of natural (also known as "endogenous") testosterone is produced, 95 percent of which comes from cells in the testicles called interstitial cells of Leydig. The remaining 5 percent is produced by the adrenal glands (small glands located above each kidney). Women also produce small amounts of testosterone in their ovaries and adrenal glands, but the normal serum concentrations are relatively low (i.e., on the order of about 0.03 micrograms per dL).

The effects of testosterone can be divided into two categories. The first is the androgenic effect of testosterone. This effect influences the body by enhancing the secondary male sex characteristics of aggression, hair growth, libido and deepening of the voice, among others. Hence, anyone with naturally low serum testosterone coupled with a depressed sexual desire can use testosterone quite effectively to spark his sexual drive. The androgenic qualities of supplemental testosterone are used quite effectively in cases of hypogonadism, impotence and stunted growth.

On the other hand, the bodybuilder and strength athlete cares little about these secondary effects. Rather, they are far more interested in the anabolic aspect of testosterone, involving tissue repair and recuperation. In fact, the very term "anabolic" refers to tissue repair and growth.

This is in sharp contrast to the catabolic steroids (i.e., cortisone, cortisol, solumedrol, prednisone, kenelog, dexamethasone, etc.). The term catabolic, as previously discussed, refers to tissue breakdown. Thus, only an idiot would think of using a catabolic steroid to build muscle. If you're wondering why they're used so commonly in athletes, it's because the powerful anti-inflammatory effects of these substances can eliminate pain and swelling to injured soft tissue. (Of course, that hardly means they speed recovery time. The medical community is currently split in terms of whether or not giving catabolic steroids can actually slow recovery and actually weaken tissue. But that's a discourse for another day.) The important point to take from this is to not confuse a catabolic steroid with an anabolic steroid; remember that they do different things.

While not a catabolic steroid, testosterone is both anabolic and androgenic. As early as the 1940s, athletes used testosterone for the purpose of performance enhancement. But understand that the improvement in these individuals afforded by testosterone's anabolic index stems mainly from the subsequent accelerated recuperative capacity. Such capacity condenses training time and effectively packs years of training into what could amount to only months.

Testosterone comes in several forms. The most common route of testosterone administration among bodybuilders and athletes is via the intramuscular route. The intramuscular route has one major advantage over the oral route — far less liver toxicity. You see, oral steroids must be absorbed through the gastrointestinal tract and thus undergo what we physicians call "first-pass metabolism." In so doing, oral steroids beat the heck out of the liver before they ever get distributed around the body through the bloodstream.

Among the testosterones, the best oral example to illustrate my point is Halotestin™. Also known as fluoxymesterone, this oral testosterone preparation is known to be pretty tough on the liver when taken in "street" dose (i.e., almost invariably exceeding the maximum recommended 20 milligrams per day). In fact, years back I recall an amateur bodybuilder who came to see me and said he was taking 160 milligrams per day of Halotestin™! I remember telling him that I didn't know anyone could take that much Halotestin™ and live to tell about it. His liver was profoundly screwed up; I warned him that there was nothing I could do for him and that if he didn't stop, his liver would eventually fail. He heeded my warning, stopped the pills, and after about a year, amazingly, his liver function normalized. I consider him pretty damn lucky, but I don't believe he's out of harm's way yet since he could one day develop liver cancer as a result of the abuse.

In contrast to the oral route, intramuscular injection delivers the drug directly into the muscle belly. By this route, the drug is gradually absorbed into the blood stream and is distributed throughout the body, ostensibly being less toxic to the liver.

Intramuscular injections are not without their own risks and problems. If you don't practice a strictly sterile technique, you risk abscess formation and even serious infection. Personally, I've treated more than my share of abscesses due to this kind of bumbling. Most end up on a fairly lengthy course of very powerful antibiotics, while others even necessitate surgery to remove the infected tissue pocket. Not a pretty sight, believe me.

In addition, it's unclear what the long-term consequences are of repeated injections. We know that calcium deposits begin to form deep in the muscle belly at the point of injection. These deposits are oftentimes easily seen on plain x-ray and are dead giveaways to heavy past users. Whether such a practice predisposes someone to more serious illness is unclear at this time. I doubt this, but I do recall a troubling case.

The case involved a fairly well known 26-year-old competitive bodybuilder from New York who shall remain nameless. He had an unusually long, continuous history of injection-based steroid use. In fact, he had been injecting himself on a weekly basis since he was 18 years old! He also practiced yet another age-old foolish method called "target muscle" injection. This involves injecting your steroid into the smallest or weakest muscle on your body in an effort to make it respond better.

In short, if you're considering this method, don't do it. Regardless of what your local self-proclaimed bodybuilding guru claims, this site-specific method offers absolutely no added benefit over the conventional gluteal route, and only increases the risk of complication. In the case of the bodybuilder I took care of, after years of "shooting his quads," he started complaining of leg pain at the site of his injections. Sadly, he was diagnosed with a rare cancer called leiomyosarcoma.

To this day, I remain unsure whether his problems resulted from his continuous drug use coupled with his site-specific injection method, or whether this case was simply one of rare statistical coincidence. Either way, he ended up hospitalized, as his condition necessitated both surgical intervention to cut tumors out of his legs and heavy doses of radiation therapy. He never made the magazines again, and the emotional baggage he carries from swinging from one extreme to another in terms of his body image still torments him.

In all fairness, this horror story is not the norm. By far, the majority of steroid users via injection rarely see any significant complications beyond a sore ass. And, in terms of injectable testosterone, despite the many different types available, life-threatening side effects are undeniably few and far between.

On the street, the most popular among these testosterone injectables are testosterone cypionate (also known as depo-testosterone) and testosterone enanthate. Like nearly all testosterones, they are both highly androgenic and highly anabolic. They are favored forms because of the relatively long-acting nature of these compounds. In other words, unlike testosterone propionate, which must be injected 2–3 times each week, the longer-acting forms need only be injected every 2–4 weeks.

In addition to testosterone propionate, other short-acting testosterone preparations of less popularity are the aqueous forms. Known by names such as histerone, testamone and testandro, these compounds are less favored on the street. The problems go beyond the annoyance and increased relative risk of high-frequency injection, extending to androgenic side effects. Few bodybuilders that use these forms wait longer than two days between injections, resulting in an overlap of dosages, increasing the levels of dangerous androgens in the body. The method oftentimes results in gynecomastia (also known as "bitch tits," an abnormal growth of male breast tissue) in an unusually rapid amount of time. In contrast, the long-acting forms don't create a steady state of androgens between injections (they tend to tail off), ostensibly giving the steroid receptors a small rest from over-stimulation.

Roid Rundown

Whether injected or oral, and regardless of the preparation, testosterone (the parent molecule of all anabolic steroids) is hardly the only physique-enhancing drug available. In fact, between underground channels in the U.S., Europe, South America and the Middle East, there so many different forms created and distributed that they're impossible to keep track of. To understand why so many different derivative compounds based on the parent testosterone molecule exist, one must first understand the "method to the madness" of creating these new substances.

To begin with, recall that testosterone is both highly androgenic and highly anabolic. Also, beyond enhanced libido and mood, most of the negative side effects of the testosterones are related to the androgenicity of these preparations. Thus, scientists and researchers have developed synthetic testosterone derivatives in an attempt to minimize the androgenicity and maximize the anabolic effects. Simply stated, these other anabolic steroids are substances in which scientists take the testosterone molecule as a skeleton, then add side chains of mostly carbon atoms or "ligands" to the basic structure. This can greatly change the molecule's properties. Such preparations are discussed in the passages that follow.

Nandrolone decanoate: Perhaps the best known of these preparations, nandrolone decanoate is by far the most popular. It's what we call a derivative of 19-nortestosterone. Such synthetic modification has produced a substance that, unlike testosterone, has only a moderate level of androgenicity, while preserving powerful anabolic properties. Thus, the side-effects tend to be minimal while its recuperative characteristics, in the form of mass and strength building, are intact.

From a medical standpoint, the official indicated use for nandrolone decanoate is almost strictly for cases of anemia of renal insufficiency, and little else. This is because of its powerful ability to stimulate an increase in hemoglobin and red blood cell mass; use for any other purpose is not recommended by the drug companies.

Still, this doesn't stop the massive flow of this largely American-made drug into the marketplace. Nandrolone decanoate via injection is one of the most common anabolic steroids I see both bodybuilders and athletes taking today, not only because of its high relative anabolic profile and low relative toxicity, but also because it's both long acting and known for strengthening joints, tendons and ligaments. In bodybuilding, nandrolone decanoate usually serves as the foundation of a drug regimen with other injectable or oral drugs "stacked" on top of its use. It's seldom used alone.

Some warnings to consider. Since nandrolone decanoate isn't very androgenic, coupled with the fact that the aspect of a 19-nor or any 19-nor derivative will actually suppress one's own natural production of testosterone, use of this drug could result in annoying symptoms when taken over many months or years. The symptoms include a blunting of your sex drive and decreased aggressiveness. In addition, although rarer than with testosterone derivatives, the side effects of gynecomastia, acne, increased cholesterol and edema (water retention) are still common enough with these drugs.

The last big problem with nandrolone decanoate involves its relatively long-lasting metabolites. This presents a great problem for the competitive athlete subjected to randomized testing. If you plan on taking nandrolone decanoate by itself, as long as you don't mind risking these problems and you don't mind putting your sex life on hold for a bit, then I wish you luck. Otherwise, you can stack it, but then you're back to basically the same thing as taking testosterone, except you'll be using synthetic derivatives.

Sustanon: Like nandrolone decanoate and most of the testosterones mentioned, sustanon is an injectable substance. But unlike these drugs, it isn't made in the United States. In fact, the majority of sustanon available in America comes from Europe (primarily Holland), and is smuggled into the country, finding its way to the black market for mass distribution.

Notoriety aside, sustanon consists of four different anabolic steroids: the rapid-onset and short-acting testosterone propionate, the fairly rapid-onset but long-acting testosterone phenylpropionate and testosterone isocaproate, as well as the slow-onset and long-acting testosterone decanoate. Thus, it's what I call "a built-in stack."

It has gained enormous popularity in recent years since it acts quickly (good for those impatient guys who can't wait the usual five weeks before they start seeing results), yet lasts fairly long. Another "advantage" of this built-in stack is that it frees you from high-frequency injections while giving you fast yet long-lasting action. But don't for a minute think that this stops your average muscle head from listening to their cronies and stacking it with another drug anyway.

The truth is, with sustanon, you may suffer the same dangerous side effects as with any of the drugs mentioned. Add to that, a fairly common problem with sustanon, as with many other foreign-made drugs like primobolin and parabolin, is it tends to come in low-quality, scored glass vials or in pre-filled glass syringes. In the U.S., we rarely dispense drugs like this because of the inherent danger. You see, the vials are scored on the neck and require you to literally break off the top to get to the drug. You then have to dump a syringe into the barrel, suck out the contents of the drug along with microscopic pieces of glass, and introduce that swill into your body. It's a sick scene if you ask me, one right out of a crack house.

Dianabol: As a general rule of thumb, taking steroids is dangerous enough, but once you start taking drugs that aren't, at the very least, approved for use in America, you're exposing yourself to incredible risk. In America, drug manufacturing and preparation for human consumption is strictly monitored and heavily regulated. Once you step outside of U.S. control, quality production standards immediately come into question. You can never be sure whether a substance made in a foreign country not approved by the U.S. was produced under sterile conditions.

Over the years, bodybuilders have shown me some pretty scary labels and package inserts. I remember one fellow from a gym on Long Island who asked me about a drug called dianabol. I told him that it was once made in the U.S. and was quite popular in the 1960s and early 70s because of the massive strength and size gains it caused. Unfortunately for the powerlifting and Olympic weight-lifting circuit who relied heavily on this oral drug, it was extremely liver toxic. Shortly thereafter, the drug was discontinued with the advent of relatively safer oral drugs like Anavar™ (which also was later discontinued), Winstrol™ (the pill form), and Halotestin™. With that, he reached into his pocket and produced a labeled bottle with a dubious package insert.

The word "Dianabol" was photocopied in English, while the rest of the sloppy label contained only Russian characters. Whether this was concocted in a Russian drug house, or not in Russia at all, couldn't be determined. A major Russian pharmaceutical company certainly didn't make it. It was obviously a fake of the lowest order, and I shudder to think of the kind of heinous crap that was in that bottle. I had to tell the poor bastard that he wasted his money.

Very few sources of real dianabol (or "D-ball," as it's frequently called) exist. The few sources are all in foreign countries and the product is exceedingly difficult to get into the U.S. Any coconut from the gym who tells you he has real dianabol is probably, at the very least, misguided. Interestingly, though very little real dianabol gets into the country, counterfeits from Mexico and Panama seem to pass over the borders rather easily.

Meanwhile, occasionally the black market gets flooded with so-called dianabol. My theory is that it's probably made in somebody's basement, and is at best likely nothing but testosterone of some kind mixed with a bunch of impurities. These clever pushers are capitalizing on a reputation of legendary proportions. It seems that anything banned or no longer available has a certain "forbidden fruit" temptation to it — so is the story of dianabol.

Anavar™: Although still made by some very legitimate pharmaceutical companies in Europe under the name "Oxandrolone," Anavar ™ production in the U.S. ceased back in the 1980s; now it's marketed here as "Oxandrin™." Any American Anavar™ you see nowadays is without a doubt a counterfeit.

Anavar™, an oral drug, was enormously popular with bodybuilders and strength athletes largely because of its relatively low androgenic index (thus fewer side effects), while its results in producing strength and size gains were said to be unparalleled among oral agents. Anavar™ also developed a reputation among the competitive sector of bodybuilders as being a favorable precontest drug because of its minimal effect on water retention.

Traditionally, bodybuilders would rarely use Anavar™ alone, instead preferring to stack it with other drugs. Popular Anavar™ stacks included combining it with injectable testosterone, deca-durobolin, primobolin or parabolin. Among the profoundly idiotic, a popular combination was a "monster stack" combining two of these injectables with both Anavar™ and dianabol. Of the population stupid enough to test these limits, I've seen a relatively large number become quite ill and even die.

Despite its black market popularity, Anavar™ fell out of favor in the medical community and was eventually replaced. It seems that this relatively small 2.5-milligram tablet provided only minimal anabolic activity when compared to newer-generation drugs. In the form of Oxandrin™, the drug is still used in the U.S. to combat AIDS-related wasting and cases of unexplained weight loss, but among the medical set, Anavar™ has a somewhat limited usage from a true medicinal and therapeutic standpoint when compared with its successor, Anadrol™.

Anadrol™: This supposedly represents the next generation of oral anabolic steroids. If you thought Anavar™ was scary, get a load of this drug. Like Anavar™, Anadrol™ was also born in the U.S.A. Also known as oxymethelone, Anadrol™, by far the most potent oral anabolic steroid ever made, has a list of notorious side effects. This drug is liver toxic in the extreme when taken in the doses recommended by street dealers. In addition, Anadrol™ is considered to be "your ticket to the plastic surgeon" as it almost invariably results in gynecomastia.

The reason we see so many side effects associated with the use of Anadrol™ is related as much to dosage as to the chemistry of the drug itself. Street recommendations for the oral predecessor of Anadrol™, Anavar™, have passed down through generations of bodybuilders. Many took handfuls of Anavar™ each day, with most living to tell about it. Those word-of-mouth guidelines for Anavar™ dosing in terms of total number of pills is oftentimes applied to those taking Anadrol™. Since an Anavar™ pill is only 2.5

milligrams on average, whereas Anadrol™ is 50 milligrams each, taking five Anavar™ versus taking five Anadrol™ is quite different, to say the least. Sadly, most dumbbell dummies count pills, not milligrams.

From a medical standpoint, my feeling about Anadrol™ is that it's extremely dangerous and won't last much longer as a medicinal. In fact, its indicated use is for patients with intractable aplastic anemia. Of those hematologists that treat such cases, I know of few that use this drug. Thus, I can't see why the medical community viewed this drug as a "next generation" substance relative to Anavar™. Perhaps it was just propaganda from the pharmaceutical company. In any case, I believe that it's only a matter of time before the drug is discontinued and replaced by some other substance. Hopefully for patients it'll be an improvement, and not just the same old crap in a brand new but even more toxic pill.

Equipoise™: Turning our attention back to injectables, another enormously popular agent among bodybuilders and strength athletes is Equipoise™. A Latin term, the prefix "equi" refers to horses, as in "equine" or "equestrian." Why? It's a veterinary drug used in horses. That's right. It's not meant for human consumption. But, leave it to our insane weightlifting brethren to cross the line and start experimenting with animal drugs.

As a fairly potent testosterone derivative, Equipoise™ gained notoriety as an abuser favorite because of its powerful anabolic index. Unfortunately for those junkies, humans are not horses. Hence, it should come as no surprise that Equipoise™ has a tremendous liver toxicity in humans.

Real Equipoise™ is just about impossible to find on the street, while counterfeits are everywhere. In fact, the only time I ever saw a real bottle at the office of a friend (he was a licensed veterinarian), it didn't look anything like the trashy fakes that people have shown me over the years. On one hand, it's sort of a blessing, because I can't imagine how many people would be hurting themselves if they could get the real thing. On the other hand, it does leave me wondering exactly what it is they're putting into their bodies if it isn't real Equipoise™.

Winstrol™: Another popular injectable anabolic steroid, Winstrol™ (or stanozolol as it is also called) is also available in oral form. This water-based injectable is considered a street favorite because it's believed to be less toxic and great for cutting up. Unfortunately, nearly everyone involved with the use of this substance in bodybuilding has woefully misinterpreted its effects.

In my assessment, Winstrol™ isn't a good cutting drug. Although it does seem to cause the body to retain less water than some of the other drugs on the street, it doesn't cause the body to be more ripped. What I have seen in Winstrol™ abusers is a significant increase in vascularity beyond that of other drugs. The problem with this dramatic relative improvement in vascularity is that it can easily fool a competitor into thinking that they're more cut. The fact is, when they get onstage, despite the pronounced vascularity, they lack deep cuts and muscular detail that only comes with proper dieting. Guys like this look great in the gym but seem to be so much less impressive in competition; the so-called "benefits" just don't pan out.

Impending Breakthroughs

Of all the synthesized substances mentioned, from a standpoint of legitimate expanded use in the future, none of these derivatives compare to the parent molecule of testosterone. I believe that we have yet to scratch the surface in terms of what this miraculous substance can do as a possible anti-aging substance and use in combating male "andropause" (a moniker referring to the male equivalent of menopause). We have yet to unlock its great potential. But we must learn through medical and scientific research how to harness the great power of testosterone, so that we know how to maximize benefits and minimize risk. Until that time, however, reckless abuse may lead one to grave consequences.

Testosterone and other anabolic steroid derivatives do have true medicinal value. But, once brought out of the realm of treating real medical problems, results can be understandably unpredictable. In addition, the risk of taking anabolic steroids is great enough, but when black market supplies are limited and the desperate take chances with substances of unsure make-up and unclear origin, they risk major health calamity.

The reality of the situation is that, regardless of my desire to dissuade bodybuilders and athletes from using anabolic steroids, there will always be those who accept the risks without waiting for science to catch up. But that doesn't mean it's right. Despite my frank words in this chapter, I in no way condone the abuse of anabolic steroids. Taking anabolic steroids "street style" with no medical guidance, for the sole purpose of athletic or bodybuilding enhancement, should simply never be done.

Historical Perspectives

As a former competitive bodybuilder turned physician, with more than a couple of decades behind me in the sport, it's fascinating to look back and see how bodybuilding has changed relative to today. In particular, one of the most striking and controversial differences between past and present can be seen in the anabolic steroids that many of these athletes have taken and continue to take.

Widespread use of anabolic steroids really didn't flourish until the late

1960s and early 70s. The craze began with synthetic testosterone, which later spawned the production of literally hundreds of derivatives, all designed with the purpose of enhancing a particular characteristic of testosterone while hopefully minimizing harmful side effects.

Perhaps the biggest difference between the bodybuilders of old and those today is the element of "cycling" on and off the stuff. In the 70s, bodybuilders tended to focus using steroids around their prep for a show. Subsequently, they would either be "on" or "off" steroids. In those days, you could easily tell when a competitor was "on cycle" because you knew what he looked like without the juice coursing through his veins.

In contrast, competitive bodybuilders of today rarely go off the juice. If they stop, it's never for very long (usually no more than days to weeks between cycles). Often this hiatus is due to health problems, a temporary scrounge for drug money or personal problems. My experience tells me that many are afraid to lose what they perceive to be their "edge" over others. Some are just insecure and fearful of what they might end up looking like without the help of chemicals. Still others follow the lemmings in front of them over the cliff's edge because they simply know no other way.

As a result, newer age bodybuilders are, not surprisingly, far bigger and more ripped than their predecessors. Sadly, side effects have also expanded in equal proportion. Several bodybuilders I've seen as patients have already developed signs of early liver failure among other things. I recall a case of a professional bodybuilder in his 30s who was taking steroids without interruption ever since he was in his teens! He had a tumor removed from his head and is now suffering other problems.

The old timers never would have stayed on steroids with no break in sight. In the golden age of bodybuilding, the majority of athletes spent most of the year off of steroids. Maybe they were less experimental, or less greedy. Perhaps they just valued their lives and health more. But whatever the reasons, the difference is clear. We live at a time of extremes. As a result, the drug habits of abusers reflect this compulsion for the immoderate and outrageous.

As if an "inability" to go off cycle isn't bad enough, the next sharp anabolic steroid contrast between golden age and new age is dosage. In the old days, the mindset of the bodybuilders was to attempt to take just enough steroids to get them where they wanted to be and give them the look that they envisioned. It was not to see how far they could push it before their heads blew up. In other words, they had in their minds a notion of what they could look like with the edge provided by anabolic steroids. They had a realistic vision of what was achievable when combining chemical assistance with hard work.

Many of today's bodybuilders take as much juice as their bodies can tolerate, until something goes wrong. They tend to lack a vision of what they will end up looking like. Instead, they simply want to be monsters. They just want more.

The combination of different steroids, also known as "stacking," began with the advent of testosterone derivatives. What started as combining two substances for enhanced effect has taken on even uglier proportions. While bodybuilders from the heyday used to occasionally stack an injectable with an oral substance, it has become relatively commonplace for many of today's professionals to stack high doses of a multitude of orals with even higher doses of several injectables. In fact, one pro bodybuilder recently reported to me to be taking five different injectable substances with four different oral pills. Insane, yes, but sadly true.

The Old-School Mindset

Reliance on the efficacy of anabolic steroids and less on proper training and nutrition is a hallmark of contrast between the ages. They did not necessarily have it right as far as training and diet in the old days, but they sure tried. Hard work prevailed. For them, anabolic steroids were viewed as being adjunctive and a means to give you the edge you needed around contest time. You would scarcely find what has become so commonplace in gyms across America today — a weekend warrior with what really amounts to a lousy build, juiced up so he can strut around the beach or stretch a T-shirt to its limits.

With the shortcut that massive doses of steroids provide in terms of quick bulk and loss of fat, bodybuilders of today (especially younger ones) are using anabolic steroids almost as a primary tool in bodybuilding. In sharp contrast to viewing steroids as an accessory, too many now think they can let the juice do the work while not investing significant time into refining their physique via training and nutrition. They never end up learning their body, so when they're finally forced to go off steroids, everything they've gained disappears, because they haven't the foggiest notion of how to train their bodies in such a way to make them respond.

As a direct result of this over-reliance on steroids, few bodybuilders of today, even professionals, train as hard as they used to. I wish every bodybuilder could've experienced what I saw at Gold's in Venice in the 1980s. Back then, truly hard training sessions were as epidemic as drugs are today. Intensity and seriousness of purpose was the name of the game. If you need more convincing, make the journey at least once in your life to "The Mecca" otherwise known as Gold's Venice. Check out the old photos that adorn the walls; it's like a shrine to intensity. Classic shots like Dave Draper and Arnold pounding out shoulder presses, or Mike Mentzer doing intense arm curls, are just a taste of the images you'd see. They just scream back at you to dig your heels in and train harder. As bodybuilders rely more heavily on drugs and less on hard workouts, steroid abuse is slowly robbing us of that central concept of bodybuilding.

To Abuse Or Not To Abuse

I remember a guy named Rich, a part-time manager and trainer at a gym I frequented years ago. He was a big dude, a real heavyweight, and juiced to the gills. Often quoting scripture, Rich was a born-again Christian who frequently talked about how you should live your life. When he got himself going he was condescending and a bit too self-righteous. But that alone wasn't a problem for me; after all, I had my own weird quirks back then. I figured if that was his thing, so be it.

Though not a bad guy at all, it always struck me as ironic that he was heavily into steroids. It didn't make sense how this self-proclaimed, holier-than-thou Christian gym minister could possibly rationalize his juice use in the face of all those religious teachings he was espousing. When he came at me with his rap a little hard one morning, I couldn't resist raising the issue.

I wasn't too rough, or at least I didn't think so at the time. But I made the point just to send him a warning so he'd leave me alone. Anyway, it was the first time I ever saw him speechless. It was worse then if I just smacked him. He looked like he was actually going to cry. I was blown away by the fact that he had never thought of it himself, that somehow he was able to bury that issue in the back of his conscience and not deal with it.

If you feel close to your religion, don't go against your gut response. Don't ignore that little voice of reason, and don't pretend the reality doesn't exist, that your principles don't match your behavior. It is what it is. It's your decision whether you want to juice or not. As I see it, you can't honestly be on some deeply religious ethical plane and at the same time decide to abuse drugs. The two don't mix. It's hypocrisy, plain and simple.

To be blunt, I still find it ironic when a bodybuilding competitor is crowned as champ and he thanks God. Thank God for what? It's all you baby, and that means the good, the bad and the ugly. I guess I have trouble envisioning God standing proudly alongside our swollen champ, let alone having a hand in yet another synthetic victory.

If you do drugs, just recognize this incongruity and don't try to say it's God's will that you won or lost. It's you. Deal with it.

A Better Way

Rather than joining the juice-fest and mindlessly participating in the bodybuilding de-evolution that has taken place, I suggest a proactive evolution instead. Begin by adopting the golden age mindset of having a clear vision of how you want to look. Don't settle for a fuzzy notion of some unrealistic, cartoonish, pro-bodybuilder physique. Instead, look for lasting improvements in your build. Learn your body and take note of how it responds. Implement smart and intense workouts to achieve your goal. Rely on hardcore training as the cornerstone of your efforts, for in it lies the key to consistent improvement and lasting preservation of gains.

Finally, don't just be a complete throwback to the old days either. Borrow from them all that was good, and improve upon the bad. This is what I mean by evolution. In so doing, drop the idea of doing drugs completely and rely instead on nutritional science and dietary supplements as your tools of choice. It is my steadfast belief that the strides we've made in these areas in the last decade are nothing short of miraculous.

In fact, with careful attention to properly chosen dietary supplements and good nutrition, one can approach the "advantages" that adjunctive drug use provides in the short run. And over the long haul, I promise that such a natural course will give you results that surpass, in a lasting way, the rapidly fading blink of satisfaction that you might experience from abusing anabolic steroids.

20 TESTOSTERONE THERAPY

Sometimes testosterone is prescribed for middle-aged or younger men who complain of symptoms like waning libido, erectile dysfunction, a drop in appetite, unexplainable fatigue, lost muscle mass and lack of motivation.

If you suffer such symptoms, assuming your doctor investigates all other potential health problems, your testosterone levels should be checked. A testosterone level below the normal total range (about 280–1,100 ng/dL) could be the culprit. It's a condition otherwise known as hypogonadism; your body, for no clear reason, may simply not be producing enough testosterone. This chart shows the typical testosterone levels in a male:

Age	Normal Male Total Testosterone Ranges (ng/dL)
1-5 months	1-177
6 – 11 months	2–7
1 - 5 years	2–25
6 - 9 years	3–30
10 - 11 years	5–50
12 - 14 years	10–572
15 - 17 years	220–800
Adult (over 17 years old)	280–1,100

Droves of men each year seek physician care for an apparently unexplainable decrease in libido and/or erectile dysfunction, only to discover that their symptoms are attributable to low testosterone. A portion of these men improve dramatically with testosterone supplementation.

As far back as the 1800s, men have been experimenting with testosterone and successfully tapping into its power. Beginning in the 1950s, supplementation with testosterone moved from the clinical setting to the sporting arena, where the substance was abused with the purpose of enhancing performance in and/or recovery from athletic endeavors. In the decades that followed, testosterone and its chemical synthetic derivatives found a way into bodybuilding for the purpose of physique enhancement, where they remain to modern day.

In recent years, however, testosterone supplementation has gradually found its way back to the clinical setting, with a plethora of derivatives and delivery systems to choose from. When used properly in the ideal candidate and not abused, supplemental testosterone can work wonders.

Even if AIDS is your problem, which I hope it's not, testosterone supplementation may help relieve some of your symptoms. In particular, testosterone has been used successfully to dramatically reverse the muscular wasting that often accompanies the disease. Testosterone therapy not only improves the symptoms by increasing lean muscle mass and strength in these individuals, but also noticeably improves the subjective quality of their lives.

Testosterone treatment has also been noted in scientific literature to do everything from improving visual-spatial memory and countering clinical depression, to improving blood count and prognostic implications in diabetics and those with renal failure.

Test & The Risks

Even though testosterone has a legitimate role in the treatment of some libido problems, the reality is that testosterone therapy is rarely appropriate for treating impotence. In fact, only five percent of erectile dysfunction is due to true hypogonadism, yet upward of 20 percent of the treatments involve testosterone. This medical mismanagement probably has a great deal to do with reverse propaganda from aging male baby boomers looking for a fountain of youth and a proverbial ejaculatory fountain to go with it.

Apart from the all-too-commonplace inappropriate prescribing of testosterone, perhaps the biggest criticism of testosterone therapy involves the possible risk of prostate cancer. There are at least seven case reports on record of prostate cancer after testosterone therapy. If you need testosterone, that's fine, but you must keep an eye on your prostate specific antigen (PSA); this is a simple blood test your doctor can easily administer. However, at this point, it's fair to say that it's still debatable whether bringing a man's testosterone up to a level of clinical significance (where he feels a meaningful difference) can actually spur the growth of prostate cancer.

In terms of non-cancerous growth of the prostate, or benign prostatic hypertrophy (BPH), we're just beginning to understand the effects of testosterone. For those that think that testosterone patches are the way to go over the injectable method because they're so much less invasive and intimidating, you may have to think again. Research is emerging that points to the low physiologic doses leeched out via the patch method as possibly being linked to BPH more so than the injectable method, whose quick spiking action and rapid attenuation may in fact reduce the size of this gland. The final answer hasn't surfaced on this point yet, but hopefully it'll soon be revealed through science.

The question of coronary risk is also an issue for men of all ages when considering testosterone supplementation. Unfortunately, the current conventional wisdom is quite contradictory. Classically, physicians have held to the belief that testosterone may be bad for the heart. This assumption was and continues to be purely based on the apparent ability of estrogen (the female sex hormone) to increase healthy high-density lipoprotein (HDL) and decrease low-density lipoprotein (LDL). As a result, it was assumed that testosterone must do the opposite. A bold assumption, wouldn't you say? Actually, testosterone has never clearly, independently demonstrated any ill effect on the heart. Further, the current belief that somehow estrogen is "heart healthy" has recently been radically and competently turned upside down by solid research.

Continued use of even injected testosterone can affect the liver. Although far less harmful to the liver than orally-administered testosterones, which are absorbed and processed from the gastrointestinal tract directly into the liver, injections can still insult the liver. Even the supposedly safe, long-acting testosterones for injection (like testosterone enanthate, for example) are plagued with what we physicians call "pharmacokinetic" problems. In particular, a disturbance in liver function still occurs. Except in the most extreme cases, this disturbance is completely reversible upon cessation of testosterone, but we know little about possible complications years down the road (including liver cancer).

If you can accept all this and you really need long-term testosterone therapy, find a physician you trust and get periodic blood draws throughout the year. Liver function testing (AST/ALT) should be done every time. A PSA should be done at least once per year.

Blood Testing for Hypogonadism:

For initial diagnosis...

Primary Testing: *Total Testosterone, Free Testosterone*
Additional Testing: *Total Estrogens, Estradiol*

Optional Physician-Guided Tests: *Estrone, Estriol, Luteinizing Hormone (LH), 3rd Generation LH, Follicle Stimulating Hormone (FSH), 3rd Generation FSH, Dihydrotestosterone (DHT), Dihydrotestosterone (DHT) Free, Prolactin, Sex Hormone Binding Globulin*

For follow-up testing...

Primary Testing: *Total Testosterone, Free Testosterone Aspartate Aminotransferase (AST), Alanaine Aminotransferase (ALT)*
Additional Follow-Up Testing: *PSA*

Examples of Current Popular Testosterone Preparations:
(Routes of administration & common dosages)

Drug	Route	Dose
Fluoxymesterone (Halotestin™)	Oral	5–20 milligrams per day
Methyltestosterone	Oral	10–50 milligrams per day
Methyltest (Oreton Methyl)	Buccal	5–25 milligrams per day
AndroGel™ (one percent)	Gel	10–40 milligrams per dose
Androderm™	Patch	2 patches (5 milligrams) per day
Testoderm™	Patch	1 patch (4–6 milligrams) per day
Testopel™ Pellets	Subcutaneous	150–450 milligrams every 3 months
Testosterone Enanthate (long acting)	Injection	100–200 milligrams every 2-4 weeks
Testosterone Cypionate (long acting)	Injection	50–400 milligrams every 2-4 weeks
Histerone (short acting)	Injection	10–25 milligrams, 2–3 times per week
Tesamone (short acting)	Injection	10–25 milligrams, 2–3 times per week
Testandro (short acting)	Injection	10–25 milligrams, 2–3 times per week
Testosterone Propionate (short acting)	Injection	10–25 milligrams, 2–3 times per week

T & The Younger Generation

What's the bottom line on testosterone therapy for younger males? Only do it when you really medically need to do it. With a potential side-effect profile scary enough to dissuade even the hardiest of men, you should be convinced not to experiment unless your doctor tells you otherwise.

Until the indications and precautions are better defined, we ought to keep testosterone in our treatment arsenal and use it strictly for those who are carefully screened as good candidates for the therapy. In individuals who pass such screening, the upside can be extraordinary and life restoring in the most positive way.

A Midlife Male Crisis

As with younger men, there are certainly cases in which anabolic steroid use is medically justified and extremely helpful in terms of an older man's quality of life. Virility and youthfulness fade too fast with age. While this is oftentimes a natural slow-down, and something most men adjust to, there are some that experience what can only be described as an over-zealous shutdown. Just like women have menopause, men can experience their own version, "andropause."

What a frightening thought! Cruising through life feeling the testosterone coursing through your veins, young and virile, seemingly invincible and impervious to the ills others around you seem to be suffering from. Then, unlike a woman's menopause, which hits fairly suddenly, your male armor begins to gradually show signs of weakening and cracking in subtle and ever worsening ways — andropause has arrived.

Maybe it starts with a bit of fatigue. Then, despite your efforts to train harder, heavier and with more frequency, you find your weights dropping, your stamina fading, and you simply struggle to get your ass in the gym. Dragging through your workouts becomes a monumental task. Your motivation sinks as you begin to experience difficulty sleeping. Then, perhaps the most troublesome of all, your sex drive flattens.

Signs and Symptoms of Andropause

Common Symptoms
Decreased libido
Sexual dysfunction
Fatigue
Decreased strength
Decreased endurance
General malaise
Insomnia
Depression
Body fat gain

Rare Symptoms
Anxiety
Panic attacks
Memory loss

As if it isn't enough dodging the bullets of cardiovascular disease, cancer and prostate problems as we men get older, now we've got a male version of a woman's menopause to contend with.

Actually, the concept of a male menopause is not new. In fact, this once vague symptomatology in otherwise healthy older men was described nearly half a century ago. But over the years, as physicians have become more adept at identifying these cases and the public has become more educated, prevalence in diagnosis has been on the rise.

Andropause has classically affected men in their 50s and 60s. But in recent years, as we've noticed at my health center, Peak Wellness, Inc. in Greenwich, Connecticut, cases of andropause in men as early as their mid-thirties are cropping up in record numbers. The medical community isn't exactly sure of the cause, but we do believe that genetic pre-programming does play a big role. Nonetheless, there are many factors that influence this condition in such a way as to make the symptoms far more severe and seemingly unlivable and/or cause them to occur at an earlier age.

One thing's for sure, excessive stress in your life as a result of everything from financial difficulties to spousal pressure to work strain can spur andropause. A high degree of physical stress can also be a precipitating factor. I've seen quite a number of cases of individuals whose andropause is caused simply by being overtrained. Heavy weight training puts different demands on the body.

Some of these guys can't get themselves out of the gym or even find the self-control to shorten their workouts, convincing themselves that they're actually not working out hard enough or long enough! This mentality leads to one of the most peculiar, destructive cycles a physician can witness. The addiction to working out is driven by a self-perpetuating fear and anxiety that the victim will lose his gains instantly if he stops, rather by actual pleasure from the activity. If this sounds like it's happening to you, back off your workouts for a while and see how you feel, before the "itch" to train excessively completely consumes you and brings out a full-blown condition of andropause.

At any rate, testing for andropause can be tricky. In addition to the signs and symptoms already mentioned, your physician can perform several blood tests that are extremely helpful in pinpointing the diagnosis. I've found that, although testing must be individualized for each person to rule out any number of possibilities, including thyroid and prostate problems, the most important and useful tests are total and free testosterone, LH, DHEA and DHEA-S. These tests are the most specific and helpful in terms of properly treating andropause.

Common Screening Tests:

Total Testosterone
Free Testosterone
LH
DHEA
DHEA-S
Note: *24-hour urine testing for these and other parameters can also be extremely helpful in determining the precise levels.*

Additional Tests:

Estradiol, Estrone, Estriol
PSA
FSH
Prolactin
GH
IGF-1
TSH
T3
T4
Note: *Additional tests such as these are often recommended to help rule out other causative, contributory or concurrent conditions.*

Treating The Affliction

Physicians experienced with andropause treatment commonly select one of three basic approaches. The first is the conservative approach, which involves restructuring the diet and activities of daily living. Although applied to nearly everyone, this approach is one I commonly use with younger patients, individuals where considerable life stress seems to be precipitating or magnifying the condition, and those with overtraining syndrome, which I've mentioned. The gist here is to reduce carbohydrates in the diet (especially those from refined sugar), increase fiber intake, and focus on getting more healthy fats from fish oils. Also, encouraging more rest, time off, and occasionally a course on stress management can make a world of difference.

A second approach is supplementation of the non-prescriptive sort. In such cases, the testosterone precursors of DHEA and occasionally androstenedione are valid choices. But one must be careful with these substances, because of their ability to form estradiol (the female sex hormone) in the system. As a result, even though these supplements are available over the counter, I suggest having your physician involved to carefully monitor symptoms and your blood hormone levels on an ongoing basis. Meanwhile, simple formulas containing ingredients like zinc, magnesium, NAC and even avena sativa (wild oats) seem to be a good bet.

Finally, available only with the help of a physician, the third approach in the treatment of andropause involves supplementation with prescription substances. The most logical and common prescriptive treatment approach is to give testosterone (in injectable, patch or gel form), because it's so often the case that a deficiency of this hormone is the underlying issue.

I frequently look at levels of LH (the pituitary hormone that stimulates testicular production of testosterone) and find this level to be deficient in male andropause sufferers as well. As a result, a short course of human chorionic gonadotropin (HCG), which acts like LH, is all that's needed to gently coax the pituitary-testicular axis back into action. If you think about it, this method makes a lot of sense. I consider pure supplementary testosterone only really necessary if the testes are truly unable to produce sufficient levels of testosterone. In other words, if your testes are functioning fine but just not getting the needed stimulation from the pituitary in the form of LH to produce testosterone, taking testosterone alone may not properly address the problem. Taking testosterone in such a case may even shut down what's left of your own natural testosterone production. While symptoms might marginally improve in that case, testicular atrophy may not resolve, and there will be a steadily increasing need for more testosterone as your own production fades. With the HCG method, you at least have a chance of jump-starting the system and not having to rely on testosterone over the long term.

21 UNCALCULATED RISK

In addition to anabolic steroids and testosterone, you can find a host of other so-called shortcuts many take in their efforts to improve their physique. While I don't recommend any of the following, in the interest of providing all of the relevant information, I briefly touch on seven common options, chemical and otherwise, used in an effort to build a better body.

1) Growth Hormone

Growth hormone (GH) and IGF-1 are not anabolic steroids. That's usually the first misconception I have to clarify when I'm asked about these drugs. From a chemical classification, they're polypeptides, with IGF-1 more similar to insulin. GH is often referred to interchangeably as IGF-1 because they're both similarly abused by many bodybuilders, yet they're different molecules that serve the same end. GH is released from the pituitary gland, and travels to the liver where it influences the release of one type of IGF-1. Muscle cells produce the other type of IGF-1.

For nearly all intents and purposes, common use and abuse is of GH, not IGF-1. This may have to do more with black market availability as well as the most common formulary brands being GH then anything else. Basically, when we talk about growth hormone use, just know we're generally talking about GH.

GH, produced throughout life in the anterior lobe of the pituitary gland, is a powerful growth factor that promotes cellular growth, suppresses cell death, and increases protein synthesis, plasma glucose and calcium levels. In youth and adolescence, GH is the key hormonal stimulator of bone growth and physical maturation. While measurements of IGF-1 concentration in the blood vary throughout one's lifespan, the normal adult levels usually range between 114-492 ng/ml.

Biosynthetic GH was originally brought to the U.S. market in 1985 for the treatment of dwarfism and short stature, Turner syndrome, and other diseases of growth and development. GH was really not originally intended for use in the adult population. With time, however, GH has been approved for use in GH-deficient adults, those with pituitary disease, pituitary damage due to surgery, head trauma or radiation, Sheehan's syndrome, autoimmune hypophysitis, sarcoidosis with pituitary dysfunction, HIV-associated wasting, and other related conditions that could affect pituitary function.

Though a presumptive diagnosis of GH deficiency in the adult is often made in clinical practice by looking strictly at the IGF-1 levels in the blood, the precise way to make this determination is by way of a GH stimulation test. The test involves measuring baseline fasting blood samples of GH, then administering up to 30 grams (0.5 milligrams per kilogram, to be precise) of intravenously introduced L-arginine (arginine stimulates GH). After that, repeat samples of GH must be taken every 30 minutes for two hours. A normal response of the pituitary to the presence of arginine is an increase in serum GH concentrations from baseline of at least 5 ng/ml. The trick is getting a patient to agree to sit in a chair with an IV in their arm for three hours while you do the test. Drugs like Clonidine®, which has the advantage of being orally administered, and even IV insulin are also used for the test.

The lore of GH among bodybuilders has more to do with its innate ability to reduce fat while promoting mass gains. Abused alone, although it can make you quite strong, GH doesn't do as much for muscle building unless it's combined with testosterone or some other androgenic anabolic steroid. When that's the case, the mass gains are epic, but the dangers are self-evident. Interestingly, GH is well known in professional bodybuilding to reduce body fat, especially around the abdomen. However, in extreme amounts GH also causes the midsection to bulge — the reason is that the intestines have a ton of GH receptors, so in the presence of excess GH, they literally get bigger. Although this is usually reversible when the user stops abusing, currently the "GH belly" is a scourge of both amateur and pro bodybuilding events.

The new quasi-legal marketing of GH is aimed toward the aging "baby boomer" generation. As we get older, we have an increased susceptibility to disease, and our reduced physical ability inevitably leads to an increase in mortality. Back in 1990, benefits of GH were shown in research to improve the quality of life for men over the age of 60. GH treatment resulted in lower body fat levels, increased skin tone and perceived feelings of greater vigor.

In two other studies, patients who received GH treatment for six months had body fat loss and an increase in lean body mass. Men between the ages of 61–81 who received GH had an increase in IGF-1 levels, an increase in lean body mass, a decrease in body fat, and an increase in lumbar bone density with no noted negative side effects. But the same researchers extended the treatment for a year and complications arose. The most evident side effect was carpal tunnel syndrome (severe, debilitating wrist pain) occurring in 24 percent of the patients; nine percent developed gynecomastia.

The term "somatopause" is a term that I use to describe the process of aging, along with the resultant decline of GH. It has been clearly established that GH levels decline as we age. The benefits of GH therapy for the elderly apparently include a retarding of bone loss, improved skin thickness, improved immune function and overall improved general fitness. With this in mind, the next logical thought is whether we should use GH to prevent age-related somatopause.

Perhaps using GH as a preventive medication might make sense in the future, but studies are conflicting. The problem is that, even if we figured out what age-related scenarios GH might be helpful for, the effects of injected GH aren't long lasting and therefore would have to be given almost daily over a lifetime. Daily injections are no easy task — just ask an insulin-dependent diabetic. I have heard some rumblings that an inhaled form of GH is in the works, but likely won't be available for a number of years. Still, this frequent injection issue, combined with the extremely high cost, makes the practical use of GH nearly prohibitive.

While uses of GH in adults range from correcting diseased and/or abnormal conditions to the very edgy anti-aging use, none of these applications include the regular guy that just wants to get big and ripped. In my view, GH abuse is like anabolic steroid abuse, in that it's perhaps just as perilous. But if that's not enough to dissuade you, check into how much a six-month supply of GH would suck out of your bank account!

2) Human Chorionic Gonadotropin (HCG)

Like GH, Human Chorionic Gonadotropin (HCG) is technically not considered an anabolic steroid, though it's a powerful hormonal stimulator of testosterone production. More accurately, HCG is classified as a polypeptide. HCG was historically extracted from the urine of pregnant females because it's a hormone exclusively produced by the placenta (a structure only found in the uterus of a pregnant mother-to-be).

In traditional medicine, we physicians generally prescribe HCG to male patients with what we call "hypogonadotropic hypogonadism" secondary to deficient pituitary function. In these cases, while the testicles are absolutely normal in function, selected patients still suffer from low testosterone as a result of insufficient stimulation from the pituitary. This pituitary-driven stimulation comes in the form of a hormone produced by the anterior portion of the pituitary called luteinizing hormone (LH). Since HCG has the ability to mimic LH, HCG stimulates a man's own natural production of testosterone.

LH is produced in the pituitary gland of both men and women, but has very different functions in each sex. In women, a spike in LH is the stimulation for ovulating. Thus HCG is used therapeutically in women for inducing ovulation and pregnancy in certain cases of infertility. Conversely, in men, LH will stimulate specialized interstitial cells in the testicles called "Leydig cells" to produce testosterone. Thus, HCG acts just like LH and stimulates the testicular cells to produce testosterone.

In the case of the male bodybuilder who uses anabolic steroids, his blood levels of synthetic testosterone go up exponentially. This high testosterone level is detected by the pituitary gland. The gland responds to what it perceives as an excessive testosterone production, albeit synthetic, by shutting down LH production. This, in turn, shuts off any remaining natural testosterone production, thus explaining the testicular atrophy (small nuts) seen in bodybuilders on extended cycles. Of course, this wouldn't be a problem if, when a bodybuilder got off the juice and his levels of synthetic testosterone began dropping, his own natural production of testosterone immediately resumed. Too bad, but that's just not the case.

Instead, what actually occurs is that, while synthetic testosterone levels drop precipitously, natural production is much slower to recover and takes weeks or even months to fully normalize. As a result, during this time bodybuilders off-cycle they often find themselves rapidly dropping size, unable to find the motivation to train, losing their appetite, gaining fat, experiencing sexual dysfunction, and even becoming depressed. So, in an effort to speed up the transition back to normalcy, bodybuilders use HCG to stimulate their own natural production of testosterone while their LH production has time to recover. This isn't so bad in the short term, and not much different from a man suffering from andropause or testicular hypogonadism taking HCG for this legitimate medical purpose. Yet that isn't always the case with bodybuilders who abuse. Too many stack them up with the other drugs they're taking and stay on them for many months or even years.

Using HCG like this is a road filled with perils. If used in excessive amounts for too long, one's LH levels will simply not recover without stopping the HCG and thus experiencing the very "crash" one had hoped to avoid in the first place. Ending up as dependent on HCG as one was on anabolic steroids is something I see all too often in the drug-abusing bodybuilder.

3) Estrogen Blockers

The so-called "estrogen blockers" are yet another classification of drugs commonly abused by bodybuilders, the most popular of which is called Nolvadex™ or tamoxifan. These are drugs traditionally used as chemotherapeutic agents for women recovering from breast cancer surgery. The reason is that many breast tumors in women are stimulated by the presence of estrogen. So blocking the effects of estrogen in these cases is believed to help prevent recurrence.

Estrogen blockers work not by stimulating the production of the male sex hormone testosterone, but by blocking the action of the female sex hormone estrogen. Most bodybuilders simply use them at the end of a cycle to knock down gynecomastia. Countless anabolic steroid abusers develop gynecomastia either during or shortly after a cycle of abuse, because the testosterone or testosterone-based drugs they're putting in their bodies are being converted to estrogen by a process called aromatization. This the way the body naturally deals with unnaturally high levels of testosterone.

Many others, under the misguided notion that estrogen blockers will give your body a higher level of testosterone, will try and use them as a muscle builder. If you're trying to build muscle with estrogen blockers, forget about it. Don't be confused. By itself, they do nothing for muscle gain. In fact, it's kind of a harsh drug in the male physiology. While it blocks estrogen receptors at some select sites, it actually stimulates estrogen receptors at other sites. So you really won't get a good fix on what it's doing to your insides until future health problems start cropping up. Also, in my experience, blockers are hard on the liver.

Anastrozole (also called Arimidex®) is an aromatase inhibitor often used like tamoxifan either alone or in with other related compounds like tamixifan or clomid. The street lore is that it can effectively reverse elevated levels of estrogen production (a common side effect of abusing too much androgenic testosterone.) The fact is that it does block the conversion of aromatizable steroids to estrogen, but this will only be temporary on a backdrop of continued androgen abuse. In other words, the estrogens go right back up if you don't lay off the sauce. Many guys use it strictly to knock down early signs of gynescomastia, and it works fairly well for this, but again, only if you are either decreasing or stopping androgen abuse. Another thing to keep in mind when it comes to Arimidex® is price. It is expensive, costing about $10 per milligram!

4) Beta-2 Agonists

Prescription beta-2-adrenergic agonists, the most common of which is clenbuterol hydrochloride, are used as bronchodilators in asthma treatment.

Other well-known drugs in this class are albuterol and salmeterol. They work by causing the smooth muscle within airways to relax after it constricts during an asthma attack. In addition to this action, and of particular interest to the bodybuilder with a penchant for drug abuse, is the fact that clenbuterol is a powerful thermogenic stimulant that burns fat while sparing lean mass.

The strong anti-catabolic nature of these drugs might result in a net muscle growth and strength gain by preventing lean tissue breakdown. This dimension of the drug has become so well known among bodybuilders that it has become a preferred substance of abuse. Also, since clenbuterol is not a steroid hormone, it lacks the androgenic side effects typical of anabolic steroids. For this specific reason, it has become a drug with elevated abuse potential among young women (especially female fitness buffs that want to be ripped).

5) Muscle Expanders

The injected muscle expanders are perhaps the most bizarre group of abused substances in all of bodybuilding. They're actually not even technically considered drugs, because this inert fatty liquid is sold in Europe (mostly Germany) as a tanning and/or massage liniment for application to the skin surface. The most common brand is called Synthol™.

When injected into the muscle, Synthol™ is extremely slow to be absorbed. This slow absorption and resultant occupation of intramuscular space is the key to its use among bodybuilders. When continuously injected over time, Synthol™ stretches and ultimately tears the fascia surrounding the muscle (fascial tissue is believed to be the limiting factor in muscle growth). So Synthol™ ends up increasing muscle size in two ways. First by simply occupying space in the muscle, thereby making it look bigger, and second, by actually expanding the fascia to allow for more muscle growth (sort of like re-potting a plant to allow for more growth).

Users of these substances are cropping up in droves among the professional and amateur bodybuilding ranks. In fact, record numbers of non-competitive bodybuilders with circus-freak aspirations are sneaking into the hardcore muscle magazines these days. But there are a number of limitations and outright dangers.

The limitations:
These substances are not used well in large muscles. Small muscles like the biceps, triceps, shoulders and calves are more commonly injected. When used in larger muscles like the chest, back and quads, the results can be unsightly lumpiness. In these cases, it's horrifying to look at the more unfortunate injections that went wrong. I recall one bodybuilder who came to my office

after trying to inject his quadriceps. What he ended up getting were a couple of big lumps in one leg and another couple of uneven lumps in the other. He ended up going back and re-injecting his quads several times, making a real mess of things. By the time he saw me his quads looked like two bags of marbles.

Despite the fiction of bodybuilding lore, there's a lack of permanence. Although quite long-lasting after you've been jacked-up, injected muscle expanders eventually get absorbed (at least in the luckier individuals). As a result, you have to keep subjecting yourself to repetitive injections in order to see measurable difference in muscle girth.

The safety issues:
As mentioned, Synthol™ is sold in Europe as a skin rubbing oil for tanning and/or massage. Hence, as a result of the label recommended means of application (use on the skin and not for injection), the glass vials Synthol™ is sold in aren't required to meet U.S. pharmaceutical-grade sterilization standards. Hence, infection and abscess formation is commonplace among abusers.

Abscesses of this nature are particularly harsh because the causative bacteria are lodged in the substance and thus equally difficult to absorb and eliminate from the body. When you start seeing these abscesses, they're often of massive proportion and must be surgically removed.

An equally stomach-curdling event is destruction of lean muscle tissue by the expanding abscess, resulting in the formation of an actual hole, divot or pocket in the muscle. Worse yet (if you're still keeping your lunch down) is the formation of a tunnel or fistula created by the bacteria as it eats away lean muscle and bores a pus-leaking channel to the skin surface.

Despite the downfalls, site-specific injection with Synthol™ has become all the rage lately, and bodybuilders with side effects of severe abscess, hematomas and septic disease have been popping up in emergency rooms with alarming frequency.

Other substances injected in a site-specific fashion with muscle expanding success include testosterone cypionate and Vitamin B12. Testosterone cypionate has the same problems as Synthol™ when administered this way, except it's not quite as much of a volume expander because it's less viscous (thick) and thus is absorbed more readily. In addition, there seems to be a higher incidence of ruptured blood vessels and emboli as opposed to the higher incidence of abscess we see with Synthol™.

Vitamin B12 is the least viscous and perhaps the worst in terms of pure volume expansion. Nevertheless, when injected in large volumes, bodybuilders are able to stimulate enough local inflammation that the muscle itself swells, expands and stretches the surrounding fascia. The other practical drawback here is the high frequency of injections required to keep the muscle volume expanded. B12 is absorbed relatively quickly, so abusers become pincushions. As a result of more frequent injections, the propensity for abscess and infection is that much higher.

6) Surgical Calf Implants

In male bodybuilders, very few saline or silicone implants are done with exception of the calves. But unlike the common breast implant craze among women, the common implants in the area of the calves for men are less certain in terms of cosmetic outcome. Furthermore, because of the difficult anatomy (namely the blood vessels and nerves that traverse this region), such implants don't have the best track record. There are a significant number of failures. Quite a number of cases occur in which problematic implants in the calves are removed due to clinical complications.

Finding an experienced plastic surgeon that has done a large number of these implants successfully isn't only a necessary prerequisite, but also a daunting task. There aren't many true experts in this particular procedure. Though countless surgeons are willing to do the implant surgery, far fewer have enough cases under their belts to make them proficient.

When performed, I feel implants in the calves should be silicone and not saline whenever possible. Silicone simply functions and feels better then saline. But silicone is considered controversial. Silicone breast implant lawsuits back in the 1980s, started in conjunction with media hype, led to a ban on use. None of this was based on credible science, but that didn't stop lawyers from painting thousands of people as victims. Hundreds of millions of dollars were paid out in damage awards. Lawyers got rich while doctors and patients were robbed of a choice. Companies went out of business. Insurance premiums in the sector skyrocketed. Countless suffered, except for the lawyers in the class-action suits that took most of the money.

Of course, it turns out that science says silicone implants don't cause cancer and are now once again being used. Unfortunately, these scientific facts were just not neatly packaged enough back during the suits and readily available for the defense.

At any rate, assuming you can get silicone for your calf implants, good plastic surgeons work with two sets of implants: One is for the outer head of the calf and the other is for the inner head. The same good surgeon generally attempts to insert the implant under the fascia and not over the muscle. The result of this is a more stable implant that doesn't move around as much; the drawback is that, in most people, you can't insert implants that improve calf size much more than about a two-and-a-half-inch increase in circumference.

So, if you want massive implants, they have to overlay the muscle and fascia and are thus innately less stable (and I believe less aesthetic).

Having the implants under the fascia does increase the pain and lengthen the recovery time (as opposed to a couple of weeks with supra-fascial, don't expect to walk properly for about a month with sub-fascial).

As far as interfering with function, a question I get a lot is, "Will I still be able to do deep squats?" The answer is, if you're getting the implant under the fascia and you don't get too greedy in terms of the size you choose, you should be okay. By the way, a good set of implants in your calves should last a lot longer then you will. So when you're long since dead, buried and decomposed, your calves should still look great. I'm sure you'll take a lot of comfort in knowing that.

In addition, chest, triceps, biceps and glutes are also implantable areas for men, but are far less common then the calves. Smaller and/or more rounded muscles have been tried, but the success rate has been poor due to structural limitations of these areas.

7) Liposuction

Liposuction is the single most popular surgical procedure among male bodybuilders, especially liposuction of the abdomen and flanks (love handles). The idea is to put you under general anesthesia and insert a catheter into your flabby rolls. After that, sterile fluid is instilled to loosen the belly butter and then it's sucked out into a jar. Sound pretty? Well it isn't, but it sure works.

Other techniques involve using ultrasound to emulsify the fat, as well as fine-tip catheters to "liposculpt" the midsection in order to delineate the six-pack look. Regardless of the method, recovery involves wearing a compressive garment for about six weeks. This keeps the bruising down and helps the skin re-adhere to the inner abdominal wall.

I'm always asked if the fat comes back. The short answer is no, because the actual cells are removed. But there are some caveats. Once fat is sucked out, a redistribution process takes place, and it's a good thing because no surgeon can be sure they're removing exactly the same amount of fat from both sides. If there are small asymmetries, they eventually even out as a result of this redistribution process. Also, it should come as no surprise, if you don't control your eating after surgery, you'll regain fat that in time can find its way back to these areas. Even so, it usually doesn't all come back (unless you're a pig, which is a reason so many people go back for revisions).

8) Nubaine

Nalbuphine hydrochloride (also known as Nubaine) is an analgesic used by doctors to treat some cases of moderate to severe pain. In other words, it is a morphine-like painkiller that works like opium. In addition to anabolic steroids and other physique/performance enhancing drugs, countless bodybuilders over the years have abused Nubaine. It is an intravenous drug abused by bodybuilders and other athletes for its phenomenal ability to alleviate all the aches and pains associated with super-heavy training. It is also well known in the gym underground to have the added benefit of improving fat burning by magnifying the action of thyroid hormone (specifically increasing the uptake of the thyroid hormone "T3"). It is a unique painkiller because, though it is in the morphine category, it doesn't give you that drugged out feeling that could interfere with your daily activities. This is a critical point and perhaps at the crux of why it has become such a popular drug of abuse among bodybuilders. While bodybuilders are all too willing to take something to kill the pain of extreme heavy training, they generally stop at any kind of heavy narcotic because that, of course, would negatively affect their training regimen.

But Nubaine is different. Professional bodybuilders that "run" Nubaine find that they walk around with just a little high yet not enough to cause the proverbial deer-in-the-headlights look. At the same time, their bodies have just a touch of numbness so they don't feel the aches and pains that come along with heavy training.

To add some more background, Nubaine is not a fully controlled narcotic, so historically, it's been fairly easy to get in the gyms. In fact, years ago, when I'd worked out in Long Island, the only empty vials we would see lying around the floors of the locker room stalls was Nubaine. It was easy to get. All you had to do was ask the guy next to you. This lack of control and restriction was, and is, because this drug is a combination opioid agonist (receptor stimulator) and antagonist (receptor blocker) all in the same drug. So it's not just a pure morphine-like substance on the order of opium. This profile supposedly makes it less addictive and mitigates the potential for abuse and overdose. Well, at least that's according to the drug company that makes it. But I know that's all bullshit and so do the underground meatheads that I've seen wash up over the many years. While I admit that Nubaine is hardly as addictive as heroine or crack, severe Nubaine related addictions, medical complications, psychiatric disturbances, and deaths are a harsh reality.

The guys that I used to train side-by-side with years ago at Gold's in Venice Beach that were into Nubaine definitely were the prime examples. The really bad ones had a sort of far-off, slightly mentally disturbed look that got kind of painful in appearance and twitchy when they came down off the Nubaine. It's difficult to describe, but when I got used to being around these guys, they became easy to spot. Funny thing was, I never really saw that glassy-eyed disconnected quasi-disturbed look again until years later during my government work as a Probate Court Physician, where I came up against hardened criminals and had to interview and examine them to determine if they should be institutionalized.

The all-to-common story I got used to witnessing over and over again was a guy taking an intramuscular shot of about 10 milligrams of Nubaine an hour or two before working out to mask the pain. Guys that were dead in the water, unmotivated, riddled with pain, and unable to crawl out of bed would jump on the "baine-train" and then whammy! Once they were running on Nubaine it was like rocket fuel. They'd miraculously come to life and be jacked up and good to go. Yet they were not just speeding either. Sure they had that going for them, but along with the buzz was a cloak of pain-liberating numbness. These guys would then go into the gym and just crush the weights. It was honestly as epic as it was disturbing to watch. They were like jacked-up supermen. They felt immortal and, seeing the way they'd pound the weights, they sure-as-hell looked the part. It was a substance that was admittedly without equal at hiding the injuries and the pain of super-heavy and intense training exertion. Guys around me were more then willing to indulge and pay any price as long as it meant they were going to get bigger and harder. Nubaine came through on the promise—well, at least in the short term.

Then cracks in this seemingly glorious armor would develop. Like any drug abused for the high, it easily promised you the world for only a small price, then, slowly took everything. Each time the drug wore off, these guys would be mortal again. The pain would be worse then before they did it in the first place. While running Nubaine they were numb enough to get through another crazy-heavy routine. Now off of it, the once diesel locomotive would feel like nothing short of a train wreck. The aches in every joint, the throbbing of every muscle, and the pain of every tendon, all would come into true focus. The harsh reality of the human condition would come back with stirring clarity. The pain would be greater in intensity then ever before, and believing like there was no other way to feel good again, they'd jump back on the baine-train!

They were hooked, and not from the pursuit of a druggie high, but from avoidance of physical pain and a subsequent fear of losing gains. Yet the result of developing dependence was the same. Repetitive use then would set up a sort of psychological dependence that I saw countless times. Eventually stopping wasn't just a matter of will. My bionic gym rat buddies that were hooked into Nubaine would be able to push themselves harder and harder and train heavier then ever before, but at a price. Each time the Nubaine wore off, the residual musculoskeletal and joint pain would become magnified.

Avoidance of this very real pain drove the guys even faster, right back to running Nubaine. Next, true addiction in the medical sense would set in. By that I mean, when they were not regularly using, they would experience uncomfortable physical side effects including extreme anxiety, shortness of breath, racing heart rate, intense stomach pains, fevers, and chills. Trust me on this one. It's not a pretty sight. Eventually the guys would be unable to break the cycle of running it again. This habit could continue for some until deep mental and physical addiction would set in.

Interestingly, while many retired professional bodybuilders might even talk a little nostalgically about their years of anabolic steroid use with the all-to-familiar bad-boy smirk, when it comes to their time running Nubaine, they always see it as a low point of embarrassment. I've always found this ironic among my bodybuilding friends because some are guys that have spent years and years on steroids. Some have done it for decades. Yet even for those that only ran Nubaine for a relative blink, say weeks or months, it is always invariably viewed as a low point. In my experience, bodybuilders who abuse steroids and growth hormone never ever consider themselves in the ranks of street addicts. They just don't view these drugs as drugs of abuse because they believe they are using them to optimize their physique and not to get a high or hurt anybody. Right or wrong, that's the way they see it. But when you ask about their time running Nubaine, they look down and away. It seems to be the one drug that just makes them feel in their heart of hearts and deep in their subconscious, just a little too close in comparison to a junkie, for their comfort.

9) Clomid

Clomiphene citrate (also known as Clomid) is an FDA approved drug for use in women struggling with fertility issues. Generally, it is the first fertility drug that a couple will be introduced to if the issue arises. Among the more traditional reproductive endocrinologists, Clomid has not been thought of as a drug for men. Yet, in recent years, the more cutting-edge practitioners have discovered a valued "off-label" use for Clomid in men with low sperm count due to genetic factors or anabolic steroid drug abuse. That said, numerous male bodybuilders have begun exploiting Clomid as a testosterone supporting drug to optimize muscular development.

Clomid is used to induce ovulation in women with ovulatory disorders. It is also used to assess ovarian function and the likelihood that a woman can still produce viable eggs.

Interestingly, Clomid is a somewhat mysterious and complex medication whose mechanism of action is not fully understood. What we do know is that it works in the body somewhere high up along the estrogen axis but is capable of reacting with any tissue in the body that has estrogen receptors. While the action of Clomid in the female physiology certainly takes place at the level of the hypothalamus and pituitary, it may also involve the ovaries, endometrium, vagina, and/or cervix. The action in the male also appears to take place at the level of the hypothalamus and pituitary, but may also act at the level of the adrenals, peripheral fatty tissues, liver, and/or testicles.

We basically know that Clomid influences the way the estrogen hormone estradiol influences three other hormones. The first is gonadotropin-releasing hormone (GnRH), a hormone produced by the hypothalamus (a gland located in the skull center above the pituitary gland) that affects the release of hormones in the pituitary. The other two are produced by the anterior lobe of the pituitary and are called follicle stimulating hormone (FSH) and luteinizing hormone (LH).

While physicians are not in agreement on the precise pharmacokinetics, it appears that Clomid fools the body into believing that the estrogen level is low. Furthermore, we know Clomid competes with estrogen for estrogen-receptor-binding sites and probably delays the replenishment of intracellular estrogen receptors. There is also some data suggesting that Clomid has both estrogenic and anti-estrogenic properties, but the test results show a variable response from one species to the next and one receptor site to the next.

The popular street and online lore is that Clomid blocks the production of estrogen. Unfortunately, this is a reckless misinterpretation of the mechanism because the drug will certainly not reduce your estrogen or the problems that come along with having a high estrogen level. In fact, in the male physiology, it actually stimulates some degree of estrogen production, though not nearly as much as testosterone. Along the same estrogen-blocking reputation, some morons also claim that Clomid is effective in reducing gynecomastia (abnormal enlargement of the breasts in males). Well, on the contrary. If you are not careful, Clomid can, in some cases, actually cause gynecomastia! So from that standpoint, one needs to watch not only their testosterone levels, but also their estradiol.

In laymen's terms, the activity of Clomid is probably achieved by interfering with the inhibitory effects of estrogen, both at the level of the hypothalamus and at the level of the pituitary. In a process called negative feedback, the higher the estrogen, the more the hypothalamus and pituitary reduce the production of gonadotropin hormones. Clomid seems to simply come in and occupy the estrogen receptors at these levels, while at the same time, not activating them. The result, is that there ends up being more GnRH, FSH, and LH. In the female, FSH and LH results in the release of mature eggs (a process called ovulation). In the male physiology, the release of these gonadotropins will stimulate testosterone (via LH) and sperm production (via FSH).

Typically, male bodybuilders use 50-milligram tablets taken orally each day for up to six months each year. While Clomid is not a steroid, has no androgenic activity, and does not appear to interfere with pituitary-adrenal or pituitary-thyroid function, it is still not a drug for sport ergogenic use.

In fact, there are no adequate or well-controlled studies that demonstrate the effectiveness of Clomid in men. What is cited in the literature are gynecomastia and testicular tumors reported in males using Clomid long term. Although in fairness, it should be noted that the cause and effect relationship between reports of testicular tumors and Clomid may be nonsense.

Yet Clomid abuse has risen sharply among male bodybuilders and athletes in recent years. I attribute this to the fact that it is not a drug typically tested for, and it's relatively easy to take because it's an oral medication available in tablet form. It is also more readily accessible when compared to more highly visible sporting drugs of abuse. As far as fertility drugs in this class go (and I think they are all grotesquely over-priced) it is relatively inexpensive. But Clomid will still cost you about $10/pill.

In my practice, when an experienced bodybuilder abuses anabolic steroids over a continuous amount of time without going off cycle (many months or years), sperm production shuts down making a man infertile. This may also occur in a man with a legitimate reason to take continuous testosterone drugs. This side effect may not pose a health problem, but it truly sucks if you're trying to get your wife pregnant. In my experience, it's not as big a deal for older bodybuilders (50+) who have been through marriage and kids.

But for the younger set, who aspire to build a family, this result can be alarming, to say the least. The general profile is that of a bodybuilder between the ages of 28-43 years of age with a history of continuous anabolic steroid abuse with no time off between cycles. This scenario is growing with ever increasing frequency as more and more bodybuilders are resistant to go off cycle. Recall in the "old days" bodybuilders would spend a significant time of the year off cycle to clean out. It was only around contest time that they would start the heavy juicing. Also, guys abuse much higher doses for longer periods as well. There was a time when guys were either on a low dose for a longer stretch or a higher dose for a shorter period, depending on their philosophy. But only now has there ever been high-dose-long-duration abuse.

When this occurs, sperm production grinds to a halt. The condition is diagnosed by testing semen under the microscope for sperm. Typically there should be 20 million or more sperm visible per cc. In those with infertility due to continuous anabolic steroid use, often one doesn't see even a single sperm!

Assuming this type of anabolic steroid abuse is at the root cause and not some genetic factor, sperm production should eventually resume. But in my experience, this may take anywhere from six months to five years in order for the system to correct itself. Also a small percentage of really heavy abusers never seem to recover, and they remain infertile for life.

On the other hand, though not yet FDA approved for this purpose, once off anabolic steroids, Clomid is being used to rescue the hormonal axis and thus trigger sperm production. Generally, we start with 25 milligrams/day.

But doses can go as high as 75 milligrams/day depending on the responsiveness of hormone production. The drug is started after anabolic steroids are stopped. Simply stated, if you're still abusing, you're cruising for a bruising. Blood levels of testosterone, LH, and FSH are all tested again in 4-6 weeks to assess the responsiveness of the pituitary and testes. If the numbers don't budge much, the dose is increased. The good news is that approximately 2/3 of these patients respond within a matter of months and guys can subsequently get their wives pregnant.

Just know that you won't see viable sperm in the semen again for about three months. So, unlike the blood tests, there is no sense in retesting semen before that time. But once you do find sperm again, you are good to go. Of course, if your body successfully resumes producing viable sperm, there is always the option of immediately harvesting a sample and cryogenically storing it for future in-vitro fertilization (IVF). This gives patients who truly have a medical need for testosterone to resume use if they so desire, while still having the ability to inseminate. Interestingly, there are occasions in which the Clomid actually does the trick and the hormonal cycle is reactivated. As a result, some patients never have to go back on testosterone drugs as their levels spontaneously normalize after a little Clomid stimulation.

Again, one can always forgo the Clomid, stop the juice, and just wait it out. In my experience, most reproductive endocrinologists will tell you that you still have roughly the same chance of recovery. But as I said already, you may be talking about years down the road. So in these particular types of cases I actually advise my patients that it is better to address it earlier with a drug like Clomid because the longer the axis remains dormant, the less likely I feel it will be successfully reawakened.

Finally, I've come across a number of bodybuilders over the years that used Clomid as a regular part of their cycle. Whenever I asked them why they did it, none could ever explain why. Fact is, it has no place in a cycle. For example, it defies logic to use it with testosterone because the effect of testosterone is to decrease production of LH at the level of the pituitary gland. This is the opposite action of Clomid. Provided there is no negative feedback driven by high testosterone levels, Clomid should cause LH to increase and thus, in time, stimulate production of ones own natural testosterone. Double dipping by stacking Clomid on a backdrop of anabolic steroids is pointless because an unnaturally high anabolic steroid level will negatively modulate LH production at the level of the pituitary. This is the opposite of what Clomid is trying to do. As I see it, it is only off-cycle in the way I discussed, or at the very least, coming off-cycle, that Clomid has its greatest utility.

10) Kynoselen

A well known competitive bodybuilder once contacted me regarding his abuse of a drug called kynoselen and what he thought was a local infection at the site of his last injection. As he went into the details, he described how he injects it like synthol. The purpose "on the street" is to do two things. The first is really to act just like synthol and expand the intramuscular compartment and micro-rupture the fascia so that the tissue can expand. The second, unlike synthol, is to cause local irritation and inflammation, which serves to further expand the capsule. This interesting substance also has the somewhat unique property of being stimulatory and restorative. This "tonic" effect improves debilitation and weakness. In fact, because it helps to enhance strength, endurance, and lean mass, kynoselen is banned by many horse and dog racing associations. Though not conclusive yet, it seems kynoselen may help increase protein synthesis, thus leading to more lean muscle mass. So kynoselen is a powerful fat burner and anti-catabolic that helps prevent muscle tissue from breaking down. Since kynoselen is so effective at combating fatigue, increasing endurance during training, and facilitating recovery, it's thought to be cheating in the animal racing world!

Kynoselen is produced by a French company by the name of Vétoquinol. Typically, this veterinary drug is used in cases of muscular dystrophy in horses. Kynoselen is also used in the treatment and prevention of muscular disorders due to selenium deficiency and whenever cardiac or skeletal muscle is compromised from disease or trauma. Other uses include certain myopathies, white muscle disease, symptoms of hypocalcemia and hypomagnesemia in cows, "tying-up syndrome" of horses, post-race for horses, symptoms of cobalt and vitamin B-12 deficiencies, arthopathies in cats and dogs, heart disease, and porcine muscle disorders.

Administration is intramuscularly, subcutaneous, or intravenous injection. Typically, the drug is administered at an average dosage of about 1cc (or 1ml)/day for every 200 lbs., and injected subcutaneously into the anterior neck region of animals. The following are typical veterinary doses:

Horse:	20ml/400kg (0.25ml/kg)
Cattle:	20ml/400kg (0.25ml/kg)
Foals:	10ml/100kg (0.1ml/kg)
Calves:	10ml/100kg (0.1ml/kg)
Sheep:	Up to 5ml (0.2ml/kg)
Lambs:	Up to 2ml (0.2ml/kg)
Adult Pigs:	Up to 10ml/100kg (0.1ml/kg)
Piglets:	Up to 1ml/5kg (0.2ml/kg)
Dogs:	Approximately 2ml-5ml (0.1ml/kg)
Cats:	Approximately 1ml (0.2ml/kg)

Doses are generally given to these animals as treatment, with one injection every few days on three or four separate occasions. After that, kynoselen is used for preventative measures at one injection weekly for 2-4 weeks.

So what specifically is it? Well, kynoselen is a non-steroidal intramuscular mix of substances! It consists of vitamins, minerals, adenosine monophosphate (AMP), and a substance called "heptaminol". The vitamins include mostly B-12. The 25 milligrams it contains stimulates metabolism and appetite. Also included is sodium selenite (a source of selenium) at 50 milligrams. Selenium is a catalyst for energy and fat metabolism plus an antioxidant. Magnesium aspartate at 1500 milligrams provides increased oxygen delivery, promotes strength, and potentiates muscular contraction. Potassium aspartate at 1000 milligrams stimulates the Krebs cycle, assisting in glucose metabolism. It also serves to increase the amplitude of cardiac contractions and has a heart-protective effect when oxygen deficiency occurs during strenuous exercise. AMP is a valuable carrier of phosphorous. The "P" in "ATP" is the currency of energy in the body. AMP combines with two atoms of phosphate to become ATP (adenosine triphosphate). As a result, an immediate source of cellular energy is available to the muscle. AMP also appears to help displace fat and stimulate energy transformation at the cellular level. Finally, kynoselen contains 500 milligrams of heptaminol. Heptaminol is a psychological and cardio-respiratory stimulant. It speeds up the metabolic processes and helps dilate coronary blood vessels. It is believed to be a key ingredient for sports ergogenics because it helps dilate coronary blood vessels, increases blood flow, and allows a greater exertional capacity for the endurance athlete.

The abuse of the product is growing in popularity among bodybuilders willing to endure the pain of site-specific injections. And they sure are painful. In fact, one of the guys I see tried an injection of just 3 ml of kynoselen in his thigh. In addition to crying like a baby for hours, he limped around on the leg for days. By the way, the typical street wisdom on dosing for bodybuilders is about 1 ml/day. Anyway, what surprises me is that more athletes aren't abusing this garbage. If someone is crazy enough to shove this stuff in their bodies, they are invariably on the juice as well and thus hardly need the relatively negligible anti-catabolic effect they provide. Also, they certainly won't benefit much from the oxygen-carrying aspects of the compound. Of course there is that sense of well-being and anti-fatigue that it provides, but I don't see that as something you can't get out of a good vitamin regimen. Instead, it's the synthol-like muscle space occupation and subsequent muscle expansion that is what the bodybuilders are after. Of course, the added dimension of acting as an irritant sets it apart from synthol. In the pure sense, synthol is actually the better static volumizer simply because it is fairly inert and very slow to absorb. But the degree of compartment expansion is dependent on the amount that is injected. This is in sharp contrast to kynoselen, which, in acting like an irritant, draws fluid and inflammatory particles to the area. So though most of the vitamins and minerals are rapidly absorbed, the heptaminol and collective other ingredients produce a volume expansion that goes beyond the proportions of the amount injected. That's where the extreme bodybuilders are cashing in.

Overall, I'd have to say that it's the distance athlete that finds the most ergogenic benefit. Increased muscle sparing, anti-catabolism, circulatory boost, cardiac potentiation, and sense of well-being for the endurance athletes could result in yet another chemistry-induced gold medal performance, if it hasn't already! Though the product is not currently banned as far as I know and there may be no current test for the product or its heptaminol component, there is a question of a future doping violation.

11) Intra-Muscular Injections

You should have seen the size of this guy. He was about 6'2" and 280 lbs with body-fat that could not have been more then 6%. While he looked huge, the problem was that he started finding himself literally tripping over his own feet. His regular doctor and an orthopedist could not figure out what was wrong with him, and like most, did not want to tell them the truth about his steroid use. He figured he was just going to hear the usual lecture from the doctors about the dangers of anabolic steroid abuse and how he was screwing up his body. I surmise he was probably right in that regard because any ethical physician is going to discourage abuse. That is something I have had to do nearly every day in my practice. But what he forgot was that, without revealing the whole truth to his physicians, they could not possibly be expected to be helpful. At least he told me the truth.

Of course, it turns out that he had been abusing anabolic steroids for years. In particular, he had repeatedly used intra-muscular (IM) injections as his delivery route. He said that "a guy with lots of experience" taught him how to inject himself and that, using alcohol wipes, he "always was sterile about it". He claimed to have been injecting himself for nearly five years, so it was baffling to him what my inquiries had to do with him repeatedly tripping and what the reasons were for my line of questioning.

But this was a major source of stress for him because he never before had any health problems. Though he had heard about tons of abusers getting things like gynecomastia and having liver and prostate problems from steroid abuse, he never even had so much as a hint of symptoms, until now. Further history revealed that he had not always been as big and actually had not taken nearly as much stuff. It was just in the past year that he really started going heavy on the juice, all in an effort to see how huge he could get. As a result, seldom did a day go by when he did not administer an IM injection to himself. He said he felt like a pincushion because at times it seemed like he was running out of places to spike!

His physical examination revealed that, although the flexing of his calves was very strong and symmetrical, he could not voluntarily point his right foot toward his head (i.e., dorsiflex). This explained why, while he could still do massive weights when squatting and even training his calves, his gait (walking) was abnormal. Analysis of his stride revealed that his right toe dragged behind him on the ground. This was the local cause of his occasional tripping. Upon further questioning, it turned out that he was right-handed and much preferred to use his right hand to do his injections into his right glute. He went on to explain that, when he ran out of space to inject and didn't feel like using his left hand or another site, he just searched around for another site on his right glute and spiked away.

I diagnosed him with a condition called "foot-drop" on his right side as a result of needle trauma to his sciatic nerve. Actually, I suspected the diagnosis right away because I had seen it before. You see, a coalescence of the corresponding nerve roots from the spine (specifically the lumbosacral plexis nerve roots L4, L5, S1, S2, S3) comes together and creates a thick nerve cord that exits the pelvis. This thick nerve cord is known as the sciatic nerve. From there, in about 90% of people, the sciatic nerve emerges under a muscle deep in the glutes called the piriformis. The nerve then divides at the level of the lower thigh into the posterior tibial nerve and the common peroneal nerve. The common peroneal nerve again divides becoming the deep peroneal nerve and the superficial peroneal nerve. The deep peroneal nerve innervates the main muscle at the front of the lower leg called the tibialis anterior muscle (originally stemming from nerve roots L4, L5, S1). This deep peroneal nerve has primarily a motor function in it that controls the contraction of the muscle it innervates. Specifically, the deep peroneal nerve (a very distal branch of the sciatic nerve) innervates the tibialis anterior muscle and controls its contraction. This muscle lies on the opposite side of the leg as the calve muscle and thus functions to lift the foot up and flex it toward the head. Though the movement is small and subtle, it is critical for a normal stride. Your body needs to hold your foot up just a little bit while walking. Otherwise, when you bring the back foot forward, your toe will drag on the ground and could get caught, causing you to stumble and trip.

This sets up an interesting problem for those administering deep IM injections into the glutes, because the proximity of the sciatic nerve can fall into common injection zones at the center of the glute. Injection trauma to the sciatic nerve at this level can result in deep peroneal nerve injury symptoms causing functional impairment of the dorsum of the foot, thus creating the foot drop and resulting gait abnormalties (tripping) that is so often seen with sloppy IM injection technique. It is for this reason that IM injections must strictly be done in the upper-outer quarter (superior-lateral aspect) of the glute.

Further complicating matters, though in 90% of us the sciatic travels through the glute region under the piriformis muscle, the remaining 10% of us have an anatomy in which the sciatic nerve exits the pelvis either in whole or in part above the piriformis muscle. This moves the sciatic nerve higher up and further over before it descends down into the leg. As a result, if the injection is too close to the center of this quadrant, the sciatic can be accidentally hit with the needle.

Healthcare professionals easily avoid this complication by properly performing the IM injections. You can avoid these complications simply by not abusing drugs. For the healthcare professional, the rules are simple.

Prior to the injection, high-order needle preparation involves selecting an appropriate sized syringe. The 5 cc syringes tend to be most practical because most single dosing generally ranges between 1-4 cc. A proper needle selection is equally important. If you select a needle of too low a gauge, it will be thicker and, though oily solutions will pass through it with greater ease, the needle itself will do more damage to your skin and deep muscle tissue resulting in more bleeding, bruising, and pain. Select a needle of too high a gauge, and the resistance created will prevent you from being able to effectively press the plunger of the syringe down to efficiently deliver the drug. I tend to use 22 gauge needles because they seem to do the least amount of damage, yet still pass highly viscous solutions deep into the muscle somewhat quickly and easily. Also worth noting is the length of the needle. Because the glutes tend to be so thick with muscle and covered in some degree of fat, I tend to favor using syringes at 1.5 inches in length for deep IM injection. This length generally best ensures that the head of the needle and thus the contents of the syringe I am injecting end up deep within the body of the muscle. At the same time, 1.5 inches is generally not so long that I can't completely insert the needle to the base for better stabilization.

Next, the needle is firmly attached to the syringe and the syringe drawn back pulling in air to the dosage mark I wish to withdraw. If the drug bottle is a multi-dose container, the top of the bottle should always be swabbed with an alcohol pad prior to use. New bottles for single dose purposes usually need only to be popped open because the rubber piercing-cap is protectively sealed. Turn the bottle upside down and plunge the needle up through the rubber piercing-cap. Inject the air contents into the bottle (these vials are vacuum sealed, so whatever amount of drug you want to get out, an equal portion of air must be injected in). Holding the plunger down, back up the needle until it is clearly well under the liquid. You do this because you don't want to just be drawing air back into the syringe. Rather, you want the syringe to instead be filling with the drug itself. As you move your thumb off the back of the plunger, the syringe should passively fill automatically with the exact amount of drug you intended. Withdraw the needle/syringe complex from the vial and then tap the sides of the syringe to make sure no bubbles are visible. If they are, simply draw back on the plunger and gently press it down again until the air is completely evacuated from the syringe (you know this by seeing no air bubbles in the syringe and by seeing the drug come out of the head of the needle just a little bit as you press any and all air out). The needle is then ready for injection.

Strictly inject in the upper-outer quarter (superior-lateral aspect) of the glute, but also stay at least 2 inches away from the center of this quadrant. More easily stated, let's say I'm going to inject into someone's right glute. The first thing I do is to envision the entire glute divided into 4 equal quadrants (it's like imagining a big plus-sign on one butt-cheek). After that, all attention is focused on just the upper-outer quarter. Then, measuring roughly a thumbs-span from the center, I have my zone. Fully gloved, an area roughly the size of the bottom of a soda can is thoroughly swabbed with alcohol. The injection then takes place exactly in the center of this area. The needle/syringe complex is completely inserted and prior to injecting, one should pull back on the plunger slightly to be sure the head of the needle is not within a vessel (if you are in a vessel, visible blood will flow back into the syringe). Once the safe position is confirmed in this way, the plunger is pressed, the needle/syringe complex is then removed, and a few minutes of pressure is applied to stop any post-injection bleeding.

At any rate, as far as my guy with the foot-drop is concerned, he ended up okay but not until I put his foot in a special support device for a while and implemented months of physical therapy. Backing off the sauce was of course mandatory. He was one of the lucky ones. And I'm quite sure he'll never use his body as a pin cushion again.

Unfortunately, with the coming of age of high-frequency injections among abusers, cases like this are all-too-common. Granted, a licensed or certified healthcare professional is the best person to do an intra-muscular injection, but I have instructed countless select patients that require long-term IM injections under a doctor's prescription how to self-administer their own medication. So I know it can be done right even by non-medical personnel. The problem is that guys are taking the juice when shouldn't be and those same guys get into trouble with poor technique. Worse yet, they then pass on their Neanderthal technical skill through incompetent instruction to the next moron in line willing to listen.

In conclusion, it's no mystery that serious bodybuilders abuse steroids and in so doing, they spike themselves with repetitive IM injections. Make no mistake about it, that's just the harsh reality of the state of our sport (and countless others, for that matter). The take-home message is that, while qualified healthcare professionals minimize complications by using or teaching proper IM injection technique to appropriate candidates, you can avoid all complications simply by not abusing the drugs in the first place.

SECTION IV

ATHLETES ON DRUGS

22 MOST ABUSED STEROIDS

It has been a long-standing controversy that somehow anabolic steroids don't really enhance athletic performance. This twisted conventional wisdom among nerd scientists calling themselves steroid experts comes from early citations in the published science. Of course, these studies were only short term and measured parameters like actual sports execution, reflexes, and similar snapshots of athletic performance. This myopia led to an incorrect conclusion on anabolic steroids and their effect in the athlete. The truth is, anabolic steroids have a profound benefit in most forms of athleticism. But to understand how, one must put the mechanism of action into focus.

Anabolic steroids exert their greatest benefit to the athlete by making repetitive training sessions more consistent, efficient, and intense. Recovery between sessions is quicker, while at the same time, the athlete can look forward to working harder each session without getting wiped out. Anabolic steroids also give the athlete the psychological grit to tough it out through difficult training sessions. Without the benefits of anabolic steroids, athletes are subjected to predictable human breakdown and typical cyclical training of the natural athlete. An elite athlete must be pushed hard to excel. But this tends to leave the athlete over-trained and possibly injured, thus invariably leading to down time or at the very least, low-intensity periods of training (called by some "cruise time"). So top athletic trainers have developed ways to cycle training intensity and periodize the workout experience for the athlete in order to minimize the down time. In this way, anabolic steroids turn months of training into weeks. In fact, when taken long enough, years of training can be reduced to a matter of months. Furthermore, over enough of a time span, the natural athlete will find it almost impossible to match the progress of the anabolic steroid using athlete, no matter how many years he or she works at it.

Of course, there are the rare exceptions of natural athletes ruling a particular sport or position. But these are usually outside of the power or high intensity sports and more those that tend to rely heavily on natural talent, instinctive finesse, and a sort of pre-programmed genetic skill set. For example, a quarterback in football will not find nearly as much benefit to taking anabolic steroids as a defensive lineman. The quarterback has a skill game that necessitates accurate throws, split second decision-making, and physical multi-tasking. This is in sharp contrast to the defensive lineman who, while some degree of finesse and skill are required at the higher levels, he basically just needs to be a big bull that charges hard through the line and at the quarterback and running backs. It's a pure power game, so anabolic steroids work wonders in such a setting. They make these types of guys much bigger, much more powerful, and much more durable.

So the temptation for the strength and power athlete is very real because these athletes aren't stupid. They know all this and most would do just about anything to assure victory. That includes taking pills and shoving needles in their bodies. There is so much at stake for so many. So it's not a matter of "if" they take the drugs. They do. That's just the reality so many don't want to face.

The issue really then becomes exposing what types of anabolic steroids such athletes tend to favor. In my experience, having seen so many athletes over the years, they tend to stay away from testosterone and the near testosterone derivatives. This is because the athlete in a sport or at a position that could benefit from anabolic steroid use is really almost strictly interested in an anabolic effect. This includes lean muscle and power building, shortening recovery time, and reducing injury. They are not interested in the androgenic effect that comes along with excessive levels of testosterone or the near testosterone derivatives. These include aggressiveness, water retention, premature baldness, and increased libido. The reason probably stems from the "juicy" look that occurs with high-dose testosterone. This look can be described as puffy eyes, acne on the face, back and shoulders, larger appearing head, more prominent facial features, visibly chunky muscle gain, and gynecomastia. In the 1980's, this was a telltale sign that a guy was juiced. So athletes made a shift away from testosterone or the near testosterone derivatives, and toward the 19-nor testosterone derivatives. These synthetic hybrid molecules with a testosterone backbone were far enough removed in structure from the original testosterone molecule that the androgenic side effects were almost non-existent, while a reasonable degree of anabolism was maintained. For these reasons they were, and in most circles still are, considered safe.

Nandrolone Decanoate

While they may well be safer in the shorter run, they have had the deleterious and often long delayed side effect of infertility in the male. In particular, the 19-nor testosterone nandrolone decanoate is a major culprit. Typical intravenous abuse in the athlete range from doses anywhere around 200 milligrams/week to up to a full gram per week in divided doses. Nandrolone decanoate has been and remains a staple drug among athletes from a wide variety of disciplines. In addition to athletes from all major sports, as well as track and field, nandrolone decanoate has even found a home among the distance and endurance set. In particular, triathletes, ironmen, and cyclists have looked to nandrolone decanoate for not only its ability to rebuild tissue and help in recovery, but also to boost hemoglobin. This is because it is actually used in medicine to help reverse anemia and wasting associated with chronic renal insufficiency. In such cases, it is not at all unusual to see hemaglobins in excess of 18 (normal adult hemoglobin is usually around 13-17 grams/dL) and hematocrits of 60 and up (normal adult hematocrit is usually around 38-50%). This allows distance and endurance athletes to increase the oxygen-carrying capacity of the blood. If the blood carries significantly more oxygen to the tissues as it does in this way, physical performance is greatly enhanced. The big problem for the athlete is that all major sports organizations are hip to the widespread abuse of nandrolone decanoate, and thus test specifically for this subclass of drugs.

Winstrol V

Another anabolic steroid in widespread use among athletes is "Winstrol V". The drug is also known as "stanazolol". It is commonly abused in its injectable form. The drug has some similarities to nandrolone decanoate in that the androgenic side effects are relatively lower then the straight testosterones. Also the reputation among athletes is that it won't make you "super-huge" so you won't draw attention to yourself. It also has the reputation of being water soluble and thus believed to be safer. For these reasons, it has remained a drug of choice among athletes for decades. The only problem for athletes looking to abuse it is getting real Winstrol V, and not some kind of dilution. For this reason, black market pricing on 30 ml bottles has climbed from about $300/bottle back in the late 1990's to as much as $1,000/bottle in 2006. Typical dosing for the abusing athlete is commonly in the amount of 2-5 ml, usually once each week.

Dianabol

Finally, dianabol (also known as methandrostenolone) is yet another top favorite anabolic steroid of abuse among athletes. In particular, Europeans, athletes from the Netherlands, Asia, and the Middle-East all seem to have a penchant for abusing dianabol. For whatever reason, dianabol abuse among American athletes is unusually low relative to our non-American counterparts. But the use is so prevalent among athletes the world over, that it makes the list of anabolic steroids highlighted in this section. I can surmise that the reason is multi-factorial. For one, dianabol is no longer made in America, so it is tougher for Americans to get. Also, in my experience, American athletes tend to have a bit more of a healthy paranoia about the risk of oral forms of anabolic steroids (they must go through "first pass" metabolism and thus affect the liver). As a result, the use of oral anabolic steroids among athletes in America has fallen substantially since the early 80's in favor of the intravenous route. Though dianabol is available in an intravenous form, it is the oral form that international athletes prefer. My experience with athletes in Europe and the Middle-East has led me to believe that they approach the use of such oral anabolic steroids with less reservation. For these reasons, dianabol is still an enormously popular drug of abuse among top athletes the world over. Common pills on "the street" generally come in 5 milligram and 10 milligram tabs with typical doses of abuse of between 10-50 milligrams/day.

Non-Steroidal Drug Favorites Among Athletes

Growth Hormone (GH)

Athletes abusing growth hormone have become commonplace at the Olympic and professional level. GH is particularly popular in the impact sports (football, hockey), the strength dependent sports (power lifting), those with a high level of explosive training (Olympic weightlifting, wrestling, sprinting, gymnastics), and those events of repetitious movement with periodic intensity (cycling, swimming, triathlon). This is due in a large part to the fact that, though GH is a banned substance, it is still not adequately tested for. So a great number of athletes get away with it. GH is not an "anabolic steroid" molecule in the literal sense, but it is a very powerful anabolic agent that falls more into the chemical classification of a linear polypeptide. The big advantage here for the athlete is in the form of dramatically increased strength, joint healing, workout recovery, and an overall greater sense of well-being. The great limitation is accessibility and price. Growth hormone is tough to get and invariably expensive once an athlete finds a source. The ugly truth is that some have to resort to extreme means of procurement. There are unscrupulous doctors out there that, if paid enough, will prescribe GH with no medical necessity and just to make the athlete perform better. In such cases, there are the incumbent costs to the athlete of paying off the doctor, compounded with the costs of the GH itself (which alone can cost $50,000 to $100,000 per year). This entry barrier forces the less well-healed athlete to resort to even more risky methods of procurement. It basically leaves the athlete vulnerable to the local pusher at the gym, whose stuff may be far from real. Another, perhaps even more disturbing way they get it done is by hooking up with an underground AIDS network of patients who are willing to part with their GH supply for quick cash. Here is how that works. The AIDS patients qualify for Medicaid and are automatically approved for GH use due to the medical necessity of prevention of wasting due to their chronic infection. So these guys get a lifetime supply of GH paid for by the government and are often more then willing to trade it off for some instant cash. Athletes that work this back-alley method save considerably on money, though at about $500-$1000/week, it still isn't cheap.

Kynoselen

As mentioned earlier, Kynoselen contains no anabolic steroids and no drugs that authorities are testing for. As a result, its abuse among athletes in America has exploded in recent years. But as with any rare black market substance in high demand, there are supply side obstacles. The first obstacle is the obvious. Kynoselen is for veterinary use only and thus can only be prescribed by a veterinarian to treat an animal. So this substance can generally only be gotten via the black market or by finding a crooked veterinarian or someone who knows one. Then there is the ever-popular internet, but the sites and sources are less then reliable. Plus the FDA is well aware of these hucksters and has already served search warrants and closed down such equine exploiters. But in the end, it hardly dissuades the athlete. Where there is a will, there is a way. As the greed becomes irresistible among the pushers, the desperate athlete, who has enough money to throw at it, eventually finds his supply source, and the cycle continues to grow.

Clomid

This female fertility drug is emerging among highly competitive male athletes as yet another popular performance enhancer. It is a non-anabolic steroid that stimulates the body to produce more testosterone. As with the truly hypogonadal, Clomid can act as a positive testosterone modulator even in those with normal testosterone. It has become popular among athletes because of the perception that it is "gentle" on the system. Interestingly, this locker-room wisdom may not be far off from truth. Clomid does not give the athlete that over-blown juiced up look and the side effects are rare. Though it is an oral, and thereby, undergoes first-pass metabolism by the liver, an athlete can stay on it for months and possibly years with no elevation of liver enzymes. If the dosage is not too high, Clomid can also be tapered and discontinued without much negative hormonal feedback or recovery lag time. Of course, the drug is not as potent as pure testosterone or the testosterone derivatives, but the logic of many athletes is that they don't always need all that fire power anyway and instead just need a little edge.

Clenbuterol

Clenbuterol is a stimulant drug prescribed outside the United States for asthmatics. Athletes love it because it perks them up and gives them energy like an amphetamine rush and thus burns fat, but without the undesirable wasting that comes along with stimulant abuse. It comes in oral form in small tablets so it is easy to take and conceal. Plus it has the added benefit of leaving the system in a matter of days after discontinuing, thus being undetectable. Clenbuterol has a rare and perhaps unique feature of being able to go beyond mild mass sparing and into the realm of significant anti-catabolic tissue building. Though an athlete won't get the gains seen with testosterone or GH, Clenbuterol can be surprisingly anabolic in the right subject. Basically, it works the same way as ephedrine as a "beta-2 agonist" (i.e., dilates the airways and reduces constrictive wheezing). However, unlike ephedrine (which is out of the body in a few hours) the stimulant and thermogenic (fat burning) qualities of the drug can last for many hours and even days without actually interfering much with the normal sleep-wake cycle. The only drawback is that Clenbuterol must be cycled on and off because of severe beta receptor down-regulation. So Clenbuterol is effective for only about 2-3 weeks at a time before a week or more must be taken off from the drug. Typically, doses of abuse for the athlete are 100 micrograms per day.

Amphetamines

Amphetamines include a wide variety of stimulant drugs with different degrees of activity. Examples include Amineptine, Amiphenazole, Bromantan, Bupropion, Ephedrine, Fencamfamine, Mesocarb, Methylphenidate (Ritalin), Pentetrazol, Pipradrol, Salbutamol and Terbutaline. Athletes that abuse amphetamines do it for the energy burst. Every athlete knows that when they get tired, even the best technique in the world goes straight out the window. So combating fatigue is essential, but not always accomplished by athletes strictly by way of training. Some athletes also abuse amphetamines for weight loss because they speed the metabolism and suppress hunger. For this reason, this was, and perhaps still is a fairly common drug of abuse among female gymnasts. One young woman I worked with was continuously encouraged by her trainer to take these pills in order to keep her weight down. Of course, amphetamines won't work for every athlete because they can cause increases in blood pressure and heart rate. This is disadvantageous for high-precision athletes.

Diuretics

Diuretics are not only widely abused among bodybuilders, but also other athletes that need to drop weight in the short term. Examples range from boxers, to wrestlers, to gymnasts, to jockeys, and a variety in between. Typical examples of banned diuretics popular among these athletes include Acetazolamide, Bendroflumethiezide (Naturetin), Bumetanide, Chlorthalidone, Canrenone, Ethacrynic Acid (Edecrin), Furosemide (Lasix), Hydrochlorothiezide (Esidrix), Spironolactone, and Triamterene. Perhaps the most widely abused of these is Lasix. In oral dose, athletes usually take in about 40 milligrams at a time. The danger is in inadvertent excess dosing and subsequent extreme diuresis. The end point is a precipitous drop in blood pressure, loss of consciousness, and a possible seizure, heart attack, or stroke.

Pain Killers

Buprenorphine, Dextromoramide, Diamorphine (Heroin), Methadone, Morphine, Pentazocine, and Pethidine (Meperidine Demerol) are the common types of pain killers abused by athletes and usually tested for by the major sports organizations. The reason for abuse is innately obvious. Athletes suffer pain and pain limits their performance. Dealing with pain is an occupational hazard for the athlete. In some sports, an ability to overcome pain and still perform can extend or even save a career. Perhaps no greater example is seen then with the linemen in NFL football. This subgroup of large athletes, often overweight and poorly conditioned, have the unique challenge of continuous explosive bone-crushing contact. These bodies are plagued with trauma and the pain that comes with it. This is no small secret and many of the sports great stars have come out and openly admitted to the widespread problem. Unfortunately, pain killers are perhaps the most common drug that is continued to be abused long after the end of a career. I knew of one patient that, long after his NFL playing days and championship glory, was seriously addicted to prescription pain pills and booze. After a half dozen knee and back surgeries and countless injections, his pain was so excruciating that it crippled his ability to even get out of bed in the morning. He just couldn't deal with his pain without heavy drugs, which detached him from his family, eroded a decent living and eventually cost him his life.

Erythropoietin

Erythropoietin (also known as "EPO") is a hormone produced by the kidneys that travels through the circulation to the bone marrow. There it stimulates the production of red blood cells. Red blood cells are critical to human life because they carry oxygen to the tissues. Since some athletes have a greater need for oxygen then others, a higher hemoglobin and hematocrit (the volume of red blood cells) is directly proportional to the oxygen carrying capacity of the blood. So EPO can boost endurance performance in athletes by allowing a greater transport of oxygen to the muscles. One way to boost EPO is simply by way of high altitude training. Sustained training at high altitudes will actually naturally stimulate more EPO because lower air pressure and diminished atmospheric oxygen at higher altitudes spurs the body to produce extra red blood cells to compensate for a perceived oxygen deficit. When the athlete returns to sea level activity, they then have a decided advantage in oxygen-carrying capacity. EPO is also manufactured as an intravenous drug (Epogen, Procrit). Due to its powerful ability to boost red cells, it enjoyed widespread use among doctors in the 1980's during the height of the AIDS epidemic to counter the anemia of the disease. Prior to that, it was almost exclusively used in renal failure patients and some cancer patients. But athletes got into it back then and the abuse skyrocketed. In particular, the drug was exceedingly popular among cyclists. The main problem was, and still is, that when abused by a subject with an otherwise normal red cell count, it will thicken the blood and form clots. These clots block circulation and have caused death. But it is so effective that, even though banned, abuse still continues. Typical doses of abuse are 250 U/kg three times per week injected subcutaneously.

Blood Doping

Blood doping basically accomplishes the same thing EPO abuse does, but just in a more gory way. Blood doping refers to a voluntary and intentional intravenous infusion of real blood into the veins to produce an increase in the blood's oxygen carrying capacity. Simply put, it's basically a blood transfusion in someone that doesn't need one. The procedure begins several weeks before a key competition, with an athlete removing up to 4 units of blood (1800 ml). This is usually accomplished with the help of a complicit doctor or nurse. Blood is then centrifuged and the plasma is decanted and immediately re-infused into the athlete. The remaining red blood cells are stored in the refrigerator right between the growth hormone and the milk and eggs. These red blood cells are then re-infused back into the athlete a few days before a high endurance event. Though blood doping can dramatically raise red blood cell count, the hyper-coagulation side effects are the same as with EPO plus the chance of additional serious side effects makes it extra frightening and thus, most certainly, one of the weirdest things athletes abuse.

Beta Blockers

Beta blockers have to be the odds-on favorite for most puzzling banned substance. Beta blocking drugs basically slow down the heart and allow for greater ventricular filling and a slower heart rate. Examples include Acebutolol, Alprenolol (Sinalol), Atenolol (Tenormin), Betaxolol, Esmolol,

Labetalol, Metoprolol (Lopressor), Nadolol (Corgard), Oxprenolol (Inderal), and Sotalol. They do nothing for bodybuilders and strength athletes. And they actually would hurt the efforts of the endurance athlete who needs a high cardiac output and faster heart rate. So what group of athletes benefit from abusing beta blockers? The answer is the shooting sports. Any elite marksman, either with gun or bow, knows full well the advantage of pulling the trigger or releasing the bow precisely at the stillness between heart beats. These athletes also try and control their nerves as well, because being nervous means having a higher heart rate. A beating heart makes the muzzle of the gun or the line of sight bob up and down ever so slightly. Beta blockers artificially slow the heart rate down so that the shot can be executed with minimal movement off the target. Abusers generally push their resting heart rate down into the range of 38-45 beats per minute. The dangers here, in an otherwise normal physiology, are hypo-perfusion and heart attack.

Prohormones

Prohormones are steroid structure precursors to the testosterone molecule. They occur in nature and can be synthesized. In the wake of the Dietary Supplement Health and Education Act of 1994, they were considered dietary supplements and available without a prescription. Only in recent years have the most popular prohormones been re-categorized as drugs. Dehydroepiandrosterone (DHEA) is perhaps the most common steroid found in the body and for years, was one of the most widely purchased prohormones on the market. It was really the first generation of prohormones used by athletes and still abused by some today. DHEA remotely resembles testosterone. In theory, DHEA is a prohormone that can be converted to testosterone in the body. However, it must first be converted to androstenedione. In any event, the popularity of DHEA slipped among the bodybuilding and athletic community once the prohormone androstenedione came along. Thanks to the nonsense that surrounded homerun king Mark McGwire, the popularity of androstenedione grew. Though no longer legally available over-the-counter, the rage among athletes over androstenedione as an anabolic steroid substitute continues. In much the way DHEA was advertised in the early 1990's, androstenedione serves as a building block for testosterone, and therefore, boosts levels in the body. While both hormones are, in fact, building blocks or precursors of testosterone, they differ in that DHEA is really the precursor to androstenedione, while it is androstenedione that is the direct precursor to testosterone. So androstenedione more closely resembles testosterone in structure. This structural similarity to testosterone, coupled with the fact that it is a step closer to testosterone in terms of synthetic reactions in the body, would lead one to believe that testosterone might be more apt to be formed from androstenedione than from DHEA. This does make intuitive sense, but science is split in terms of telling us what exactly happens to androstenedione when taken orally. Yet, there is a painful fact that athletes must be aware of when considering the prohormone androstenedione as a testosterone booster. As easily as androstenedione can be converted to the male sex hormone testosterone, it can just as easily be converted to the female sex hormone estradiol, if given to the wrong person. This is a dangerous fact that far too many athletes still ignore. In answer to the problem of DHEA and androstenedione becoming estradiol and not testosterone (a process known as "aromatization"), the dietary supplement industry came up with "19-norandrostenedione" and "19-norandrostenediol". These newer, synthetic prohormones were basically chemical structure modifications of the molecules androstenedione and androstenediol (an alcohol form of androstenedione). These substances theoretically have less of a propensity to aromatize and form estrogen. In the case of the "19-nor" prohormones, we know that if an athlete takes in even small amounts, their urine will test positive for nandrolone in as little as three days. If you are an athlete facing a drug test, taking the 19-nors are as bad as taking real prescription nandrolone because nandrolone is exactly what will be detected in the urine. Of course, whether 19-nors actually behave in the anabolic sense like prescription nandrolone is still unknown. But the bottom line is that, in my opinion, they do not.

Estrogen Reducers

Estrogen reducers are divided into two classifications. The first are the "aromatase inhibitors". These substances block the conversion of testosterone to estrogen. The three most commonly abused are Aminoglutethimide, Testolactone, and Anastrazole. They work by temporarily crippling an enzymatic dumping pathway, whereby your body gets rid of what it perceives as excess testosterone. The problem after extended abuse is the cross reactivity on the corticosteroid receptors, which can then affect blood pressure and blood mineral content. The second group of estrogen reducers is the estrogen blockers. Examples include Tamoxifen and Arimidex. These drugs are basically weak competitors with estrogen for estrogen receptors. While estrogen and testosterone levels don't change much with estrogen reducers, response is seen in the body as being less sensitive to the existing estrogen levels.

24 Tricks Athletes Use To Avoid A Positive Test

The Clear

"The Clear" was thought to be the steroid tetrahydrogestrinone (also known as "THG"), a testosterone-like molecule originally sold as a dietary supplement until the FDA categorized it as an unapproved new drug. It was undetectable for some time until testing procedures caught up with it. It was for this reason, that the clear got its name. But the truth is, THG is nothing but a purely synthetic "designer" steroid derived by some simple chemical modification of another banned anabolic steroid (probably Stanozolol). While for some time athletes avoided detection, the cat is now out of the bag. The Clear was unknown until track coach Trevor Graham, after finding out that a number of athletes were using it, anonymously mailed a syringe full to the U.S. Anti-Doping Agency. It was later found to be THG and believed to be distributed by a company called BALCO. U.S. sprinter Kelli White was quite vocal in her admission that THG made winning two world championships "easy". But she also admitted that THG gave her acne, big muscles, and changed her voice. Several athletes were allegedly connected to "the Clear" provided by BALCO founder Victor Conte. Perhaps most notable was and still is Barry Bonds, whose trainer, Greg Anderson, was said to be on the supply side. *The San Francisco Chronicle* reported that Barry Bonds acknowledged in grand jury testimony that he used "the Clear" provided by Anderson. Bonds apparently claimed he did not know the substance was a steroid and instead thought the clear substance Anderson gave him was the nutritional supplement flaxseed oil.

So who fathered this hybrid molecule? Well, there are a number of theories, but perhaps the one I've heard the most in the press is that it was designed by none other then prohormone steroid guru Patrick Arnold. Patrick was basically a self-proclaimed steroid expert who was responsible for bringing prohormones into widespread use in America. While not believed to be a medical professional or published researcher in the field, I must admit that Patrick was quite clever. I remember years ago, long before the BALCO scandal, when he came to my office and later attempted to get me interested in some kind of prohormone testosterone stimulator he was hawking at the time. After a careful look at what he was doing, I remember calling and telling him that his greatest concern should be that he might be manufacturing unapproved new drugs. He dismissed it. Now it seems that things finally caught up with him as the fed dragnet nabbed him as well. In a strange sort of way, it's too bad. I liked Patrick and he actually reminded me of Dan Duchaine—an eccentric steroid guru with no real credible professional healthcare training, but with a great personality and a fascinating and inventive mind. Though most major athletic organizations test for THG, buyers and sellers can still be found on the internet.

Mabrook Method

The Mabrook Method is a clever method of allowing a male to bypass a supervised urine test. Popularized by a professional bodybuilder by the name of Mohammed Mabrook, the use of this method grew immensely among Olympic and professional athletes. In fact, it was so effective that it fooled examiners for years until one finally figured it out. The "Method" as it's called, entails taking normal urine from another person and putting it into a small ball-like squeeze tube. Usually, these athletes use what is called a Jackson-Pratt suction tube (a small, soft, and compressible plastic bottle with a closable hole-top). The procedure involved pre-filling the tube with fresh urine and placing the closed tube under the scrotum. When the athlete would walk in and disrobe stark naked for the test, the examiner traditionally would see nothing on the person and would basically let the athlete "urinate in peace" and not with the examiner's eyes focused on the athletes genitalia. I mean think about it. Human nature almost dictates that, even if an examiner is required to "observe the collection" he won't likely be staring directly at the guys private parts to see where urine is coming out, especially if he's stark naked! Well that's what went on for years. The athlete would then simply reach under the scrotum, pop the top, and squeeze the tube either between his legs or with his finger. Some guys got so good at doing it that it almost didn't matter if an examiner was looking directly at the jewels, since they'd have to be within inches to see what was really going on. But eventually the examiners got hip. The tip off occurred when an Olympic athlete and first-time method-man actually made the mistake of collecting his room mates urine the night before and saving the sample in the refrigerator. The result was ice-cold urine that was far from a normal 98.6°F, and thus a dead giveaway. So the method is not as widespread these days, but I hear it's still popular in some circles and remains a problem for the examiners.

Catheterizing Method

If the Mabrook Method seems a fascinating oddity, just read on about the Catheterization Method. Again, the intention is to get past a urine drug screening. But in the wake of the failures of the Mabrook Method, athletes started reaching for more elaborate methods. As the name implies, the Catheterization Method involves the insertion of a urine catheter through the penis and directly into the bladder. Collection of a volunteer's clean urine is the same as with the Mabrook Method except that, instead of being stored and dispensed in a receptacle, the urine is instilled directly into the bladder through a urinary catheter. After that, the subject simply enters the testing area, disrobes and urinates. It may sound extreme, but it is extremely effective and remains popular today, though drug testing agencies have countered this abuse by simply scheduling sudden random urine tests at unpredictable times. This precludes exploitation of the Catheterization Method simply because, purely from a technical standpoint, at least a few hours lead time is needed to get ready to be tested.

Dilution Method

Another way athletes approach getting around a positive drug test is from the other side of the proverbial fence. The idea is to dilute the blood and thus make certain levels appear normal on a blood test. Obviously, this only works for substances that already naturally exist in the blood, and not synthetic molecules for which any level of detection is prohibited. For the most part, it is for this reason that the athletes that use this method are primarily EPO, some thermogenic stimulants, and to some extent, testosterone abusers. The idea is to set up an intravenous access into one of the veins and instill 0.9% normal saline. Typically, a half liter is introduced through the veins an hour or so before the test. In close enough proximity to the blood draw exam, the fluid should have circulated around enough and integrated itself into the serum contents while not yet "third-spacing" out of this compartment. As a result, the concentration level tested should be more dilute. Drawbacks include vulnerability to a sudden random screen due to need for prep time, the fact that very few organizations do a blood collection, the limitation of what it can be helpful for, the difficulty of judging how much dilution is enough to achieve a concentration decrease to within normal limits. For these reasons, it's now a seldom-used method.

Detox Products

Detoxification products are generally a combination of vitamins, minerals, and herbs that supposedly detoxify your system. Some claim that they work by "un-stacking" red blood cells. They describe a seemingly impressive method of acting as an oxygen catalyst, thus freeing up oxygen and preventing "Roulex-Formation". All the products I've seen so far seem less than credible to me. Anyway, they are not used by any athletes I am aware of that abuse hard pharmaceuticals. Most guys that try this one are pot smokers applying for jobs etc. But it's worth a mention, because most major athletic organizations do ban and test for cannabis use.

Masking Agents

Masking agents are drugs that mask the use of a banned substance. Typical masking agents that athletes abuse are Bromantan, Epitestosterone, and Probenecid. They tend to be drugs that in some way alter urine flow and/or pH of the urine itself. The most popular is Probenecid, a drug normally used for patients with excess uric acid. It masks by inhibiting renal excretion of the drug. I recall back when Australian winger Ben Tune tested positive for Probenecid. It came as a surprise and puzzlement to so many. It turned out that it worked by changing the concentration of components in the urine, thus altering tested concentrations. In the case of epitestosterone, this can also be an effective masking agent because urine is typically tested for the testosterone:epitestosterone ratio (T:E). Since a ratio greater then six becomes suspect, by taking in more epitestosterone, the ratio will actually decrease even though testosterone levels might even be on the rise!

BODYBUILDING LIFESTYLE

25 Getting Your Training Terms Straight

To begin with, bodybuilding, as in every discipline, has its nomenclature. Of particular interest to the athletes embracing the bodybuilding lifestyle are those terms that apply to advanced training concepts. These references are so often thrown around the gym incorrectly. Unfortunately, this misuse blurs a clear understanding of our standard. As a result, a guy might recommend doing giant sets when he really means super sets. Maybe he means he trained to failure, while he's telling others he did forced reps. This simple, yet disturbing, corruption of our art by misuse of terms is pervasive and undermines the legitimacy of our sport. But little if anything has ever been written to establish the industry standard definitions of advanced training terms used by experienced bodybuilders. That said, what follows is a list of the most commonly used, advanced training terms. Every serious bodybuilder should clearly understand these terms and convey them with accuracy when talking about our sport.

Failure

Performing a set to the point of a total muscular inability to move the weight through the intended range of motion is called training to failure. This method must be performed with a spotter when doing certain motions that would either trap you under the weight (chest or shoulder pressing) or put you in peril (squats, leg press, etc.). Smaller movements that do not place your body in jeopardy require no spotter to train to failure. Once failure is reached, the set is over. The benefits of going to failure are that you are assured a fairly high degree of intensity without definitively overtraining, assuming you are careful. The downside is that, if done with regularity, your body tends to subconsciously gear for the failure and hold back a little bit. This robs the muscle of full late-stage muscle recruitment, and thus growth. A good general caveat when using this method of training to failure, is only to do so on the last set of a given exercise, and not every time.

Forced Reps

Forced reps go one step beyond failure and utilize a spotter to help you complete the intended number of repetitions of a given set. This method helps you through extra reps after you have failed on your own. It raises the level of intensity and deep muscular stimulation to a very high level. But the key here is getting a good spotter. A bad spotter will let you collapse under the weight with the bar either not moving or moving in the opposite direction before offering assistance. A good spotter will give you just enough help to keep the bar moving at all times, but not too much. So the bar should slow but never stall. As with training to failure, try to keep forced repetitions to no more then the last set of a given exercise, and even then, not every workout. This is because the likelihood of overtraining is higher then when just going to failure. Still, when done correctly, forced repetitions represent the single best way to spur muscle growth.

Split Set

I coined this term back in the late 1980's to describe a training method we began to incorporate to raise the level of intensity and burn the muscle deeper. We did this by using a method that spurs recruitment of more individual muscle fibers into firing but without going to failure or forcing out a repetition. The split set is executed in what I call "mini-sets". It is basically a "set-within-a-set" concept. The idea is to work in continuous motion through each repetition of a given set, but divide the set into predetermined sections, where you intentionally pause briefly in the near-lockout position just to grab a breath. Done correctly, this should stave off failing or necessitating assistance with a forced repetition. Yet it will allow you to train with a slightly heavier weight then you would, had you done each repetition continuously throughout the entire length of the set. So for a ten repetition set, it might run like this: five reps, pause and breathe, three reps, pause and breathe, two reps, done! Just note that the split set does not work well if your weight isn't geared for a set lasting at least eight repetitions, and you must not take your pause for more then one breath. If you do that, you're not just pausing anymore. You're resting and thus actually decreasing intensity.

Super Set

A super set simply describes a sequence of two to three different exercises for different body parts, lined up in sequence to condense training. To be a super set, the chosen exercises must be for different muscles, otherwise you're doing a giant set. For example, you might decide to hit both chest and back by doing barbell incline bench press in super set with a lat pull-down movement. When done correctly, it should intensify your routine and save you time in the gym. Unfortunately, too many people don't do it correctly and fall into the inherent trap of holding back on the first exercise just a little bit and, consciously or subconsciously, gearing for the next exercise in sequence. As a result, they end up turning a super-set into more of a circuit and, though they might work up a sweat, they never really pump up the muscles. So if you're going to do a super set, be sure that you're throwing out maximum intensity on every exercise in the sequence, regardless of whether it's your first, second, or third movement. For this reason, I've never been a big fan of the super sets and never seen huge growth as a result of doing them among the many guys I've worked with over the years. Perhaps this is because, while one of the body parts usually gets inadequate stimulation for extreme growth, the time lag between the next set makes the other body part ice up and flatten. If you're going to try them, some of my caveats on the subject include doing only a super set with visually developed and fairly strong body parts. This is because the super set will almost invariably soften your ability to focus and concentrate on a single exercise set—an element essential to bringing up a weak body part. So pick your battles carefully as to exactly when and how often you incorporate super sets, if at all. Also, don't go too low on your repetitions. If less then six reps on each exercise, you simply have no chance of stimulating the muscles well enough to grow.

Circuit

A circuit is a sequence of four or more exercises, lined up in sequence, with the purpose of getting a whole-body or near whole-body workout without rest. It is done exclusively with machines and not free weights. For this reason, circuit training is ideal for the youth or novice interested in general fitness, or for those coming back from a hiatus or injury, or for light maintenance. In other words, you won't build extreme muscle doing a circuit.

Giant Set

A giant set works just like a super set except it involves multiple exercises in rapid sequence for the same body part. In other words, you could do a set of leg presses and then go right to leg extensions. It's a good way to key up intensity and stimulate muscle growth in either your strong or weak areas. The only caveats are to be careful adding a third or fourth exercise to the sequence. More is not necessarily better. In my experience with the pros, the big juicers in the gym might be able to handle a third or even fourth exercise in rapid sequence with an honestly high level of intensity. But the natural bodybuilder will over-train in a heartbeat trying to do the same. So I like giant sets, but seldom, if ever, use a sequence of more then two exercises.

Drop Set

Properly executing a drop set starts with a relatively heavy weight set, followed in rapid succession with another set of the same exercise but with a lighter weight. This can continue for almost any number of sets. For example, after a good warm-up doing dumbbell shrugs for your traps, let's assume you work your way up to a strict 100 lbs in each hand for 10 reps. After that, a drop set would involve immediately picking up the 80 lb dumbbells for another 10, followed by the 60 lb dumbbells for 10, and finally 50 lb dumbbells for 10-15. When my diet is on and training is clicking nicely, I love a good drop set. It gives me the added intensity I'm looking for, while at the same time, it doesn't take my focus and concentration away from either the body part I am working or the specific exercise I am absorbed in performing correctly. Simply stated, drop sets are a stupendous way to build muscle and finish off the target body part.

Negatives

Negatives are performed after you've completed a set to failure. A spotter then lifts the weight for you to the top position and then slowly releases it for you to fight on the way down. For example, a guy reaches failure on his sixth repetition with 315 lbs on the barbell flat bench press. The spotter then comes in and basically dead-lifts the weight off the guys chest and back up to the top position for the guy to then resist as it settles back down to his chest. Sound stupid? Well it is. In fact, the only one who's more stupid then the guy doing the set is the guy about to get injured giving him a spot. In a few words, negatives are senseless and inane. Though they might have some role among your tomato-can powerlifters trying to max out, but they won't help you build extreme muscle.

Cheat Reps

Doing cheat repetitions means performing a rep in sloppy form by using momentum to raise the weight. The swing is produced because a given weight is too heavy. The result is that deep muscle fibers are never really fully recruited into action. When training alone and without a spot, a little form-break here and there on the last repetition of a given set may actually be necessary and even helpful. But try not to cheat your repetitions if you don't have to. Also cheating on your early reps is a big mistake, as it reduces the degree of deep stimulation and exposes your body to injury. Try to come up against failure or rely on a spotter to help you just a little bit in getting through the last rep of a set in perfect form. That's the best way to build the most extreme muscle. I should note, as an interesting aside, that over the years, I have seen a few bodybuilders cheat their reps, still grow, and not injure themselves. One was the great Arnold. He would do heavy barbell cheat curls like they were going out of style and no one would dare question his arm development. Even so, these few bodybuilders have almost invariably told me in later years that had their form been sharper they believe their development would have been far greater. Furthermore, I've never, ever seen a guy bring up a weak body part by cheating his ass off. They have always involved guys with a freakishly good body part that decide to overload the weight for ego, or whatever. So it's not to say that you definitely won't grow from cheating your reps, but rather, it's simply not an optimal way to stimulate deep muscle fibers, and certainly, should never be at the centerpiece of any competent routine, regardless of what big guy you might see doing them.

26 Sex Factor

Okay, here it is according to yours' truly—the purpose of life is the act of procreation. As a result, most healthy men generally gravitate toward the need to have regular sex. In so doing, the act of ejaculation supports a healthy male physiology. That's the primary reason why we exist and that's precisely how we are wired. Our bodies are nothing more then vehicles created to support the primary directive of perpetuation of our species.

I remember Joe Weider telling me that everything came back to the sexual act and that this attraction between a man and a woman is the primordial root purpose of our existence. "Sex is the driving force behind why man is programmed to respect big muscles, and seek power, riches, and dominance over others. It's also why the woman is programmed to attract and seduce the man. Women use makeup and dress a certain way to appeal and attract men of prowess and power." Another great inspiration in my life has been Mike Ellis. On the subject, he concurred. He felt that man has ostensibly overrated himself. "We are much closer to animals then we'd like to admit." In particular, herd animals. "The root of man's pursuit of social and physical power and women's attraction to safety, a secure life, a good provider, and a strong procreator, is the very essence of the desire for the sexual act." I couldn't agree more.

It is this instinctive passion for the sexual act that our physiologic makeup is based upon. As men, we are designed, built, and fitted to the specifications of achieving this genetically imprinted pre-programmed purpose. If you contemplate it for a while, you may find that this makes absolute sense both from the standpoint of evolution or divinity, whichever way you want to look at it. I think Freud would agree. But breaking things down further, specifically for men, at the heart of this core purpose is the basic act of ejaculation. I firmly believe our nervous and circulatory systems, our hormones, and our senses exist with this in mind. As a biologist long before I was a practicing physician, I took a very scientific approach to this matter. I still do. While I believe our bodies are built around supporting the sexual act, for the purposes of extreme muscle enhancement, I'm really specifically talking about ejaculation, and how that helps your health and development.

Use It Or Lose It

Without fulfilling this ingrained purpose, our physiology must change. In other words, use it or lose it. Look at it another way. If you've ever broken an arm or leg and had it in a cast for a while, remember what happened when you finally got the cast off. The muscles were small and shriveled from atrophy as a result of the disuse. Well, it's no different when it comes to ejaculating. In fact, when taken to an extreme like a few of my patients with unhappy home lives that have not had sexual relations with their wives for years, eventually all desire is lost. For these poor souls, they can forget about getting excited over an attractive woman and end up settling for the prospect of a few beers and a lawn chair. Of course, though your libido eventually flattens and your testosterone production will fade without regular ejaculation, that's not to say you won't live. In fact, the next pope might very well out live the last one and perhaps you and me in the process. So you certainly can live without ejaculating. But for our purposes—that of extreme muscle enhancement—it's quite necessary to regularly "unload your gun", so-to-speak.

It is interesting to note that practitioners of the Chinese Taoist religion (popular in ancient times) would profoundly disagree with me. Their spiritual leader, Tao, developed sexual practices thousands of years ago that supposedly improved health, promoted a long life, increased mental powers, and sharpened spiritual awareness. These practices centered on the notion that semen was considered to contain man's energetic essence. So while getting excited was okay, you just weren't supposed to ejaculate (or do so very rarely, perhaps for purposes of procreation). Don't ask me how they did this and got everyone to follow. At any rate, at the extreme, they thought that if a man never ejaculates, then his essence will be preserved.

The way I look at it, the entire body is interconnected. One part of the body communicates with another by way of neurotransmitters and hormones. This network of negative and positive feedback maintains the delicate balance of our physical constitution with amazing speed and precision. The pathways that support ejaculation are no different. Tracing things back, a man's ejaculate is the fluid matrix responsible for the safe transportation and deposition of live sperm into the female genital tract. It is produced by glandular fluids from the cells in the prostate and surrounding gland cells. A man's sperm, in turn, contains the very makeup of his genetic code, a set of DNA for matching with a woman's to create new life. Prior to ejaculation, sperm coalesces with ejaculate in the seminiferous tubules within the testicles. Sperm grows and matures in the walls of these tubules in direct response to testosterone produced by neighboring interstitial Leydig cells. Testosterone production at this level is stimulated by the presence of luteinizing hormone (LH) in the blood surrounding the Leydig cells. Blood loaded with LH comes all the way to the testicles from the pituitary gland at the base of the skull. The anterior portion of this gland produces LH in response to gonadotrophic releasing hormone (GnRH), which is produced by a gland above the pituitary, called the hypothalamus. The hypothalamus gets its stimulation from a number of places of input that we still are just beginning to get a handle on. Some forms include neuro-psychological stimulation from the senses (touch, sight, smell, taste, etc.), mood (periods of low stress, joy, bliss, etc.), and just about any type of parasympathetic stimulation. Of course, this sequence of events is also stimulated by the need to produce more mature sperm and thus more ejaculate as these materials are lost after sex. The man who ejaculates regularly is much more apt to enjoy a higher libido, a higher testosterone level, a happier life, and for these reasons, will certainly have an easier time putting on lean muscle.

On the contrary, if the higher neuro-psychological stimulation that starts this whole chain of events is blunted by unpleasant sensory input, high stress, periods of insufficient happiness, or simply disuse, the result will be the opposite. Libido will be the initial casualty and the system eventually starts to shut down. For example, a guy who just got injured, lost his job, and someone close to him suddenly died probably won't feel much like having a passionate love-making session with his woman. Temporarily, your body just shifts gears and bounces back pretty quickly, assuming you get out of your funk sooner rather then later. But too much time in the dumps in the absence of the prerequisite positive neuro-psychological stimulation to foster your libido to the point you feel like getting laid, and you've had it. Chronically, erectile dysfunction eventually sets in and you won't be able to get it up. Even the prostate gland starts to suffer. It is a strongly held belief among a number of healthcare professionals that disuse is directly linked to prostate problems. The prostate is encased in a capsule made up of fibromuscular bands believed to be necessary for squeezing out ejaculate. When these bands are not called upon to contract, they atrophy, while the centrally located cells of the gland itself may slowly enlarge over time. This enlargement (a condition called benign prostatic hypertrophy or "BPH") obstructs urinary flow. At this point, when lifestyle changes, supplements, and medications don't work, the only alternative may be a surgery that could result in impotence.

All right boys, sorry for that harsh reality. Take a breath and relax. It's all going to be okay. Just remember, for reasons that go far beyond your pursuit of an extreme physique enhancement, good ole Dr. C says to just do whatever it takes to keep the plumbing working and it's all going to be just fine.

27 Gaining Muscle As You Age

The fact that the body changes with age hardly means that you have to stop improving your physique or are destined to lose your gains. The truth is, things only get worse and you see yourself shrivel if you don't adapt a new style of training to accommodate a changing and aging physiology. Provided we are not talking about nursing home geriatrics, a man can continue to improve and sharpen his physique well into his later years.

For most guys, the brakes start tapping at about 35 years old. But again, that doesn't mean you can't continue to dramatically improve your build and add mass in the years ahead, but just that you will have to adjust for age-related changes, in order to keep reaching the extreme. Actually, the years from age 35 to your mid-forties, should be some of the most productive years of training in your entire life. You may not pile on mass quite as fast as you did when you were 10 years younger, but you should have developed the advantage of knowing to some degree what motions work best, what motions you should avoid, and how to eat well to gain muscle and not fat. Your routine should be much more efficient and pointed and far less meandering and exploratory. Now you just have to make a few changes to the following elements, and your physique will continue to improve in the years ahead.

The Mind-Muscle Link

First of all, with enough years of bodybuilding under your belt, you will develop the ability to recover quicker between sets. As a result, you should be able to speed through your workouts with greater efficiency, while still reaching a high level of intensity. This has everything to do with the increased deep tissue vascularization and age-cultivated neuromuscular adaptation that only comes from years of training. Once warmed up (which truly may take a little longer then it did in your teens), your muscles will pump up faster. Utilize this to your advantage. In fact, with enough experience, you will cultivate a self-awareness of your "mind-muscle link". In this way you should be able to execute just the right exercises in just the right form to bring out maximum pump with no wasted effort. With the overall muscle conditioning that only comes from putting in your time at the gym, you will be able to speed from one set to another at a rate that cannot be matched by younger bodybuilders. An intense set of bench presses that might take your pec muscles 60-90 seconds to recover from prior to another set, might take a younger bodybuilder two or three minutes. This opens the door for getting more done in a given workout session without overtraining. Routines can be more diverse and you can safely add useful exercises and body parts for training that you might not have otherwise been able to in your younger days without overdoing it by spending too much time in the gym.

However, though your recovery between sets will reach maximum efficiency and shorten as you gain years of experience, don't get too excited. Because the overall time you need to adequately recover between workouts in order to continue to make gains must increase dramatically, and that's my next point. While you will find yourself increasingly able to key-up your intensity and train with greater efficiency, you will need to take more days of rest before training the same body part again. The remedy for this is to incorporate routines that stretch out the cycle of getting through all your body parts before starting over. These include a 2-on, 1-off/2-on, 2-off routine, a 3-on, 1-off/2-on, 2-off routine, a 7-day push-pull routine, or a 10-day split.

But whether you choose one of the routines I've mentioned or some other variation, one of the best tricks to keep your routine stretched out is to never train on more then two consecutive days without at least one day off. This is a strategy that great champions like Mr. Olympia 2006 Jay Cutler utilize to keep from overtraining. In fact, Jay will tell you that few guys love to be in the gym as much as him and if it were up to him, he'd probably be in there training every day. Nevertheless, utilizing the mandatory day or more of rest after at least two consecutive training days has been critical to his bodybuilding success.

Next, as an older bodybuilder, odds are that you are natural. Most guys that experiment with the juice do it in their daring and foolish younger years. Once you get to 35, unless you are a professional looking to compete, the lure of juicing loses its luster. So the point is that you must contend with being a natural bodybuilder who is aging. As a result, you must make the most of each working set you do. Once you're past your warm-up set, it is go-time. Without the assistance of drugs, there is simply so much less room for training error. A lax effort here and a cheated rep there, which you might otherwise get away with and actually still grow from when you are young and/or on drugs, simply won't cut it when you're older and/or clean. Treat every set as if the fire alarm is about to go off while you're training and you'll have to clear out of the gym, cutting your workout short. That way each set gets the maximum effort of the strictest intensity and focus that only comes with the mindset of each working set being your last.

The Fat-Reduction Challenge

Gaining excess body fat is also something that, while it should be avoided at all ages, is of particular importance to the 35 and older bodybuilder. The reason is simple. When most young bodybuilders gain a little extra fat, they just make a few adjustments and they tighten up. The results are seen in days. When you get older, it's just not always that simple. The 35 and older crowd will cut the calories and instead of seeing things start to tighten within a day or two, we just flatten out. Sometimes this flattening will persist for days before any appreciable change in fat loss is seen. In the worst cases, I see guys lose slabs of muscle before they ever see their flank-fat begin to subside. The trick here is that one must allow a much more gradual approach to fat loss. The diet must be very clean. Don't push for those miraculous changes overnight. Changes occur much more slowly and much more modestly, though they do occur.

The moral here is that, though you certainly don't have to be ripped, the older bodybuilder must never gain too much fat because of the ever-increasing challenges faced in taking it off once it's gained. I theorize that this issue might be the result of the high cortisol activity and decreased IGF-1 that comes along with natural age. These hormonal challenges make shedding excess fat, particularly in the abdomen, a true challenge when one wants to still pursue an increase in lean muscle.

To counter this, first pay attention to the cleanliness of your diet. Where you used to get away with the occasional couple of fast-food burgers and a chocolate shake, it just won't cut it now. These forays off the strict path should be rare and countered with cardio. Secondly, while you should be enjoying lots of healthy foods and not starving your body, you will not have the same caloric need or tolerance as you did when you were younger. Simply put, the metabolism is not as high when you're over 35. A prescription of a little less overall caloric intake is in order because, though you may still suffer the compunction of wanting to stuff your face, the truth is, your body just doesn't need as much food as it once did.

Supplementation

As a final point, I have found that certain dietary supplements work extremely well in the older bodybuilder. The ingredients that support natural growth hormone secretion, like arginine, glutamine, and BCAA's can be immensely helpful. Also, the aging body tends to have a higher aromatase activity (this is the enzyme that converts your testosterone to estrogen). It is for this reason that testosterone levels tend to fade with age, while estrogen levels and the feminizing characteristics they bring on, tend to increase with age. I am a bit leery of a lot of the fancy so-called aromatase inhibitors on the market. But simple indole-3-carbinole (I3C) extracted from desiccated broccoli works very well. This naturally occurring substance is currently being researched in the field of cancer prevention and a number of applications. The only problem I've found is, though I see small doses included in some of the formulas, I really don't know how they do this because I've always known I3C to be somewhat unstable. The form I get is custom formulated at one of my vendor pharmacies for my patients and it must be kept refrigerated at all times. I generally use between 2000-3000 milligrams/day for a six-week cycle. I also like to monitor free and total testosterone and total estrogens both before and after the cycle. Interestingly I have found that, while bodybuilders 35 and older find the cycle rejuvenating, with a boost in their ability to burn fat and increase muscle growth, I have not seen similar observations in younger bodybuilders. Finally, I have also found that zinc and copper-enriched formulas have particular benefit in older bodybuilders.

COMPETING IN BODYBUILDING

28 Deciding To Compete

Deciding to compete is an intensely personal decision. It means exposing your physique to the utmost scrutiny and having yourself compared to others. While you might feel like a big-shot hulk when you're wearing three sweatshirts and all covered up in the gym, stepping on stage to compete against other bodybuilders is a whole different ball game. I would say that 99% of muscle builders never step on stage and subject themselves to the scary truth. Most would rather just train and gain as best they can, and I believe they should. But for a select few, there is a higher level they dare to challenge.

Over the years, I have seen guys with countless reasons to compete. Younger guys are fearless and often in a "body-dysmorphic" denial about how they really look. But they're the most enthusiastic about wanting to test their mettle. Some get out there looking pale with no tan, hair they forgot about under their arms, no concept of posing, or completely missing everything but a couple of little lumps for biceps. But sometimes you can spot a real freak that displays quality beyond their years with enough to compete in the men's division. Perhaps the greatest such teen freak competitor I can remember was Casey Viator. He actually won the Mr. America in 1971, while still a teenager. He was only 19!

Sage Age Advice

My advice to the prospective young competitor is to not compete until you are at least 18 or 19 years of age. This is because many amateur organizations won't make a class distinction based on age. In fact, many promoters won't make the decision to split a class this way until they see how many competitors show up that day. As a result, if you decide to compete at too young an age, like 17 or younger, you may find yourself up against insurmountable competition from guys 18 and 19. At such young ages, those couple of years make a huge difference. I mean, bodybuilding aside, just think about comparing the average 19 year old to the average 17 year old. There's no comparison and on stage, it can be embarrassing and I think unfair. But it happens, so you need to be aware of it and plan for it if it applies to you.

Practice With A Primer Show First

Also, prior to your first show, planning a rinky-dink "primer" show to compete in some distant town is a good strategy. By keeping it quiet and just among the close buddies helping you, you can hit this show a week or two before the big one and work out the kinks. This way you can get used to being on stage, get some pictures, improve your skin-tone, work out the posing kinks, and polish things up overall before appearing in front of all the friends and family that will inevitably crowd the auditorium just to see you. I remember using this strategy years ago with a young and freakishly good teenage bodybuilder. Mark competed at 17 years old. I let him do it at such a young age because he had the potential for success. He really wanted to get up there, plus we found a show that included a 17-and-under class. But as the family fanfare grew over what was to be the young guy's first show, and he was inundated with well-meaning inquiries from countless relatives and friends, the pressure increased. It wasn't fun anymore. Mark was just plain worried and nervous about how he was going to do. I presented my strategy of a primer show to him in order to take the heat off. He loved the idea and really felt that it would take the pressure off him. So I planned a small competition out on Long Island about two weeks before his publicly announced show. It worked like a charm. He got through his posing routine with some key errors we had to fix, we got some pictures to show him first-hand how to improve his poses and color, and he got rid of his nervousness and fear because now he knew what to expect. Surprisingly, he actually placed second and took home a trophy (which he kept in my car until after the next show). By the time he got to the main show, he was stellar, kicked the competitions ass, and looked so polished and impressive, that Mark was the talk of the show, even among audience members that were there just to see the open-class competitors.

Beyond strategy, when it comes to your conditioning, the best thing you can do as a teenager looking to compete, is to get your body fat as low as possible. This will give you the best chance to look good on stage and beat out competition. Generally speaking, teenagers don't have much mass compared to the open class. But nor are they expected to by the judges. I mean let's face it, it's tough to build much mass when you've had so few years of training under your belt. So the best showing you can offer is to display a hard body. Most teenagers make the mistake of trying to show as much mass as possible, not realizing that they won't end up with much and just look fat onstage. You can exploit this perpetual oversight and take advantage by being lean and cut. In short, training hard and waiting until you're in your late teenage years to compete, and being as well-groomed, tanned, and shredded as you can be is the way to have a proud showing.

Bodybuilding competitors from 20 to about 35 are generally the most serious. The physique quality tends to be at its highest between these ages, at all levels of competition, both among professionals and amateurs, as well as natural and drug shows. Competitors in these open divisions tend to not only have the best physiques, but they're the most competitive and tenacious about winning. These guys that compete in the open are often resolute about bodybuilding because many are trying to make a living at it and build a future in the sport. Most fans are coming to see the biggest and freakiest physiques on stage, which are almost always found in the open class.

Competition Is Not For Everyone

With the open class as competitive as it is, my advice to the prospective competitor is to be brutally honest with yourself and if you aren't as sure as you can possibly be that you can stand toe-to-toe with the big boys, don't get onstage. As a safeguard, find some mentors that will level with you. Remember, that 90% of open-class bodybuilders you talk to say they are top 10% material. Think about that for a moment. They obviously can't be right. So relying on your own self-assessment in this case is riddled with perils. My advice is to play it safe and get one or two qualified people to tell you how you really look and how they think you would fare in the open class competition you want to enter. If they feel you have what it takes, then go for it. Just make sure you're ready to give it 100% effort in preparation. Any less will result in a disappointing showing.

As an ever-increasing number of bodybuilders age, we have seen the masters competition grow in popularity over the years. Classes have expanded from what was just the "over 40" class to also include at many levels, "over 50", "over 60", and even "over 70" classes. These guys don't always carry the mass of the open class bodybuilders and sometimes hold a little extra stubborn body fat on a wider waist. Even so, they often show some of the best muscle density and maturity as well some freaky body part development. These guys are past their prime and compete for the pure love of the sport. They are the most inspiring. For these reasons, I have to admit that sometimes seeing the masters compete is the most enjoyable part of the bodybuilding shows I go to.

Due to obvious age, master class bodybuilders generally have the admiration of the crowd, and even get overly generous accolades at times. They have the least chance of embarrassing themselves. While my advice to the prospective master competitor is to have a proud showing by looking as good as possible, you have a little more latitude then the competitors in other classes. So enjoy yourself and the experience.

My old buddy Doug Morgan was a guy I helped to national level masters competitive success. He was ripped at about 6'2" and 220 lbs. Though a real bona fide heavyweight and serious about competition, he always had a smile on his face, enjoyed the ride, and simply felt lucky to be up there. I always remember his admirable attitude and the fun he felt. In this way I probably learned as much from him as he did from me.

29 Show Strategy

Tested Vs Untested Shows

Bodybuilding competitions can be generally grouped into drug-tested shows versus non-tested shows. Bodybuilders in natural shows are obviously much smaller then their drug-taking counterparts, but you can expect the competition to be as tough because everyone is tested and on a level playing field. The polygraph is the most common method of testing for these shows. If this is the type of show you decide to enter, I always suggest trying to get tested as far in advance of the show as the promoters will allow. This way you don't risk a surprise failure on the day of the show. The accuracy of the polygraph is very much dependent on the skill of the examiner. As a result, it is not at all unusual to find guys that fail the polygraph, while not having taken drugs or violated the rules in any way. A combination of a poor examiner and a nervous examinee is a formula for disaster. So it's good to get it out of the way as early as possible. If you ask, which most guys don't, many promoters will allow you to be tested in the weeks prior to the show, provided you make your own arrangements and travel to the polygrapher.

Knowing you passed prior to the show not only takes that stress off your shoulders, but it's one less thing you have to do on the day of the contest. Knowing you won't be disqualified prior to the day of the show also saves possible embarrassment. In the summer of 2003, I attended a bodybuilding show to watch an old friend of mine compete in the masters class of a local natural show. He knew my advice about getting tested ahead of time but chose to do it his way. In addition to me attending the show, a number of people close to him showed up to give their support. Unfortunately, and surprisingly, he failed the polygraph and was not allowed to compete in the show. It was an intense humiliation for him and something I know he will never forget, and neither will his friends.

Of course, if you can't arrange testing in advance of the show or the promoter does not allow it, relax. Just get it done the day of the show. As long as you know you have not screwed up, you are telling the truth, and you have nothing to hide, just go with the flow and relax.

Untested bodybuilding shows are another matter. You have nothing to worry about in terms of testing. You just have to worry about the competition. Since there is no drug testing, there are basically no rules to follow in preparation. Thus, guys can and will do anything to win. If you are a drug-free bodybuilder and want to try and make it in an untested show, it's next to impossible. No bodybuilder I know of ever made it to the big-time professional level without drug use. It's a sad reality, but that's honestly what you are dealing with. So if bodybuilding is more of a fun hobby for you, my advice is to stay natural and stick with the drug-tested shows. If you are more serious about competing in bodybuilding, there is no question that the higher level of competition is found in the untested shows. You'll have some tough decisions to make in terms of whether it makes sense to litter your body with drugs in order to hang with the competition at this level. The way I see it, you better be killing the competition at the drug-free level before remotely considering the risk-to-benefit ratio of no longer being natural. There are few things more pathetic than a guy who risks dumping a truckload of anabolic steroids into his body, only to place out of the top five in his competition.

But that said, assuming you decide for whatever reason that you're going to try your hand at an untested show. You'll be faced with another important decision. The major amateur division right now is the National Physique Committee (NPC). Their shows are not drug tested and freaks abound. Among the choices of competition, you'll need to consider the type of show you are facing. Some types of NPC shows are just local or regional shows and nothing more (i.e., they don't lead to anything greater). A select few across the country, however, are considered national qualifier events. Generally finishing in the top two of your class in such a show will qualify you to move on to national level competitions. Subsequently, class-winners at the nationals transcend the amateur level. They can get their professional cards with the International Federation of Body Builders (IFBB) and compete in professional shows for prize money, contracts, and endorsements. Just remember, the competition will be a heck of a lot stiffer in the national qualifier show, than the NPC show.

If this is the road you choose, my suggestion is to take it in steps. Try your hand at a regular NPC show first. If you have trouble there, then there's no sense in competing in a national qualifier until you improve. On the other hand, if you win at least your class in the open, then anything short of a subsequent national qualifier is a waste of time.

Adam was a guy I helped to get to the nationals. At around 6'4" and 275 ripped pounds, this guy was impressive, to say the least. But what really made him one of the most phenomenal "freakazoids" I ever helped, was the fact that he was good enough for me to put him in an NPC national qualifier for his first show! Needless to say, he won his class and qualified for the nationals. Shortly thereafter, life threw poor Adam a couple of curves that he had trouble handling and he never found his way back to bodybuilding. But, by competing at a level appropriate for his physique, at least he didn't waste his effort in competition.

30 Contest Dieting

Once you decide that you are going to compete, the next and most important consideration is diet. Make sure you check with your own physician first. Review your entire approach in detail with them and get their blessing. Keep them in the loop every week and make sure they are intimately aware of your every move before you make it. That's important because in my book, you have to get completely ripped. In the old days, you could get away with being a little smooth as long as you were big. But those days are over. Anything short of being shredded leaves the door open for you to get beat. If you get ripped, you can beat guys much bigger and better then you. At the professional level, Andreas Munzer is a perfect example of a guy with limited genetics that soared through the professional ranks and onto magazine covers, all because of his shredded condition. Clarence Bass even wrote a book on being ripped, and no one would have given his build a second look if it weren't for his incredibly low body fat. On the other hand, guys blessed with amazing genetics but just can't get super ripped can end up losing to worse bodybuilders. Though examples like Mike Matarrazo, Lee Priest, and Mike Quinn abound at the professional level, guys that never reach a truly ripped overall state can be found at every level of competition. So the greatest equalizer is being shredded, and being shredded has everything to do with perfect pre-contest dieting.

Pre-Contest

That said, most amateur shows are scheduled throughout the summer months, so timing is critical. Assuming your body fat is within reason (generally <10%), dieting for a bodybuilding competition will require a minimum of 12 weeks of contest prep. So if your body is above the 10% level, you will need to lose that weight first before entering the rigors of pre-contest dieting. Remember not to kid yourself on this one. Unlike your training, where you can skip a day here and there with little or no detriment, dieting for a show just does not work that way. Once you are too far behind, you won't be able to make it up. So being accurate and honest with your baseline condition is essential.

If there is any doubt, the best bet is to have your body fat tested at your local doctor's office (if they offer the service), nutritionist, or even university. Hydrostatic weighing (water submersion) may be the best conventional method, but it tends to be only offered at major universities that have exercise physiology departments and offer the service to the general public. If you can get it done, that's great, but if you can't, bioelectrical impedance analysis (also known as BIA or plethysmography) is perhaps the easiest and most available way. It's even offered at most gyms and simply requires the placing of some electrodes. Just be sure you're fasting beforehand. Also widely available are skin calipers, which involves an examiner using the device to pinch areas of skin with underlying fat from sites around the body. Usually, both 3-site and 7-site measurements are offered. The 7-site is more accurate. When performed properly, both BIA and 7-site calipers are accurate within reason.

Diet Baseline

Next, after making sure you're within acceptable shooting distance for the show and you've mapped out your timeline, you need to nail down your diet baseline. If you don't have a precise fix on what you've been eating, you need to immediately do a 3-day diet log. Don't change anything in your diet yet. Just eat as normally as you have been but write down each and every piece of food, supplement, and drink you put into your body and at exactly what times you consumed them. Using a piece of paper, a pencil, and carbohydrate counter that you can find for free online or purchase for a few dollars at your local bookstore, this simple exercise will allow you to precisely calculate the amount of carbohydrates you've taken in each day. Once you figure this out, take an average of all three days. That will give you a precise establishment of your baseline carbohydrate intake.

Your protein intake amount should stay stable throughout the pre-contest period. This will come out to about 1 gram per pound of bodyweight or roughly 20-23 grams every 2-3 waking hours, with the exception of the post-workout meal, when you can add an additional 10-20 grams of protein. Your fat intake should also remain stable throughout this period. This should come out to roughly 30-40 grams of strictly healthy dietary fat each day. So with the macronutrients of protein and fat really being non-variables, it should be clear that contest dieting is all about carbohydrate management.

The first dietary adjustment you need to make has nothing to do with drastic cuts and going overboard too early. Instead, before we cut back on anything, what we want is 3-days of rigorous dietary consistency. Prior to these three days, you precisely map out and plan the schedule for all the meals you intend to take in, along with the exact timing of these meals. The subsequent three days should be nothing more then an exercise in precise dietary consistency, and nothing more. You must plan how to get in all your protein meals along with your requirement of essential fat, plus properly spacing the daily average carbohydrate intake that you calculated during your 3-day diet log. Surprisingly, this may end up being either less or even more of the total calories you're used to taking in. That's why relying solely on caloric intake is so problematic. During these 3 days you should just be eating exactly the same things at exactly the same times, each and every day. The idea is to nail down your baseline with exactness. This may seem boring, but it is the absolute best way to get control of your diet and make proper changes. Otherwise, you'll just be shooting in the dark when it comes time to start cutting things.

Let's take an example of a 25-year-old, natural, 220 lb bodybuilder at 9% body fat. With no other special considerations, he may likely come in with the following baseline profile:

30 grams of protein for 6 meals + one meal of 50 grams	= 230 grams/day = 920 calories
40 grams of fat from mixed sources	= 360 calories
300 grams of carbohydrates	= 1200 calories
Total calories	**= 2480**

Using this model, the next step after 3-days of standardization and consistency are firmly established, is to be sure that your protein and fats are at the correct levels. Remember that, though dietary fat will come down a little, these levels are going to stay virtually consistent right up until the show. So if you find that your protein is too low or too high, your fat is too low or too high, or either is from a poor source, you must make those changes immediately. Based on a body fat of 10%, protein intake should be roughly a gram per pound of bodyweight and fat intake should be about 25% of your total baseline calorie intake. In the example given, it would mean that this guy would have to slightly reduce his protein intake, clean up the types of fats he's eating to focus on the essential fatty acids and reduce that amount to about 30 grams/day. Once these levels are reached, they should remain fairly consistent throughout the diet period despite the inevitable drop in bodyweight, carbohydrates, and total calories. These adjustments should be executed immediately and maintained for a 3-day adjustment period.

On the last day of the first week of your diet, it's time to add in sodium. Don't get nervous, I'll explain later. But as long as your own doctor says it's okay, your sodium must be temporarily high, not low, in the early stages of dieting. It will definitely cause you to retain more water and make you smoother, but that is actually what I want to happen this early in the game. So make sure that you have at least 8 grams of salt (roughly 3200 milligrams of sodium) in your daily diet somewhere. If your calculations from food and supplement labels seem to come up short, just use table salt. Don't worry if you are a little over either. That's okay, I'd rather you overshoot the mark a little. Sodium levels that are too low this early will negatively influence your final condition.

Carb-Cutting Concerns

By now, we're on to the second week and only have 11 to go. It's time to draw our attention to carbohydrates. This is where it gets tricky because you have to rely on how you look to determine if and when to cut carbohydrates. Since we rely on the mirror, I have a couple of tips. Try to have one or two more experienced guys help you out and assess your physique every three days, and avoid daily stares in the mirror. In the last few weeks, you can stare at yourself every day, but overly scrutinizing your conditioning this early will quickly become maddening in the weeks ahead. Keeping these assessment sessions to every three days and having outside input from guys with experience is a good way to prevent you from driving yourself crazy, or simply making the wrong call. A bad call would be to cut carbohydrates, while you're still getting harder. Remember, if you're still getting tighter every three days on the same amount of carbohydrates, there is no need to drop the amount just for the sake of dropping it. Only when you and your colleagues are certain that your condition is unchanged from one assessment session to the next, is it ever time to drop carbohydrates.

Nevertheless, as a general guideline, given the 12-week preparation and adequate base lining, I generally don't like dropping more than 10% of your original baseline level of carbohydrates in any one-week period. Over the years I've found that an 8% drop tends to be the most accurate overall number I can use without flattening the muscle. It doesn't seem like such a big drop at first, but really catches up to you because what begins as a small portion of total carbohydrate reduction ends up increasing in proportion exponentially as this same amount is dropped. Take the example I gave, where the guy is base-lined at 300 grams of carbohydrates each day, 8% of which equals 24 grams. Since he's got roughly 11 more weeks ahead, if his body allows him to push to the extreme to get him ripped by dropping carbohydrates by 8% of his original baseline each week, he'll end up taking in less then 40 grams/day. Now that's not necessarily a bad thing, but you just want to make sure such a schedule is necessary. Again, remember that it's critical to avoid overshooting the mark by being too aggressive with your carbohydrate cutting. You will be training fairly intensely this whole time, and if your nutrient needs are not met, you'll flatten out and lose mass fast! To maximize the effect, follow the diet directions I have just given you and you should enjoy excellent results.

Training For The Show

Virtually nothing has been written about how you adjust your training for the bodybuilding competition, yet a tremendous body of conventional wisdom does exist. Traditionally, old-school bodybuilders have subscribed to the theory that you have to start training lighter and with higher repetitions in order to bring out more cuts as you get into the pre-contest phase. Unfortunately, this approach led to too many guys losing valuable size.

The Method Makes The Man

A better method is to try to keep your repetition range consistent. For example, while you're losing body weight during training, you'll naturally have to back off your poundage a little just to keep the repetition range the same. In other words, you must keep pushing significant poundage, but you must also back off the weight a little in order to accommodate the fact that with each week you will be progressively weaker as a result of the weight loss. This approach will preserve size, while avoiding the injuries that you'll be more susceptible to as your body fat becomes progressively lower.

Another popular but controversial training adjustment involves incorporating more of what are called "cutting movements". These include cable movements and machines as opposed to the more standard free weight movements. For example, incorporating more cable cross-over to train the chest versus dumbbell press. My advice on this point is that the results are variable so you have to be careful. As a general rule of thumb, if you have a good chance of being ripped, while maintaining some good size, these adjustments can work wonders and bring out muscle density. For example, leg-extensions for quads was just about all former Mr. Olympia Lee Haney used to do leading up to competitions. Then again, if you're on the smooth side and don't see yourself truly getting ripped and/or you just don't have the mass to sacrifice, making these adjustments may produce disastrous results. This can happen as you do less of the basic movements that built your muscle in the first place and more of these cutting movements that tend to sacrifice a bit of size.

Increasing the amount of cardio is also a consideration when adjusting your training in the pre-contest period. As everyone knows, cardio is a great fat burner. But generally, my advice to the natural bodybuilder is to stay away from cardio because it tends to deplete muscle mass, especially in the legs. At the very least, it will cause muscles to lose their fullness everywhere on the body. Instead, let the diet do the fat burning. The only natural exception is the bodybuilder with thick legs who has a fairly low percent of body fat to begin with. A guy with this kind of build can get super shredded using this approach. Natural bodybuilder Peter Neff was a perfect example. With his massive quads and low body fat, he used to do these little jogs and bike rides that got him so shredded that many to this day refuse to believe he was natural, but he was.

But cardio for the drug-using bodybuilder is a different story altogether. In almost every case, the results of incorporating liberal amounts of cardio into the pre-contest regimen are terrific. I attribute this to the drugs allowing the body to tolerate the systemic load that the cardio places on the body, while not sacrificing muscle mass. It seems that the drugs almost create a new internal milieu that puts body fat first on the front line of incineration priorities, while exerting a protective effect against the catabolic destruction of muscle mass that so easily occurs in the natural bodybuilder.

One major point to remember during this pre-contest regimen is to stop all training, including cardio, at least 4 days before the show. This will allow all the muscle to be rested and as full looking as possible. On the other hand, if you don't stop, the rigors of weight training during this vulnerable time will cause your body to incinerate all your muscle. Also, if you choose to do cardio during this phase, you'll retain more water because cardio triggers secretion of an adrenal hormone called aldosterone. This hormone is an anti-diuretic and will cause your body to hang on to water and look smoother.

Getting Ripped

Once you officially begin your pre-contest diet and training and things start getting dialed in to a regimen that gradually drops fat while preserving mass, the challenge shifts solely to getting the body as ripped as possible. Getting ripped is really the most important element to competitive success. I would even argue that it is more important than being big. In fact, I've seen the ripped guy beat the bigger, smoother guy, countless times. Perhaps this is because a guy that is ripped looks incredibly impressive under the lights and in front of the lens. This is in sharp contrast to being big and smooth, which looks terrible under the lights and even worse in front of the lens. In addition to the obvious merits of being shredded, I have always felt that this prejudice by the judges is simply a logical favoritism toward the guy that appears to have taken the show more seriously. For these reasons, many a too-small man has entered a show ripped, beaten a slew of big smooth guys, and won his class. Nevertheless, your goal should still be to be as big as possible, while still getting ripped. That's where proper pre-contest dieting comes into play.

Assuming your calorie cutting and training adjustments are working to peel progressively more fat from your body, you are then ready for the next step. At this point, the most critical facet in understanding how to get super-chiseled has far less to do with fat burning and much more to do with salt and water management.

The Salt Solution

To begin to comprehend this curious assertion, one must first understand the importance of salt in the diet. It all starts with short-sighted physicians misinforming their patients about salt, combined with ensuing media-hype that has put us on the wrong road. In this case, sodium (also known as simple table salt) is the so-called culprit. We're nearly all convinced that sodium is somehow bad for us, including bodybuilders. It most likely started from early medical evidence in patients with salt-sensitive hypertension or kidney problems who saw their conditions exacerbated. But these are the exceptions that only occur under conditions of abnormal physiology (i.e., disease). The truth is, in otherwise normal physiology, dietary salt certainly does not cause these diseases. In fact, in the form of sodium, salt is an absolutely essential mineral that the human body is intimately dependent upon. Everything from serving at the cellular level as an electrolyte during neuromuscular activity, to working as a critical component in molecular transport systems, to functioning as an enzymatic cofactor in countless reactions throughout the body, sodium must be present. Therefore, dietary salt intake is healthy and quite necessary.

As bodybuilders, we have fallen into the same trap of misguided conventional wisdom. Simply put, I believe dietary salt intake is one of the most powerful yet underestimated anabolic substances readily available to each and every one of us.

My old training partner Greg Valentino and I stumbled on the magic of salt quite serendipitously. We used to train at an upstate New York gym in Yorktown Heights called Bob Baff's. Back then we would spend hours in the gym. We loved the gym so much but were hopelessly over-trained. That said, sometimes we'd meet in the parking lot and, despite a sizeable breakfast, just decide on the spot that we needed more food to get through the impending lengthy workout. Short of driving back to the diner, the only place within a short walk was this crummy Chinese restaurant in the same shopping complex as the gym. Though convenient, the food sucked. They would load up everything with salt, salt, salt, and extra salt. We used to joke about it not really mattering whether you would order the chicken, beef, shrimp, or whatever, it all tasted the same—salty. So why did we keep going back? Well, every time we'd come out of there and hit the weights, we'd pump like crazy. I mean, it was freakish. Gregg and I both saw the immediate results with the pump lasting far longer. For a while we just figured it was the extra calories that did it. But after trying diner food and some other options just because we got tired of eating at that same stink-hole every morning, we found out the hard way that there was no substitute for our ritual Chinese salt torture. Nothing produced the same results.

As to how much sodium we were taking in one sitting, I don't know, but figure it must have been at least 5 grams of sodium! To put this in perspective, table salt contains about 40% sodium. So a teaspoon of salt (which weighs about 5 grams) is going to contain roughly 2 grams of sodium. It seems like a huge amount, especially when measured against American Heart Association recommendations that salt intake not exceed 2400 mg each day. Then again, in many other countries, salt intake is amazingly high. Some groups regularly ingest up to 8 grams or more of salt each day. Again, as a cause of disease in an otherwise normal physiology, the link has simply not been proven. That's not to say you should run out and consume mass quantities, but it does explain why high salt intake seems so well tolerated in so many, and why we survived our regular forays unscathed.

So what exactly is going on in the body that makes an acute, orally ingested sodium load such an effective pump enhancer? To understand this better, one must examine the role of sodium in muscle activation. Before a muscle cell contraction occurs, the inside of each cell has a negative electric charge when compared to the positive exterior of the cell. This state of "polarization" is not achieved passively. It's an active process created and maintained by a series of cellular pumps that produce higher concentrations of positively charged sodium molecules (Na+) outside the cell, while keeping in higher concentrations of negatively charged chloride molecules (Cl-) within each muscle cell. The concentration of sodium outside the muscle cell is some 10 times greater than within, resulting in a net negative "resting muscle cell potential" charge of about -75 millivolts (mV) relative to the cell surroundings. So each muscle cell sitting there waiting to contract exists with a negative charge as a result of the hard work of cellular pumps that set up this electrical gradient.

When the muscle cell is stimulated to fire off and contract, special sodium channels in the membrane of the muscle cell open. As a result, sodium rushes into the cell to balance out and neutralize the gradient. Sodium floods in and, as the signal is propagated throughout the muscle cell, a confluent muscle contraction begins. Entry of sodium is balanced by the exit of potassium molecules (K+), whose concentration inside the muscle cell is about 20 times greater then outside the cell. As stimulation comes to an end, sodium channels close and potassium channels open. Sodium molecules are again actively moved out of the cell by the work of the sodium pumps, while potassium molecules are pumped back in, thus restoring the gradient.

This basic electrophysiology of the muscle cell tells that vigorous contraction is intimately dependent on a high concentration of sodium molecules outside the muscle cells. It would seem to make sense that a bodybuilder looking to create maximal muscle contractions during weight training in order to facilitate a great pump but whose sodium concentration was too low, simply won't have muscle cells that perform optimally at the molecular level. Augmenting this gradient with orally ingested sodium might be the factor that sets off a more rigorous influx of sodium molecules into the muscle cells, resulting in a more efficient contraction. I call it "contraction potential". It's akin to having more water built up behind a damn. Open the floodgates and water careens through with explosive force.

Once this greater contraction potential is exploited during intense bodybuilding training, cascades of anabolic effects are triggered. The first and foremost sign is the brisker contraction. The muscle just seems to respond more vigorously when called upon to contract. This greater responsiveness sets up the ability to call upon deeper muscle fibers to move the weight. In other words, you should be acutely stronger because more individual muscle fibers will be more easily available for active recruitment. It's a sensation that your novice bodybuilder or guy with less muscle mass is just not going to appreciate. But with a reasonable degree of mass on your body and a few years of consistent training under your belt, you should easily notice the difference. To better explain, while each muscle cell fires in an all-or-none fashion, individual fibers simply don't all recruit at once. In other words, you need far fewer fibers to pick up a glass of water and drink then you do when performing standing alternate curls with 65 lb dumbbells.

That said, exploiting the greater contraction potential by training heavier and/or more intensely sets up the need for local vasodilation in the area of the muscle being trained because more lactic acid is produced. This lactic acid must be cleared from the muscle. Doing so requires increased circulation. Circulation and pump go hand-in-hand—the greater the local circulation, the greater the pump.

Additionally, sodium is what I call "the world's cheapest cell volumizer". Though much less sodium exists inside the muscle cells than outside, as explained, there is still a significant concentration within muscle and within the other cells of the body. Tendons, ligaments, organs, and connective tissue are all made up of cells. The cells of the body are bathed in the substances we ingest, including sodium. Sodium obviously attracts and retains water. Having the cells well hydrated protects them from injury. In this way, an optimal level of sodium, and thus water in the cells, as long as you are not in the final stages of preparing for bodybuilding competition, is decidedly advantageous for the bodybuilder desiring lean muscle mass gains.

So with all that in mind, it should be clear to you why dietary salt is so important. The biggest mistake you can make in preparing for a contest is to cut salt out of the diet too early. For reasons explained, your dietary salt intake should actually be high, and so should your water intake. In fact, except for the last few weeks before the show, I like every bodybuilder I work with to actually look somewhat watery during the dieting process and stay that way for most of the pre-contest phase! This helps anabolism and protects the body from injury. But what gets guys off track is the intimidating concept of looking like they're retaining water at any point in the pre-contest period. It's tough when you're in the gym training and everybody knows you're going to compete and, as the contest date looms ever closer, they start thinking and saying you're too smooth. Typically, guys get nervous and start cutting salt out too early. The problem is, these guys flush out a little water early on but in the process flatten out like pancakes and drop lean mass like crazy. It's a stupid move. Most nervous moves are stupid moves. This is no exception.

The trick is to avoid getting nervous. Instead, learn what to do and how to use it as a great advantage over the others. Managing this critical period is one of the things I've always been best at. Countless bodybuilders over the years have turned to me for my expertise in pre-contest fluid and electrolyte management and how to safely get rid of subcutaneous water prior to competition. There are some real super, yet simple tricks here, and I'll reveal them to you.

First of all, don't cut dietary salt until three weeks before the show. In fact, if you make it a point to salt nearly everything up until that time, you will get the best result. Beware, however, that it will cause you to retain a boat load of water. But that's the idea. Meanwhile, everyone around you will probably be in a panic, which you'll find hard to not get drawn into. If you have a weight class to make, you may easily be 10 pounds or more above your final weight. This must also be considered and counted for. The key is not to deviate from this path of liberal salt and water intake until you reach the next critical step.

Cut The Salt, Keep The Water

The next critical step works best at the three-week point, prior to the day of the show. At this point, you must suddenly go from the super high salt intake you were used to, to a super low salt intake. You do this by eliminating all forms of table salt and all high salt foods and condiments. You must do this, while at the same time, continuing to take in the same liberal amounts of water. So again, you must cut the salt but not the water. Since water follows salt throughout the body, the natural water shedding that occurs is dramatic. In the few days that follow, literally pounds of water are released and the body quickly begins to tighten like a drum. But you must remember, that it is still critical that you not dehydrate your body at this point. The more water you take in, the better, but no other fluids whatsoever.

Though a tiny bit of incidental salt will still be in your body from the natural foods you eat, all identifiable additive salt should be eliminated from the diet. Using de-mineralized water instead of tap water is a popular practice during this time that I find unnecessary and probably counterproductive because the small amount of salt in regular tap water is actually essential for normal bodily functions. But if you want something to really be concerned about, be aware of some protein shakes and certain supplements that have high amounts of sodium. While some of these products are awesome, those with a lot of salt will kill your condition within three weeks of the show.

I generally like to cut out supplements and just rely on food these last few weeks. That way I don't have to drive myself nuts with what might or might not be in the different products I use. Also, this is a good time to knock out all artificial sweeteners since some contain sodium or salt moieties that amount to table salt equivalents. So the diet at this point is going to not only be minimal in calories, but will be very bland—and most challenging.

Carb Up

Once you make the sudden switch from a high sodium intake to purging all excess salt from your body, you'll be unable to retain water no matter how much you drink. For this reason, in the days and weeks ahead, you will shed fluid and many pounds of body weight. Unfortunately, you will see the greatest strength drop as well and you will feel increasingly crummy. The trick is, even though your body won't be able to hold on to much water, you keep drinking a great deal. Anything less then a gallon each day is probably a mistake. Of course, anything more then two gallons each day is also probably a mistake. It's a touchy balancing act. While you must maintain a steady flow of water intake because your body simply won't be able to hang on to it, if you overdue the intake, you can run into a condition called hypotonic hyponatremia. This condition is caused by excess water diluting the existing sodium level in your blood. In its mildest form the condition results in light-headedness and fatigue. At its most severe, it can cause seizures, loss of consciousness, and even death.

As long as you're smart about it, it should be smooth sailing. That is of course, until you have to drop the water as well! During these last few weeks of liberal hydration, the idea is to simply focus attention back onto progressing the diet by continuing to reduce carbohydrates in the way I discussed. Once you're within days of the show, it's time to "carb-up". The purpose of carbing up is to replace all the glycogen that is usually stored in the muscle, but has now been depleted from dieting. Once glycogen returns to the muscles, they appear fuller. They also pull in more fluid from the subcutaneous layers and into the muscle, thus helping in the "drying out" process.

I generally like to carb-up my guys two days before the show, more one day before the show, and the day of the show. To estimate the amount of carbohydrates you need to consume on the first day of carbing up and on the second, use the table I've provided.

Estimated Daily Carbohydrate Range for Carbing-up

LCL Multiplier

		DAY#1*	DAY#2*
Lowest Carb-level (LCL)	100+g	2-4x	4-7x
	75-100g	4-6x	6-9x
	50-75g	6-8x	8-11x
	25-50g	8-10x	10-13x
	10-25g	10-12x	12-15x

Day#1 occurs two days before the show and is the first day of carbing-up, while Day#2 refers to the day before the show and is the second full day of carbing-up.

For example, assume you've worked your carbs down to between 10 grams (incidental carbs even in protein foods usually preclude anyone from ever really getting to a true zero) and 25 grams on the last day of caloric restriction. According to my table, you will need to carb-up on this first day by consuming between 10-12x this level. So if we take 25 grams as the number, you will need to add in 250-300 grams on the first day of carbing up and 300-375 grams on the second. At the other extreme, if you take in 100 or more grams of carbohydrates on your last day of restriction, you will need to add in 200-400 grams on the first day of carbing up and 400-700 grams on the second.

Choosing the lower or upper limit of your range, or somewhere in between, is a challenging task that requires a great deal of accurate self-assessment. It really will depend on your condition in relation to how low you were required to drop your carbohydrates to achieve this ripped status. Yet, different body types have different responses. Also, psychosocial challenges (life's usual hassles) naturally happen during the course of a diet that will influence your compliance and success. Thus, it can take you off schedule. But as a general rule, if you look like you're peaking in ripped condition for the day of the show, then the upper limit of your estimated range is probably in order, whereas if you're looking like you're peaking but find you didn't need to push your carbohydrates much below 100 grams per day to get there, the lower range limit may suffice.

Carbing up my way would be pure fun if not for the fact that I also severely limit fluid intake during this time and right up through the day of the show. When carbing up, choose what I call "dry carbs". Though you will need to take in some oral fluids, which I will explain, the reason that the carbs must be dry is so that you can more precisely control and accurately measure your fluid intake. If your carbs are wet, you simply won't have any idea how much fluid you're getting and could take in too much. I tend to like plain boiled or baked potatoes and corn. I also like liberal amounts of dried fruit because of the laxative effect. With dried fruits, the colon empties. As a result, fecal matter is evacuated along with more water. The waist will be smaller and the abs will be flatter, sinking into the ribcage, thus easier to control and flex. Ironically, even though you're trying to dry out by avoiding fluids during this time, you must ingest a small, controlled amount of fluid on this day. If you don't have a little fluid on board, you just won't get the fullness you're looking for. A small amount of orally ingested fluid is still required to efficiently draw the ingested carbohydrates into the muscle. For fluid on the first day of carbing-up and the first day of dehydrating, I usually use 10 ounces of all-natural grapefruit juice, sipped throughout the day. For the second day (day before the show), I drop this level to 6 ounces. I like it in the form of grapefruit juice because of its acidity and unique nutritive fat-burning content (for what it's worth at this point, I do realize you won't have much time to burn off any more fat). Since the body is now thirsty for both water and carbohydrate, most all of it will end up in the muscles. Just remember to enjoy the little sips because that's all the fluid you get all day!

Finally, assuming you are officially ripped, it's at this point that I usually use sherbet as my only source of carbs on the day of the show. Since prejudging is usually around mid-day, you won't have a lot of time to eat. Sherbet is ideal because it is cold and thus quenches the thirst, while providing the body with a good soaking to keep the muscle full on the day of the show. You should drink absolutely no fluid. Sherbet provides all the moisture you will need. Avoiding solid carb foods and relying instead on sherbet is also advantageous on contest day because this will keep your stomach flat and your waist in.

33 Contest Posing

Once you get inside five weeks of the show, the adjustments you'll need to make come fast and furious. In the fifth week out, I like to start adding regular posing. From here on in, you should set aside an hour every day to practice your posing. This measure gets you polished and ready for a good stage showing and gives you enough lead-time to work out any glitches. Also, pre-contest posing tends to sharpen your physique, bringing out a higher degree of cuts and vascularity.

Mandatory Poses

The first thing you'll need to work on are the mandatory poses (i.e., those that all competitors will likely be subjected to by the judges either alone or in comparison to others). This begins with simply standing front and center and then making four quarter turns. When standing from the front, it's always important to keep your chest high, lats and shoulders flared, and arms and legs tensed. Ideally, the trick is to do all this while smiling, or at the very least. not looking like you're in pain. Next are the quarter turns. Quarter turns are always made to the right, never the left. Let's get it straight right now. If you make a turn to the left, you'll look like an ass, so don't even think about it. The first turn is to the right in order to show your left side to the judges, followed by a turn to show your back, another turn to show your right side, and finally a turn back to the front. Don't make your turns like you're Frankenstein. Heavy feet make you look clumsy onstage. Instead, make your turns in military style by putting your right foot behind you and using the right toe to initiate the turn. Gradually bring your left foot around to follow.

Practice and do this with consistency and you'll quickly get the hang of making each turn look and feel smooth, consistent, and effortless.

Correctly standing from the side is one of the most challenging poses in bodybuilding. Unlike the front and back, everyone looks narrower from the side. So the trick is to make the side that faces the judges as substantial as possible. You do this by starting from the ground up. Assuming we're talking about a first quarter turn to the right with your left side facing the judges, begin with splitting your stance just a little bit. You do this by moving your left foot slightly in front of your right foot. This makes your lower body look wider and more substantial because, assuming your feet are snug together, you can turn your left knee a bit in order to push out your left hamstring toward the judges. In addition, the judges will be able to see parts of your right leg as well as your left, thus adding depth to the lower body. Just remember not to push by getting your left foot too far out in front of your right. The furthest you should go is where your heel is in your arch. Also keep both feet flat on the ground. These are critical pet peeves with quite a few judges and if they catch you pushing it too far, they'll call you on it right then and there, and embarrass you on stage.

Again, from the side view, you must hold your abdominal muscle in. Above all else, this is perhaps the most critical adjustment from the side. If your gut is hanging, the judges will hang you. But if you're truly ripped and you have enough twisting torque between your upper and lower body, this should not be a problem. Of course, endurance is sometimes an issue because posing is hard work and if you're sucking wind, your gut will flop in and out. So practice is key for getting you in good enough shape to hold the pose without breathing hard.

From the side, your chest should be high and your shoulders slightly turned toward the judges. This again creates depth and makes you look more substantial. Note that, while your shoulders are angled toward the judges, your left knee is angled against you and thus away from the judges. This creates the necessary tension and torque in the waist region that better allows you to maintain abdominal control in order to keep your waist in.

Final notes from the left side include tightening the left arm for the judges and, if you have large pecs, flexing your right pec, while angling your shoulders toward the judges. Practice all of this on the right side as well.

When you make your quarter turn to the rear, the posing elements are essentially the same as those from the front (i.e., chest up, lats flared, and arms tight). Just remember to flex the muscles in the back of your thighs and your calves instead of your quads, which won't be seen in this pose. Also keep the triceps hard and not the biceps, since they too will not be seen in this pose.

The next mandatory posing considerations involve variations from the front. These include the following five poses:

- Front double biceps
- Front lat spread
- Arms-overhead abdominal pose
- Most muscular—"the Crab"
- Quads

The front double biceps pose is one of the most classic poses in bodybuilding. There have been many subtle variations over the years but the best way to do it is Arnold-style. Check out an old poster or picture of The Austrian Oak doing the pose and you'll know what I mean. Legs should be tight and flexed with striations, abdominal muscles should be pulled in (not flexed), chest should be up, and the upper arms out to the elbows should be parallel to the ground. Biceps, of course, should be maximally flexed and you should have a relaxed look or smile on your face. Note that some guys point their elbows a little higher up in the air. Steve Reeves popularized this version, but Lee Haney also held his elbows a bit higher on his front double biceps pose. These subtle variations are basically up to you to decide which looks better as either is fine with the judges.

The front lat spread is primarily a pose that showcases your degree of shoulder width and whether or not your lats are big enough to see from the front. In addition to arms and legs being tight and flexed, the key here is to not over-flex your chest. Instead, keep your chest and entire rib-box as high as possible and flared out as much as possible. Guys like Franco Columbo used to pull his elbows into his chest and flex his chest and abdominal muscles. This is an acceptable variation if you have the thickness to carry it, but I much prefer the classic version displayed by guys like Lee Haney and Ronnie Coleman. But again, the key here is getting your chest and shoulders as high and as wide as possible.

Invariably, you will be asked to put your arms overhead and flex your abdominal muscles. The key to the arms-overhead abdominal pose is to breath most of your air out and flex as hard as possible. Don't forget that your legs are quite visible on this pose because you're still posing from the front. So be sure and keep them flexed as well.

The "Crab"

The most muscular pose (also known as a "crab") is intended to show the judges the overall thickness, development, and degree of cuts in the chest, shoulders, and arms. In this pose, the trick is to figure out how close or far your arms should be from your body. In general, the weaker your chest and shoulders look, the further your arms should be from your body (assuming that at least your arms are worth looking at). The stronger your chest and shoulders look, the closer your arms should be to your body. Perhaps the most recognizable, most muscular pose was that of Lou Ferrigno, since he spent so much time hitting this pose when he played the Hulk on television. His chest, shoulders, and arms were absolutely huge. Yet the best, most muscular may well have belonged to Sergio Oliva. It's the tensest pose you'll hit since you're flexing the most amount of muscle to the highest degree at the same time. It's an important pose because the crowd loves it.

Although not generally standardized as a formal mandatory pose, you will likely be asked, at some point, to pose your quads. Obviously, this occurs from the front. Generally, you want to place your hands on your hips or at the edge of your trunks. Your upper body should be relaxed but held wide without your belly hanging. I prefer to flex the quads in a straightforward fashion. Put your best quad forward and flex hard. Some guys like to shake out their quads before flexing. This is okay for some of those with huge quads, just don't get too cute on this one and get to the pose.

The next mandatory posing considerations involve variations from the rear. These include the following four poses:
- Back double biceps
- Rear lat spread
- Calves
- Hamstrings

The back double biceps pose is similar to the front double biceps pose in that your position is somewhat the same, however, different muscles must be showcased for emphasis. In particular, the pose is intended to show back thickness and detail as opposed to biceps development. For this reason, the elbows should be back behind you just a little bit, thus allowing you to flex the muscles of the upper back. These include the rear deltoids, inner back, and traps. Your lower back should be slightly curved, allowing for flexion of the inner muscles of the lower back (also known as the "Christmas tree"). Also, make sure your rear end sticks out a bit and your hamstrings and calves are held tight and flexed.

The rear lat spread showcases the width of the back. On this pose, it's less to do about thickness and more about wingspan. So you want to trick around with your hand height and position on your sides in order to give you the maximum lat display.

Though not always mandatory poses, you may be asked to flex your calves and/or hamstrings from the rear. Hamstrings are flexed by drawing one heel up to the glute, while flexing the leg biceps muscles. Calves are flexed by going up on your toes. There are no strict standards here and not every set of judges will ask you for them, but they still need to be practiced just in case.

The next mandatory posing considerations involve variations from the side. These include the following two poses:
- Side chest
- Side triceps

The side chest shot begins with lifting the foot and pointing the toe down into the floor. Once this is done, point the knee in toward the opposing leg to force the showing hamstring out in the direction of the judges. Simultaneously, clasp both hands together under your ribcage, with the hand of the arm in back, on top of the hand of the arm facing the judges. With one hand over the other, use a thumb-less grip. Raise up the chest as high as possible and slightly tense the rear pec bend angling your shoulders slightly down toward the judges and raising the rear shoulder. There should be no air space between your arms and torso. Finally, flex the arm facing the judges. Hold your head tall and still, and look in the direction of the judges with a smile.

Like the side chest, the side triceps shot begins with lifting the foot and pointing the toe down into the floor. Once this is done, point the knee in toward the opposing leg to force the showing hamstring out in the direction of the judges. Simultaneously, clasp both hands together behind your back. Straighten and flex the triceps facing the judges and keep your chest high and abdominal muscles sucked in. A good tip here is to use your lats to push your triceps in the direction of the judges. Again, hold your head tall and still, and look in the direction of the judges with a smile.

By now it should be obvious to you just how important it is to practice all of these poses long before showtime.

What The Judges Are Looking For

What the standard bodybuilding judge at any level is looking for can generally be summed up in five categories. They are as follows and in descending order of importance: cuts, mass, shape/proportions, symmetry, and appearance.

When it comes to cuts, as discussed, it's all about the diet, and the final condition you display at the show will tell it all. If you're ripped, you're ripped. If not, well, you had better be close because there are four more categories to go. As I mentioned earlier, it's the single most important category. In my opinion, you must be ripped or close to it, or you should not be on stage. Being ripped means that all muscles are visible under the skin. All excess fat is gone. No muscles are smoothed over by water retention. All separations between muscle groups are evident. A six or eight-pack of abdominal muscle are deep and clear and even in repose. Cross striations are seen when big muscles like the quads are flexed. Vascularity is abundant and the striations ripple everywhere when you walk. That's being ripped.

Mass is a rather obvious criterion. You want to be as big as possible. In fact, that's what "bodybuilding" is all about. If you haven't built up some degree of muscle mass to display, you really should not be standing on stage. Interestingly, it's not so easy. I've seen droves of guys who looked huge walking around the gym disappear after only a few weeks of dieting. Every meathead mass monster thinks they can walk onstage and wow the world. But the fact is, the slabs of beef on many of these guys just disappear after only a few short weeks of dieting. That's what makes competitive bodybuilding a real art form. You need to be big, but you need to be ripped. It's a contradiction of ideals that you must come to terms with.

Shape is primarily dictated by your genetics and body type. Ideal shape starts your basic structure. The best structure reveals a dark image outline of wide shoulders, a narrow waist, seeping quadriceps, and calves and forearms. Once the lights come on and the poses start, shape can be taken one muscle group at a time. Starting from the top down, traps should sit up on the shoulder and be full and diamond shaped from the back of your head down to the middle of your back. Proper shoulder shape is roundness and full development, front to back. Chest should be full and developed all the way to the upper inside of your pecs. A good test is it should be full enough that if you look straight down in a completely relaxed state, you shouldn't see even the edge of your nipples. Back should be wide, yet dense and fully developed inside and out. The best lats flair out wide, yet insert down low on the spine. Biceps should be peaked, above being massive. The higher the peak generally means the better your shape. Triceps should be big from the side and fan out on your front lat spread, but they must also dip down in an arc on your double biceps from the front and back. The abdominals should be sharp and delineated but the waist should not be wide. Forearms should be muscular but not overdeveloped. Glutes should be circular and display roundness. Quads should sweep out to the sides yet be full both on the upper-inner aspect. In other words, there should be no air space between your legs. They should be touching when doing mandatory poses. Hamstrings should sweep out away from the leg from the side. Calves should be diamond shaped. Overall, the best shape tends to be guys with the biggest muscles on the smallest joints. Small joints make all the muscle bellies look bigger. The best thing you can do in the off-season to improve your shape is to be honest in your criticism of your body and priority train to bring up the areas that are lacking proper shape. At contest time, the best thing you can do for your shape is to bring down your waist with hardcore dieting.

Proportions involve how the presentation of one body part or area relates to another. It is so closely related to shape that they must be considered together. Though, along with shape, this is a tertiary category, many a contest has been lost due to proportion problems. As an example, the classic proportion problem on the amateur level would be the guy with the monster upper body but no legs. Other classic amateur proportion problems are big chest and shoulders but no arms, and big quads but no calves or hams. At the professional level, proportion problems tend to be more centered on a lagging single body part as opposed to a whole area or region of the body. This is due to the fact that guys with big proportion problems just don't make it to the professional rank. Yet even some of the greatest professional bodybuilders struggle to achieve proper proportions.

Symmetry describes the way one side of your body relates to the other. It is one of the more obvious and easy elements to judge. It is a quaternary category and of less importance, yet one that still must be considered. Simply divide your body down the middle and compare one side to the other. They should look as similar as possible. While everyone has a "good side" and no one really has perfect symmetry, the point is that you don't want one side to look too different from another. If this is happening, you want to analyze what you are doing and adjust your training accordingly to address the issue long before you think about stepping on stage.

Appearance is the final category that influences the judges. It is a subtle and almost silly category when you think of how superficial this cosmetic element is, when compared to the magnitude of the very real and substantive muscle building and cuts you have worked so hard for. Yet there it is. It does make a difference. All body hair should be removed and your skin should be tanned and unblemished. I recommend using an electric beard trimmer to bring the hair down prior to shaving with a razor (in the off season, the electric beard trimmer alone works wonders at keeping the ape look at bay). Tanning should begin long before the show. Using the sun, the tanning bed, or both is fine. When it comes down to contest time, I generally like to use a self-tanning product to produce the extra bronze look. Just be sure you experiment with different products and methods early on so you're not playing a guessing game at contest time. The hair on your head should be simple and understated, or not there at all. Big hair, ponytails, fros, and mohawks are all out. They de-emphasize the physique and might offend the judges. Posing trunks should be simple and understated. I always like straight black or red colors and steer away from anything multicolored or shiny. Finally, smile! It's always more favorable on stage and in life to smile. This shows everyone that you are comfortable, confident, and having a good time.

Your Posing Routine

Though not part of your mandatory posing requirements, you will also need to put together a posing routine. You may be asked to move through all or part of your routine at the prejudging either without music or with house music in the background. But if you make it into the top group (usually top five in each class) you will be allowed to perform your routine onstage at night in front of the whole audience and to the music of your own choice. So you really need to work on it. The maximum length of the routine at the amateur levels usually ranges between 60 and 90 seconds depending on the promoters, the sanctioning body, and the number of expected participants (in the bigger shows, you are almost always limited to 60 seconds).

The best way to get this right is to have someone help you that really knows what he is doing and has posed, competed, and won a competition himself. But that said, the key here is to weave different poses together, and not necessarily just the mandatory ones. In your routine, you will have free reign to throw out whatever poses you choose. The ultimate clips of how to thread poses together are those of Ed Corney. You can see him with Arnold in the old *Pumping Iron* movie. To me, he was the greatest free-poser of all time. You will also need to choose music and coincide your poses to the music. Make sure your music matches your personality and is something the crowd will enjoy as well and easily relate to. Picking weird music and sound effects work for some freaky looking pros that really know how to move and present their physiques (like the great Ron Brown), but don't try it yourself, unless you're prepared to chew what you bite off.

I guess the key here is, unless you're some kind of creative genius or super performer, be sure to lean toward the conservative side and stay restrained in your choice of music. As I stated, routines are limited to about a minute and you'll have to bring your chosen theme with you already cued up and ready to play. So plan it that way, and keep it simple. Though some shows allow you to hand in your music slightly ahead of time, most will ask you to hold on to it and hand it over to the sound guy just before you get onstage.

When you do your routine, whether just moving through it with the house lights up at the prejudging and only house music as a background, or if it's the full-blown night show version, don't make too many fast movements on stage. Generally speaking, the more unsure or uncomfortable you are on stage or the smaller you are in mass, the slower you should move. Furthering the point, the smaller you are in stature or weight class, the slower you should move. There are few things more embarrassing and strange to witness for an audience member then a fast moving little twitchy guy on stage.

To best illustrate this point, two of the greatest training partners I ever had were Carlos and Dominic. While both champions in their own right, these guys were as different as it gets. Carlos was a suave Cuban lady-killer with a million-dollar smile and dance moves to back up his phenomenal physique. While not hugely muscled, his shape, symmetry, and cuts were near perfect. He was in a lighter weight class then me and we never competed against each other head-to-head. But Carlos was so comfortable in his own skin and thus on-stage, that I swear this guy could pull off just about anything and get away with it. In fact, the night he won at the New York State Championship, he actually had the balls to wear leopard print posing trunks and bust out dance moves between poses! It just came naturally to him. The crowd went wild and the ladies in the audience practically rushed the stage to get to him.

On the other hand, my buddy Dominic was a big, tall Italian guy with mass (a bonafide heavyweight plus) that lacked good shape and struggled getting ripped. Even so, he was a champion in his own rite and did himself proud onstage the year he won at the Tri-State Bodybuilding Championships. But he did this without the flash and fancy moves that Carlos was known for. Though he was an extraordinary athlete and incredibly strong in the gym, he was simply not a comfortable poser and was even physically clumsy at times. As a result, I was careful to coach him, with slower poses and more serious movements and gentle transitions. In other words, no high-risk maneuvers. Just get the job done and get off the stage.

Personally, I was somewhere between my two buddies. Though with hard work, I earned a reputation with the judges as being a solid poser onstage with a noticeable stage presence, I certainly would never have tried to pull off stuff like Carlos did. So understanding your personal limits is critical for free-posing success.

While moving in a slower more controlled fashion is important for most, don't overdue it or you just end up boring and unimpressive and that's not what bodybuilding is all about. This sport is about showing the human physique at its high point. So while you should certainly err on the side of caution and work within your comfort zone, you are there to impress. The way to impress starts about five weeks before the day of the show by expanding your degree of comfort. You do this by choosing your music, nailing down your basic working routine, and practicing it repeatedly. Work to refine your movements and sharpen your presentation. The more practice you have, the more comfortable you will be onstage. The more comfortable you are moving through poses, the more drama you can add and the more chances you can take. With enough repetition, you can synchronize your poses to the beat of the music and add speed and bigger movements to the high points of your chosen theme. This makes it much more interesting for the audience and thus fun for you. Plus it can, on occasion, impress the judges, especially if you are called to move through your planned routine at the prejudging.

Assuming you've found a one-minute excerpt from a song you like, transfer it to a new blank tape and get it cued up from the beginning. Try and pick a song that fits within the minute time slot because if it abruptly ends, it will make you look bad. Simple recording equipment can create a fade out, although I've never really much liked the fade because the audience is usually left momentarily puzzled that your routine has come to an end, so applause, if earned, tends to be delayed, with a silence that softens their ultimate response. The best way to handle a music choice is to have a DJ or audio-tech friend help you master your sound track. A good sound man can work wonders and get 60 seconds out of just about any song, while creating a clear end. They can also weave together samples of a few different songs to make something very original. That said, I am always sure to keep my guys from posing to any popular song on the radio at the time. This is because you'll invariably have a couple of boneheads that choose the same current popular song to pose to, and if you're not the first out with the song, you'll hear the groans of disapproval from the audience. So try and be original, or at the very least, unique.

Five weeks before the show I usually like my guys to start working on their routine by taking a few hours on a non-training day and really work on the guts of the routine. I do this by making sure that they're moving through poses that suit their physique. There have generally been two schools of thought on this subject. The first is Arnold's approach. Since his legs were okay but certainly not awe inspiring, yet his arms and chest were mind-blowing, most of his poses were large sweeping movements that almost invariably ended in a display of his arms. Though he could be accused of being somewhat one-dimensional, he designed these beautifully choreographed sequences to play to the crowd with the clear intent of showing off his best body part in order to get the biggest response. On the other hand, Tom Platz, whose quad development is still unparalleled even by today's standards, had a very different approach. At his best, he had a fairly good all-around physique, but his quads were perhaps even more mind-blowing then Arnold's arms. Nonetheless, he chose to display a balance of poses that revealed his physique in a more complete fashion. The choice is yours, but I much prefer Arnold's approach. Choose poses that showcase your best body parts and best angles. If you have a freaky body part, go with it and don't hold back on displaying that area in a number of different ways. Remember, you've only got 60 seconds to impress, so if it's up to me, I say you should put your best stuff forward.

When beginning your routine, be sure you're not standing in some kind of uncomfortable position. Coming in from off stage once the music starts is the easiest way to avoid all technical problems. But finding the right tune that allows you to do this in a visibly comfortable way can be challenging. There is also the issue of such an approach cutting into the total time you're on the stage. The better your condition and the better you look compared to others, the more time you should want on stage. This must be carefully considered.

34 Showtime

Assuming you made it this far, it's finally show time. Wake up and eat light. Have a few plain eggs and then start carbing up with sherbet. Be careful though, because you'll be completely fluid restricted today, so your body will intensely crave the sherbet and you will feel compelled to immediately wolf down a half gallon. The result might be bloating and stomach discomfort. This would be exactly what you want to avoid on the day of the contest. Resist the urge to gulp and instead take your time with the sherbet. A steady stream throughout the morning makes much more sense.

After breakfast, go through all your mandatory poses in front of the mirror. Pose exactly as if you are onstage. Go through your entire posing routine as well. Double check and make sure your music is cued up and ready to go. Get dressed in a loose fitting warm-up suit with your trunks on underneath. Pack your music along with a small towel, and your oil. You can bring a couple of dumbbells, stretch bands, or home resistance pieces if you want. But it is usually unnecessary since even a local amateur show has a promoter with enough sense to stock the warm-up area backstage with some basic weights for competitors to pump up with before they go onstage.

Get to the show a little early because being there late and pressed for time is unnecessarily stressful. Once you arrive, check in and register. You'll be given a number and a pin, which you should immediately attach to the front of your trunks on the right side. You may be asked to weigh in or be measured for height. This will place you in a particular class. Find out the order of appearance for all competitive classes. Knowing this order is critical to properly time your last-minute preparations. Large shows that include women, teenagers, novices, masters, and lighter weight classes, can have a prejudging that lasts from the early afternoon to all the way up to the night show. For example, if your prejudging starts at noon and you're a light-heavyweight in the open class of such a competition, you may not find yourself getting onstage for the prejudging until 2 pm. So knowing when your class will be called to the stage is critical.

Prejudging

The prejudging is where you'll be compared to all other competitors in your class. Expect to be asked to go through all the mandatory poses as they're called out one-by-one by the head judge. If the class is small enough (ten or less), all competitors will likely be asked to line up and do the poses together. The judges will quickly identify the stronger competitors and start moving competitors around on stage so that they can make the appropriate comparisons. If the class is large, competitors will generally be asked to line up in the background of the stage and be called forward in small groups. Occasionally, competitors may be asked to file off stage and be called one-by-one onstage to go through their intended night-show posing routine, but with houselights up and either no music or just low volume house music. You must be prepared to do this without the accompaniment of your own music.

A good showing at the prejudging is everything because what most people don't realize is that by the time you get to all the fanfare of the night show, the top five places in each class have already been selected at the prejudging. These results are, of course, not announced until the night show. It's only the comparison between class winners for the overall title that takes place at the night show.

Once you've figured out when you'll be taking the stage for the callout, many bodybuilders take in about 100 milligrams of pure niacin about 90 minutes beforehand. This simple B vitamin found naturally in a number of foods is an essential water-soluble nutrient involved in cellular energy pathways. But in a concentrated dose, pure niacin produces an effect that flushes the body and brings out vascularity under the skin. This should not be confused with niacinimide, which does not produce this same effect. Niacin, overall, is pretty harmless. I've never seen anyone get in trouble with a niacin load, and I've seen some guys take as much as 500 milligrams at one time. Nevertheless, if you push it a little too far, the flushing can become annoying, itchy, and even a painful distraction. At the highest levels of overdose, niacin has been cited in the medical literature as causing liver complications. But I've never seen of or heard of such a case among bodybuilders in all my years.

Warming Up

About a half hour before you expect to be called out on stage, you should head back stage and start warming up. This generally involves heading to the designated pump-up room or area and doing your standard bodybuilding movements just to get the muscles looking a little fuller. A little lifting at this point is critical to emphasize muscularity, but just don't go for that crazy big pump you usually go for in the gym. You simply won't have time to effectively do this with all your body parts. Plus, even if you did try it, you simply won't hold such a pump through all the poses of prejudging. You just want to get the start of a pump in certain areas of your body and let the onstage posing bring out the size and density of a fuller pump. In other words, over pumping will result in nothing but subsequent deflation. Instead, I generally superset three different movements in no particular order using light weight and a very high repetition scheme. But I tend to make sure the arms, upper chest, and side delts are all a little pumped. If time allows, I'll also pump the back, calves, and hamstrings, but tend to do more hard, repetitive flexing to bring out these areas. Do not pump the quads or abdominal muscles since they will tend to smooth out with a pump. Instead, pose these areas the hardest. That will bring out enough density and fullness without losing separation. So while a few deep knee bends are okay to start things off, get right to posing them hard as a way to bring out the fullness, separations, and striations. Overall, though, I like some degree of resistance work in preparation for the stage. I find that nerves tend to make most resistance-induced pumps fairly flat and that you get much more mileage out of pumping the weights a little, then quickly getting to hard flexing in front of a mirror.

At this time, a good tip is to keep your warm-up suit on until you are five to ten minutes into your pump-up routine. This will allow the blood to circulate to the muscles better, thus more easily countering the pump-robbing forces of stress, dehydration, and caloric depletion. Once you feel the blood start flowing, you can remove your sweats down to your trunks. Continue your pump-and-pose routine, but don't look around too much at the other competitors. It doesn't matter what they look like. It only matters that you look your best. The truth is, how you look backstage can be amazingly deceiving. Some guy that looks huge, may end up showing no cuts onstage and thus end up being very beatable. Essentially, you should not get distracted with what's going on with the other competitors around you. It's for the judges to sort out once you get on stage, and not for you to get caught up in.

As you or your class get close to being called out onstage, you should begin oiling up. It's nice to try and sneak a buddy backstage with you to help with this task, but you won't always get away with it. Most competitions are very strict about who is allowed backstage. So competitors usually help each other out. Either way, oiling up properly is kind of an art. If you do it the right way, posing is unimpeded and muscle separations are highlighted under the stage lights for the judges and audience. If you do it the wrong way, posing is impeded and these same separations become washed out by over reflecting the stage lights. Oiling properly begins with making sure you have the right kind of oil. Most guys use baby oil or cooking spray. I don't like either. Baby oil tends to be too over-reflective due to the relative low viscosity of the liquid. And because of the propellants and additives, cooking sprays tend to be hypo-reflective. Plus, they are very messy. I find the best oils to be the thick, highly viscous tanning oils. Hawaiian Tropics® makes a great, thick tanning oil in a small, easy-to-carry brown bottle with a gold cap. I use these types of oils because they can be applied sparingly and worked into the skin to create what I call a nice skin-sheen. With the exception of the face, the bottoms of your feet, and the sides of your waist, all areas of the body should get a thin application of oil, worked deep into the skin. Make sure the bottoms of your feet do not contact any oil or you might slip. Also, dry your hands thoroughly. There are only two poses in bodybuilding, the front and rear lat-spread, that rely heavily on grip. Your thumbs and first fingers must be dry enough, along with the dry sides of your waist, to allow you to plant your thumbs and fingers on your sides and use them as an anchor point to draw out your lats during the pose. Too much oil here, and you'll never get the pose right.

Once it's time to judge your class, you'll be lined up in numeric order along with other competitors and escorted out onto the stage by a stagehand and at the direction of the head judge. The head judge runs the show so always direct your attention to him and listen carefully to his instructions. Take your position on the stage, on the spot where you are directed, and face the judges and audience. Standing at attention with lats flared, legs flexed, and a relaxed smile, wait for the instructions of the head judge. He will usually begin by asking everyone to do four quarter-turns. This gives the judges the first point of comparative reference in seeing how everyone looks from the front, back, and sides.

After that, the head judge will begin calling out the mandatory poses in any order he so desires. Judges often confer throughout this process and might ask you to switch places with another competitor. As a result, you might be center stage, or find yourself relegated to the sidelines. Try not to read too much into this. While it is true that the guys that end up moved to center stage are usually vying for a top spot in the eyes of the judges, I've seen plenty of guys who just instantly blew away their line-up and thus were asked to step to the sidelines, while the judges tried to figure out the rest of the order. So the important thing is not to read tea leaves at this point. Put it out of your mind. What you should be doing is making sure you're holding yourself flexed and at attention, even if you're in the back row and out of center stage. While it may be difficult, and perhaps inappropriate to smile while this happens, don't relax and deflate your chest or let your arms fall to your sides. Such mannerisms signal to the judges a sense of giving up and not caring.

After the mandatory poses are complete and the judges are finished with all comparisons, your line-up will likely be escorted from the stage. Each competitor may then be called out one-by-one to move through their posing routine without their music. This allows the judges to see you in a non-comparative way. They're not only looking at your development, but your fluidity of movement, onstage presentation, and charisma. It also allows the smaller daytime audience of fans to be entertained and cheer for their favorites. After that, it's usually over. The judges have made their decisions (usually the order of the top five places in the class). So you can start thinking about the night show.

Though the decision of where you placed has already been made at the prejudging, if you honestly feel that it was a very tight race between you and some other guy for first place in the class or if you are fairly certain that you won your class, there is more work to do. If you win your class, you'll then be compared at the end of the evening show to the winners of the other classes to determine the other overall title winner. Individual routines are performed by class competitors, and shortly thereafter, the awards for the top five class places are then handed out. Once this takes place for all classes (i.e. in the open: bantamweight, lightweight, middleweight, light-heavyweight, heavyweight, and super-heavyweight), the showdown between class winners begins.

My Secret Weapon

It's for these occasions that I reserve a special secret in my bag of tricks. Recall, that for weeks now, you have been severely salt restricted, and for the last few days, severely fluid restricted. My trick is this; right after the pre-judging, I load in about half a teaspoon of salt by way of a salty food like French fries or some other gastronomic sin. I do this at least 2 hours before the night show and without drinking any additional fluid. It's a tough, dry haul, but with only a few hours to grin and bare it, it can be done. After all, you came this far. The effect is astounding, and can make the difference if you expect you might be facing a close competition, which will be decided in comparison at the night show. What happens to your body is that, assuming you take in no additional fluids, when the salt gets down into your gut it will draw any extra subcutaneous water and soft tissue fluid into the gastrointestinal tract to dilute. As a result, you'll appear even more shredded by evening time. By the way, you're probably wondering why I don't just dial things back and use this trick of salt loading while dehydrating for the prejudging. The answer is twofold. First, you would risk flattening out because you would miss the morning carbohydrates and accompanying fluid intake, which are needed to make the muscles full. Secondly, it's risky. You can't do this if you feel like crap. It's very taxing on the physiology and certainly carries with it some risks. You will only know how you tolerated the dehydration phase once the prejudging is over. Also, you should have a good idea of what the competition is like and thus how far you have to push things to win. This way you can accurately assess the risk to benefit ratio and whether it is necessary or even possible to push your body any further.

Just be careful at this stage of the game. A lot of competitive bodybuilders rely heavily on diuretic drugs during this time. They do this so that they don't have to play around with this delicate salt-to-fluid balance. While diuretic abuse works great to get rid of the water, without any second guessing, it can be a perilous road. Two of the most popular diuretic drugs of abuse in the final days and hours leading up to the competition are Lasix® and Spironolactone®. Lasix® is often abused because of its quick onset of action, coupled with its ability to act in the body for up to six hours. Spironolactone® is also abused because it spares potassium in the body and thus makes cramping less likely. But again, I can't reiterate how dangerous this stage of the game is. Andreas Munzer and Mohammed Benaziza were two great champion bodybuilders that were about as ripped as anyone has ever gotten. These guys shred themselves to unexplored heights of dehydration and water loss. But they died. Even the great champion Albert Beckles, with all his sage wisdom and experience pushed it too hard and collapsed back stage into the arms of Berry DeMey and came near death.

But whether you decide you need to push it that extra little bit or whether you just coast through the prejudging, either way, it's time for the night show. Ostensibly, the drill is the same in terms of prepping and pumping up. The only difference, is that you'll have to make sure your music is cued up and ready to go and in the hands of the sound guy before you're asked to do your routine. Different shows have different protocols. The better shows will ask for your music way ahead of time and will simply be ready when you're called out to do your routine. The worst ones ask for your music just before you take the stage and, while the guy ahead of you is doing his routine.

The Night Time Is The Right Time

Once the night show hits, the most obvious difference that will quickly become apparent will be the energy. Prejudging crowds are usually very small, there is no announcer, house lights are up, and the tone is very serious. This is in sharp contrast to the night show, where the crowds are thick and wild with energy. The house lights are down and the stage lights are focused. With showmanship, the better charismatic announcers usually create excitement by teasing the crowd and getting things riled up. The night show is usually a circus freak-show environment that's a boat-load of fun.

Usually, the first thing to expect is when it's time for your class, each competitor will be called out to do their posing routine to their respective music. When it's your turn, get it right. That shouldn't be hard if you've done everything I've said and practiced as much as I've indicated. In fact, it should be a foregone conclusion that you will get it right and nail your routine like second nature. Everything under your control should be in control. That said, you should be having a good time, and look every bit that part. On the other hand, if something out of your control happens, don't panic. The most common problem is that the sound guy screws up your music. This usually means the music starts late or not at all. When this happens, just smile and try and get the crowd on your side. If your conditioning is great, that will be all they care about. Give it a few seconds and, if no music, just start posing. The crowd will always get behind you because the brethren of bodybuilding know full well how much it sucks to work so hard and get to the big day only to have some dimwit screw up your routine. The trick is to smile and show the crowd that you can take it in stride. That will make you look like a winner. Bitch and moan, show a bad attitude, and the crowd will grow increasingly uncomfortable and you'll start to look like a loser.

But more often then not, you'll never have to worry about this. When you're up there, be sure and have a great time. Show some passion and artistry. Remember, that friends and family will be there watching and cheering. So put on a great show for them.

After the routines, it's on to the next part of the evening competition. Once all class members that made it to the night show complete their routines, they'll be called out together in a lineup. Competitors stand side-by-side as they did in the prejudging and are either situated together or called forward individually or in small groups, to be compared. This allows the evening crowd to see how one competitor looks directly compared to another. Some of the mandatory poses are called out and then the competitors are asked to leave the stage. Usually, the next step is the class awards, where the top five places are announced in reverse order one-by-one to take the stage and accept their award. The award is usually a trophy. But sometimes plaques, medals, and statues are also given out. This progresses through each class until the final phase of the show, when all open class winners (the winners of each weight class) are then called out for a final comparison in order to award the overall championship show title.

You Can't Lose

Whatever the decision, show some class in winning or losing. Even if you feel like you got ripped off, try to contain yourself, and smile, shake hands with the winner, and wave to the crowd. Odds are, people that really care about you, friends and family, have made it a point to show up and support you. Being a candy-ass baby makes your whole posse feel crummy and just ruins the experience for them. I made this mistake once when I felt that I got shafted. This guy who I had trounced only three months earlier, edged me out for first. I felt like I got ripped off because he trained at the gym of the guy who promoted the show. But as the crowd booed the decision and agreed with me, I saw my friends in the audience going crazy. They got me going and I started shaking my head in disgust and looked every bit the part of a sourpuss sore-loser. Unfortunately, it only made me look bad to everyone, including the judges (who tend to have a pretty good memory). I always regretted that and, with hindsight always being 20/20, improved my character and vowed never to do that again. Fortunately, I never had to.

In victory, the rules are the same. Have class. Be nice. When I finally made it to the top of the podium, I made sure to shake the hand of every guy I beat. I took the time to smile and wave to the crowd, but I did not overdo it. While ecstatic, I didn't gloat. I always focus on victory with everyone I help. I tell them to feel the victory down to their core and with every fiber in their body. I tell them to let that feeling of undeniable joy bathe their very being and come up and out through their smile and eyes for all to see and share. On this day, regardless of placing, everyone should see what a winner you are.

AFTERWORD
Other Bodybuilding Resources

OTHER BODYBUILDING RESOURCES

The following are the most well known bodybuilding magazines on the market today.

Muscular Development

My old friend Steve Blechman, publisher of *Muscular Development (MD),* has had limitless faith in me as both a columnist and contributing editor. Steve has always given me creative freedom; he has let me write about what I thought was important to the reader, never dictating or forcing editorial direction on me. He also never once refused to publish my column (and that's saying a lot, considering that I haven't always had the most popular opinions or the kindest things to say when something tweaked me).

In addition to having highly-qualified writers, perhaps the greatest strength of the magazine comes from Steve himself. I think the most impressive thing he does is to personally comb the scientific research on literally a daily basis and relay it to the reader. I recall many times helping him to his car with a milk-crate full of scientific publications for him to get through over the weekend. He simply never stops working for his readers.

My exclusive bodybuilding magazine endorsement goes to *MD* and to the wonderful staff at ARP with whom I have worked so closely for many wonderful years. Simply put, *MD* is a superb hard-core resource for the serious bodybuilder.

Muscle & Fitness

I can't imagine not acknowledging Joe Weider, creator of *Muscle & Fitness,* for years of sage wisdom, inspiration and education. Some of my most profound lessons in bodybuilding came from the great master himself. I cherish his friendship and value his lessons, many of which I reiterate in my own teachings.

M&F was the first bodybuilding magazine I ever picked up. In my early teens I marveled at the images, hung up favorite pictures in my makeshift garage gym, and tried to emulate my heroes. I am proud to say that I was commissioned by Joe himself to write the very first medical and science newsletter for the magazine.

Flex

Launched in the early 1980s by Joe Weider, Flex is a source for pro bodybuilding training and nutrition information, as well as insider gossip. While M&F is now packaged for mass consumption, Flex is still aimed squarely at ardent gym rats who follow the sport religiously.

Muscle Mag

Owned by Bob Kennedy, Muscle Mag has always been a fun magazine for bodybuilders. The strength of the magazine is in its pure entertainment value, covering bodybuilding with a quirky spin. Muscle Mag is also well known for its plethora of hot young fitness babes wearing thongs (hardly objectionable to me, but also not really relevant to bodybuilding). Chances are, if you're into bodybuilding and enjoy the T&A interludes, you'll like Muscle Mag.

Ironman

Ironman magazine has developed a loyal core of readers over the years. A much smaller-scale publication than Muscle & Fitness, Flex or Muscular Development, it still offers an interesting mix of training science, competitor profiles and contest coverage.

IN
CONCLUSION

While in medical school, I spent time in Israel. One of my training partners was a guy named Sam Schwartz. Somehow, despite the vigorous schooling and the crazy war zone we were in, we found a way to train and keep our sanity. Finding a place to train wasn't easy, but it wasn't impossible either. Having traveled the world over, it amazes me how I always seemed to find at least one cruddy gym to train at *somewhere*. It's a testament to the resilience of the human spirit and the undying passion for bodybuilding that cuts across all races, colors, creeds and countries.

Tel Aviv was no different. Deep in the dirty, downtown manufacturing sector, through a passageway and into an industrial building basement, there it was — a bomb shelter with a huge steel door that must have weighed two tons. Inside, a guy by the name of Benjamin Jaffe presided over Jaffe's Gym. No question about it, this place was as hardcore as it gets. Amazingly, despite being nothing more then a cold cement cavern, it was still pretty cool because Jaffe had managed to get all the necessary equipment into this windowless cement cavern.

Plenty of big guys trained there. Where they came from was usually a mystery. No one cared. Israeli, Arab, Russian, American, it didn't matter. What mattered was that this bomb shelter gym was a place where we all mutually paid homage to the iron without prejudice. While we didn't always speak the same language, we always helped one another with a lift, a spot or just some verbal encouragement. We used to joke that with six feet of cement and steel doors to protect us, if they started bombing, most of us meatheads wouldn't bother missing a set, much less stop our workout.

It was in that subterranean hole in the Middle East that I learned something about myself, and something about what bodybuilding meant to me that stays with me to this very day. I realized the sport had long since transcended the superficial level of me just doing it to impress people with my biceps. It was something much deeper. Therein lay the greater question. Would I still be doing it if I was the last person on earth and there was no one else to look at me? My experience there gave me the answer, which was and still is most definitely yes.

Of all the gyms I've trained at over the years, training at Jaffe's with Sam was most memorable and meaningful. Workouts were uncertain back then, and good food was war-zone scarce. We were so thankful when we could embark on our pre-dawn training ritual at our dank temple. We were waging our own daily war, a war to get ourselves into the gym and not miss a workout. Add to that, it was a low-point in my life from a personal standpoint, so I was grateful to be getting in my workouts. It kept my sanity.

Being thankful may sound odd for such a non-religious, skeptical physician-scientist (for those who know me), but my situation taught me an important spiritual lesson — *it seems the best evidence I have that a greater force exists in some form is that when times were at their very lowest and darkest for me, I curiously found myself praying.* It's interesting to me, since I can't explain it and it was me who was doing it. By pray, I don't mean some big get-down-on-your-knees bible revival, but just quiet, powerful, positive thoughts focused on some greater force outside me. Call it what you will.

My next spiritual epiphany was inspired by a quote from the great baseball pitching legend Satchel Paige. He once said, "Don't pray when it's raining if you don't pray when the sun is shining." So once in a while I pray when the sun is shining, but at these times it's more of an exercise in thankfulness and appreciation for what I have.

At any rate, these were difficult times with tough challenges, so they weren't my best years of training from a mass-gaining standpoint. Yet from a psychological, emotional and meditative standpoint, I never valued my training more. Sam felt the same. Each day was a battle and a sacrifice to get to Jaffe's, but it was a momentary introspective victory if we got there because the training sessions were so worth it. After each workout, we would always stop on our way out the door and give thanks. One of us would always announce to the other, "We won again." With a ritual high-five, we'd tackle the rest of the day knowing that no matter what was thrown at us, it likely wouldn't be worse then the physical pain that we just extricated from our bodies. At least that was our attitude and, real or not, it was what we believed and the key to our survival.

Gut-busting training is still my way. The Marines are right. An extreme physique and calluses from more than a quarter of a century have taught me that the pain of training is nothing more than weakness leaving my body. Through this ritual self-sacrifice, my body and mind are cleansed.

The gym still is my meditative temple and my silent, consistent partner that never lets me down. It has taught me every important lesson I've ever learned. It has saved me from the evilness in my circle. It has saved me from myself. As it was then, it is now. Each day I come out of the gym, my daily re-birth is complete. I'll never stop bodybuilding.

About The Author

Carlon M. Colker, M.D., F.A.C.N., is the Chief Executive Officer and Medical Director of Peak Wellness, Inc., Greenwich, Connecticut, and an attending physician at both the Beth Israel Medical Center in New York and Greenwich Hospital in Connecticut. His specialties include internal medicine, sports medicine and sports nutrition. He's also credited with assisting in the design of the first wellness program on the East Coast.

In addition to his practice, Dr. Colker is a premier researcher in the field of dietary supplements, and is widely regarded as one of the world's foremost experts on human performance. A Fellow of the *American College of Nutrition*, he has a wealth of scientific research publications and published articles to his credit. Dr. Colker is also a long-time contributing editor and columnist for *Muscular Development* magazine, and has appeared in many other popular publications, such as *Muscle & Fitness, Ironman, MuscleMag, Flex, Mind & Power, Body, Runner's World, Walking, Let's Live, Self, Strive, Men's Health, Men's Fitness* and *Cosmopolitan*, among others.

With over 20 years of experience in the health and fitness industry, Dr. Colker is an internationally-recognized consultant, and has worked with government agencies, large health-care systems and private companies, as well as with Olympic and professional athletes and celebrities. His commentary can be seen on national television, appearing as a regular guest correspondent on the America's Health Network "Ask the Doctor"

segment and Fox News Channel's "Fox & Friends." He has also had guest appearances on ESPN's "Outside the Lines," NBC News "Health" segment, Court TV, ABC's "World News Tonight," "The View," "Jenny Jones" and "The Roseanne Show."

A champion bodybuilder himself, Dr. Colker has combined his real-life success in the training trenches with his advanced knowledge as a practicing physician, developing an unparalleled approach that has helped countless bodybuilders and athletes unleash their power and reach their true maximum potential.

Notes

Notes

Notes

Notes

Notes

Notes

Notes